# Contents

*PREVIEW TEST*

Write in place-value form.

**1.** three hundred nine

**2.** four thousand ninety-six

**3.** fifty million, sixty-two

**4.** nine hundred and nine tenths

Name the place value of each underlined digit.

**5.** 2_5_.091    *ones*

**6.** _3_64.89    *100*

**7.** 6.0_5_8

**8.** 7.8_4_

Compare. Write <, =, or > for each ●.

**9.** 573 ● 572    *<*

**10.** 438 ● 458    *>*

**11.** 987 ● 1230    *>*

**12.** 6.40 ● 6.4

Find each result.

**13.**     857
        +987
        *1844*

**14.**     2051
         +5239
         *7290*

**15.**     18.064
         +70.989
         *89.053*

**16.**      37
         +41.61
         *78.61*

**17.**    1208
         − 949
         *259*

**18.**     157
         − 79.8
         *78.8*

**19.**    225.4
         −139
         *86.4*

**20.**    12.061
         − 9.78
         *2.281*

Round to the nearest hundredth.

**21.** 34.8157    *35*

**22.** 2.0643    *2*

**23.** 90.6538    *91*

Estimate each sum or difference.

**24.**    75
         +23
         *98*  *100*

**25.**    291
         +130
         *421*  *400*

**26.**    507
         −387
         *120*

**27.**    1979
         − 843
         *1,136*  *1,000*

Solve.

**28.** During one month a hit record sold 74,209 copies. The next month the sales dropped to 48,318. How many more copies were sold during the first month?

*25,891*    *74 209
48 318
25,891*

**29.** In the last month, John worked 16, 9, 13, and 14 hours at his part-time job. How many hours did he work in all?

*16
14
13
9
52*

9

# READING AND WRITING WHOLE NUMBERS

**In the last census, 226,504,825 Americans were counted.**

The place-value chart for whole numbers below shows **periods** and three **place values** in each period. The value of any digit in a number depends on its place in the number.

| Periods | BILLIONS | | | MILLIONS | | | THOUSANDS | | | ONES | | |
|---|---|---|---|---|---|---|---|---|---|---|---|---|
| Place values | hundred billions | ten billions | billions | hundred millions | ten millions | millions | hundred thousands | ten thousands | thousands | hundreds | tens | ones |
| | | | | 2 | 2 | 6, | 5 | 0 | 4, | 8 | 2 | 5 |

In numbers with more than four digits, commas (or spaces) are used to group the digits into periods.

**Example 1:** Read 226,504,825.

Two hundred twenty-six *million,* five hundred four *thousand,* eight hundred twenty-five.

The symbols < and > are used when comparing two numbers. < means *is less than* and > means *is greater than.*

To compare two whole numbers, start at the left and compare digits having the same place value.

**Example 2:** Compare 14,351 and 8796.

**1 4 3 5 1**
**0 8 7 9 6**
⬑————————1>0, so 14,351>8796.

**Example 3:** Compare 975,384 and 975,834.

**9 7 5 3 8 4**
**9 7 5 8 3 4**
**same** ⬑⬑⬑ ⬑————3<8, so 975,384<975,834.

## EXERCISES

Read.

1. 4316
2. 60,197
3. 411,235
4. 31,918,497
5. 5,080,046
6. 672,000
7. 92,850,706
8. 80,548,003
9. 8,016,309,045
10. 234,087,509,465
11. 745,730,208

Write in place-value form.

**Example:** four million, thirty-six thousand, twenty-nine **4,036,029**

12. seventeen thousand, one hundred forty-nine    017,149

13. nine million, four hundred twenty-two thousand, five hundred eighty-one    009,422,581

14. three billion, two million, six thousand, five    3,002,006,005

15. eleven million, thirty-five thousand, six hundred thirty-four    11,035,634

16. seven hundred twelve million, eight hundred sixty-seven thousand    712,867,000

Name the place value of each underlined digit.

17. 4<u>1</u>,368    T
18. <u>8</u>08,679,112    m
19. <u>9</u>1,763,819,413    B
20. 404,<u>1</u>09,366    T
21. 346,129,0<u>7</u>1,546    T
22. <u>9</u>46,787,113,802    B

Compare. Write < or > for each ⬤.

23. 25 ⬤ 28    <
24. 43 ⬤ 34    >
25. 270 ⬤ 268    <
26. 349 ⬤ 378    <
27. 561 ⬤ 605    <
28. 425 ⬤ 225    >
29. 5128 ⬤ 5217    <
30. 6391 ⬤ 6931    >
31. 8447 ⬤ 8744    >
32. 6410 ⬤ 4732
33. 29,005 ⬤ 29,003
34. 3000 ⬤ 786

Arrange in order from least to greatest.

35. 64, 76, 47, 81    47 64 76 81
36. 125, 150, 201, 98    201 150 125 98
37. 780, 970, 890, 870    970 890 870 780

Arrange in order from greatest to least.

38. 2040, 2094, 2009, 2490    2490 2094 2040 2009
39. 502, 510, 259, 592    592 510 502 259
40. 708, 780, 870, 807    870 807 780 708

**11**

NIU photo by Barry Stark

The Jazz Band concert had three performances. The number of tickets sold was 362 for Thursday, 404 for Friday, and 417 for Saturday. What was the total number of tickets sold for the three performances?

**Example 1:** Add 362, 404, and 417.

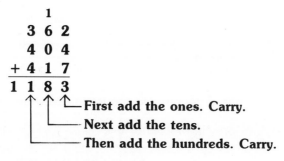

```
      1
   3 6 2
   4 0 4
 + 4 1 7
 1 1 8 3
```
First add the ones. Carry.
Next add the tens.
Then add the hundreds. Carry.

1183 tickets were sold.

When adding more than two numbers, you may want to group digits whose sum is 10. This makes addition easier.

**Example 2:**
```
  6 ← 10
  7 ←
  5        10
  4 ←
 + 3 ←
  2 5
```

**Example 3:**
```
      2
    3 8 ← 10
    4 9 ←
 10 9 2 ←    10
  + 6 1 ←
    2 4 0
```

## EXERCISES

Add.

**1.** 9+8+2   19

**2.** 6+7+4   17

**3.** 9+4+1   14

**4.** 8+7+3   18

**5.** 7+4+8   19

**6.** 9+3+6   18

**7.** 7+5+4+3   16

**8.** 9+5+8+6   28

**9.** 28 +76   104

**10.** 84 +67   151

**11.** 56 +79   135

**12.** 37 +95   132

**13.** 86 +74   260

**14.** 97 + 85 _182_      **15.** 72 + 68 _140_      **16.** 54 + 87 _141_      **17.** 93 + 48 _141_

**18.**  75
146
+ 38
_259_

**19.**  64
266
+ 93
_423_

**20.**  72
5
+258
_335_

**21.**  27
8
+385
_420_

**22.**  19
58
+432
_509_

**23.** 294 + 86 + 594 _968_      **24.** 777 + 65 + 433 _1215_      **25.** 615 + 91 + 871 _1577_

**26.** Find each player's score.

### Miniature-Golf Scorecard

| Hole | Par | Handicap | Susan | Lou | Lori | Jenny |
|---|---|---|---|---|---|---|
| 1 | 2 | 8 | 3 | 3 | 2 | 3 |
| 2 | 3 | 5 | 4 | 3 | 4 | 3 |
| 3 | 2 | 12 | 3 | 3 | 2 | 2 |
| 4 | 3 | 15 | 4 | 4 | 3 | 3 |
| 5 | 2 | 10 | 2 | 6 | 3 | 3 |
| 6 | 2 | 9 | 3 | 3 | 2 | 6 |
| 7 | 2 | 16 | 4 | 3 | 7 | 2 |
| 8 | 2 | 14 | 6 | 2 | 3 | 2 |
| 9 | 2 | 7 | 3 | 3 | 4 | 3 |
| 10 | 3 | 3 | 7 | 5 | 3 | 7 |
| 11 | 2 | 13 | 2 | 3 | 6 | 4 |
| 12 | 2 | 11 | 4 | 4 | 3 | 3 |
| 13 | 3 | 1 | 3 | 4 | 5 | 5 |
| 14 | 2 | 6 | 5 | 3 | 3 | 3 |
| 15 | 3 | 4 | 4 | 7 | 5 | 5 |
| 16 | 2 | 17 | 3 | 2 | 3 | 2 |
| 17 | 3 | 2 | 3 | 3 | 3 | 3 |
| 18 | 1 | 18 | 1 | 1 | 1 | 1 |
| Par 41 | | | | | | |

**27.** Find the total score for each bowling team during the season.

**Team A**

| | |
|---|---|
| Purcell | 14,355 |
| Donahue | 4,409 |
| Phillips | 13,910 |
| Hammond | 7,051 |

**Team B**

| | |
|---|---|
| Stergulz | 14,569 |
| Lykins | 11,784 |
| Lynk | 5,987 |
| Stube | 13,970 |

**Team C**

| | |
|---|---|
| Koenig | 14,430 |
| Pflaumer | 8,131 |
| Klein | 12,007 |
| Zapel | 10,916 |

**Team D**

| | |
|---|---|
| Agnifilo | 12,284 |
| Gossett | 13,491 |
| Umbro | 13,110 |
| Sclafani | 10,918 |

*EXTRA PRACTICE page 473, set 1*

# EXTENDING PLACE VALUES TO DECIMALS

By using a decimal point, we can include digits to the right of the ones place. These digits have place values that are less than one. A decimal point separates the part of the number that is less than one from the whole-number part.

| Place values | ten thousands | thousands | hundreds | tens | ones | . | tenths | hundredths | thousandths | ten-thousandths |
|---|---|---|---|---|---|---|---|---|---|---|
| | | | | 3 | 2 | . | 5 | 8 | 7 | |

**When reading decimals, follow these steps:**

1. **Read the part before the decimal point as you would any whole number.**

2. **Next read the decimal point as *and*.**

3. **Then read the part following the decimal point as you would a whole number, and name the place value of the last digit.**

**Example 1:**  Read 32.587.

thirty-two and five hundred eighty-seven thousandths

**Example 2:**  Read 0.0084.   eighty-four ten-thousandths

**Example 3:**  Read 0.84.   eighty-four hundredths

**Example 4:**  Read 0.840.   eight hundred forty thousandths

You can write 0's to the right of a decimal without changing its value. For example, $0.6 = 0.60 = 0.6000$, and so on.

To compare two decimals, write them so that each has the same number of digits after the decimal point. Then compare digits having the same place value, starting at the left.

**Example 5:** Compare 0.41 and 0.409.

**Write 0.41 as 0.410.**

$$0.4\ 1\ 0$$
$$0.4\ 0\ 9$$

**Then compare.** ↑ —1>0, so 0.41>0.409.

**Example 6:** Compare 6.53 and 6.57.

$$6.5\ 3$$
$$6.5\ 7$$

↑ —3<7, so 6.53<6.57.

## EXERCISES

Name the place value of each underlined digit.

**1.** 0.4<u>7</u>
**2.** 0.62<u>9</u>
**3.** 4.5<u>9</u>1
**4.** 27.800<u>5</u>
**5.** <u>6</u>.2425

Write a decimal for each.

**6.** sixty hundredths  *, 0 6 0*

**7.** four hundred twelve thousandths *.4 12*

**8.** eleven and eight tenths *11. 80*

**9.** two hundred ten and two thousandths *210, 002*

**10.** twelve thousand and thirteen hundredths *12, 000. 13*

Compare. Write <, =, or > for each ●.

**11.** 4.95 ● 9.45
**12.** 0.01 ⟩ 0.001
**13.** 0.612 ⟨ 0.7

**14.** 0.3 ⟩ 0.30
**15.** 0.112 ⟨ 0.211
**16.** 0.121 ⟨ 0.2021

**17.** 4.0506 ⟨ 4.506
**18.** 17.9 ⟩ 0.179
**19.** 0.402 ⟩ 0.4020

Arrange in order from least to greatest.

**20.** 0.409, 4.09, 0.49
*1    3    2*

**21.** 2.23, 0.223, 0.322
*3    1    2*

**22.** 0.7, 0.68, 0.91
*2  6    3*

Arrange in order from greatest to least.

**23.** 9.4, 0.94, 0.094
*1    2    3*

**24.** 0.05, 0.5, 5.0
*3    2    1*

**25.** 0.68, 0.86, 0.068
*2    1    3*

Write a decimal for the given number.

**26.** A honeybee beats its wings once every five thousandths of a second.
*.005*

**27.** A lightning stroke takes about one thousandth of a second.
*.001*

## 1.4 ADDING DECIMALS

S. Calabi/Leo de Wys Inc.

**Nora bought a down jacket for $129.36 and cross-country skis for $78.75. How much did she spend in all?**

You can find the answer by adding $129.36 and $78.75. To add decimals, line up the decimal points, and add in the same way that you add whole numbers.

**Example 1:**  Add 129.36 and 78.75.

Line up the decimal points.

$$
\begin{array}{r}
1\ 1\ 1\ 1 \\
1\ 2\ 9.3\ 6 \\
+\ \ \ 7\ 8.7\ 5 \\
\hline
2\ 0\ 8.1\ 1
\end{array}
$$

Nora spent $208.11 in all.

**Example 2:**  5.2 + 6.7 + 9.4

$$
\begin{array}{r}
1 \\
5.2 \\
6.7 \\
+\ 9.4 \\
\hline
2\ 1.3
\end{array}
$$

**Example 3:**  25 + 3.68 + 4.9

$$
\begin{array}{r}
1\ 1 \\
2\ 5 \\
3.6\ 8 \\
+\ \ \ 4.9 \\
\hline
3\ 3.5\ 8
\end{array}
$$

When no decimal point is used, it is understood to follow the last digit.

## EXERCISES

Add.

**1.**  4.6
+5.7

**2.**  7.8
+3.5

**3.**  2.38
+0.64

**4.**  6.96
+5.89

**5.**  8.53
+9.78

**6.** $\begin{array}{r} 29.61 \\ +22.08 \\ \hline \end{array}$  **7.** $\begin{array}{r} 41.49 \\ +60.09 \\ \hline \end{array}$  **8.** $\begin{array}{r} 6.85 \\ +7.019 \\ \hline \end{array}$  **9.** $\begin{array}{r} 5 \\ +4.08 \\ \hline \end{array}$  **10.** $\begin{array}{r} 12.3 \\ +\ 8.74 \\ \hline \end{array}$

**11.** $0.9 + 0.31 + 1.8$ **12.** $7 + 2.3 + 13.09$ **13.** $8 + 6.9 + 7.85$

**14.** $6.5 + 9 + 0.09$ **15.** $117.4 + 2.08 + 3.9$ **16.** $412 + 8.35 + 2.99$

**17.** $46.3 + 87.06$ **18.** $89.61 + 28.5$ **19.** $76.19 + 84.675$

**20.** Donna bought the following items. How much did she spend in all?

| eggs | $0.89 |
| milk | $1.95 |
| yogurt | $0.59 |
| apples | $1.29 |
| bread | $1.11 |
| peanut butter | $1.79 |

**21.** Bob wants to buy the following items. What is the total amount?

| video recorder | $895 |
| blank cassette | $12.75 |
| movie cassette | $49.95 |
| movie cassette | $58.95 |
| television | $565 |

*EXTRA PRACTICE page 473, set 2*

---

## CHECKPOINT

Write in place-value form.

**1.** forty-three thousand, six hundred eight    43,608

Write a decimal for each.

**2.** fourteen hundredths   .014

**3.** nine hundred five thousandths

Compare. Write $<$, $=$, or $>$ for each ●.

**4.** 657 ● 675 **5.** 8.09 ● 8.090 **6.** 0.438 ● 0.44

Add.

**7.** $\begin{array}{r} 56 \\ 213 \\ +\ 64 \\ \hline \end{array}$ **8.** $614 + 49$ **9.** $\begin{array}{r} 5.84 \\ +3.6 \\ \hline \end{array}$ **10.** $76.7 + 7.82$

**17**

## RECOGNIZING ADDITION PROBLEMS

**When there are two or more groups of objects, you can use addition to find how many objects in all.**

**Example 1:** Susan made 25 plant hangers to sell at a craft show. She sold all of them and received orders for 19 more. How many plant hangers did she sell in all?

*Solution:*   Add 25 and 19.

$$
\begin{array}{r}
1\phantom{0} \\
2\ 5 \\
+\ 1\ 9 \\
\hline
4\ 4
\end{array}
$$

So Susan sold 44 plant hangers in all.

**When there are two or more like amounts or measurements, you can use addition to find how much in all.**

**Example 2:** A video game costs $34.95. Sales tax is $2.45. How much is the total cost?

*Solution:* Add 34.95 and 2.45.

$$
\begin{array}{r}
{\scriptstyle 1\ \ 1} \\
3\ 4.9\ 5 \\
+\quad 2.4\ 5 \\
\hline
3\ 7.4\ 0
\end{array}
$$

So the total cost is $37.40.

## EXERCISES

Each of the following problems can be solved by using addition. Write the addition. Solve.

1. Sally made 5 dry-flower arrangements and needs to make 7 more. How many will she make in all?

2. Bill has refinished 3 chairs. He has 5 more chairs to do. How many will he refinish in all?

3. Nicholas walked 0.6 mile from his house to Matthew's house. Then together they walked 0.5 mile to the library. How far did Nicholas walk?

4. Lou had 6 video games. He received 2 more on his birthday. How many video games does he have now?

5. The length of a table is 48 inches. A 12-inch table leaf is inserted. What is the length of the table now?

6. Jennifer has collected 7 miniatures. Her display case has room for 5 more. How many miniatures can the case display?

7. Michael had 24 model cars. He bought 4 more. How many model cars does he have in all?

8. Juan bought records for $9.95, $12.50, and $8.88. How much did he spend in all?

9. Kumi bought a gym bag for $8.99 and a racquetball racquet for $14.95. Tax was $1.20. How much did she spend in all?

10. During the closeout sale, one salesperson had sales of $1862.34 on Friday and $1490.49 on Saturday. How much did the salesperson sell in those two days?

*EXTRA PRACTICE page 473, set 3*

## MATH NOTE

You have 10 coins totaling $0.59. None of the coins is a half-dollar. What are the 10 coins?

## 1.6 SUBTRACTING WHOLE NUMBERS

H. Armstrong Roberts

**A new car costs \$8347. A rebate of \$450 is being offered. What is the cost of the car after the rebate?**

**Example 1:** Subtract 450 from 8347.

```
    12
  7 2̸ 14
  8̸ 3̸ 4̸ 7
 −  4 5 0
  7 8 9 7
```
↑ ↑ ↑ ↑──── Subtract the ones.
       └──── Borrow. Then subtract the tens.
       └──── Borrow. Then subtract the hundreds.
       └──── Subtract the thousands.

The cost of the car after the rebate is \$7897.

**Example 2:** 56,438 − 49,229

```
  4 16    2 18
  5̸ 6̸,4 3̸ 8̸
 −4 9,2 2 9
    7,2 0 9
```

**Example 3:** 6003 − 2368

```
        9 9
  5 1̸0̸ 1̸0̸ 13
  6̸ 0̸ 0̸ 3̸
 −2 3 6 8
  3 6 3 5
```

You can check a subtraction result by adding.

**Example 4:**

Add these numbers.
Record the sum. ──→

```
   1 9 6 2 ←
  −1 8 2 3
   1 3 9
   1 9 6 2 ←
```

It checks if these two numbers are the same.

## EXERCISES

Subtract. Check your results.

**1.** 113 − 85  **2.** 172 − 98  **3.** 180 − 94  **4.** 215 − 79

**5.** 294 − 105  **6.** 250 − 119  **7.** 512 − 283  **8.** 416 − 379

**9.**   763
   −241

**10.**   9876
   −5034

**11.**   11,374
   − 9,032

**12.**   6187
   −3147

**13.**   734
   −519

**14.**   816
   −407

**15.**   9324
   −8155

**16.**   14,602
   − 8,327

**17.**   36,415
   −18,248

**18.**   9002
   −6435

**19.**   17,113
   − 6,248

**20.**   4905
   −3897

**21.**   456,040
   −137,894

**22.**   22,111
   − 8,763

**23.**   10,203
   − 5,681

**24.**   39,041
   −28,951

**25.**   600,000
   − 12,346

**26.**   901,110
   −302,405

**27.**   8,370,120
   −6,093,214

Parentheses ( ) show which operation to do first.

**Examples:** a. $(22-10)+8$
   $12+8$
   **20**

b. $22-(10+8)$
   $22-18$
   **4**

Find each result.

**28.** $(53-37)+9$

**29.** $53-(37+9)$

**30.** $(84+39)-(62-18)$

EXTRA PRACTICE page 474, set 4

*SKILLS REVIEW*

Add.

**31.**   743
   +591

**32.**   415
   +284

**33.**   1256
   +1434

**34.**   9120
   +4684

**35.**   2.8
   3.5
   +14.6

**36.**   17
   24.3
   + 8.39

**37.**   32.5
   6.95
   +70

**38.**   34.68
   +149.7

Vytas Beniusis

**Mr. Umbro earned $347.20 last week. After deductions (for taxes, union dues, and so on) his pay was $274.29. How much was deducted from his earnings?**

To find the amount deducted, subtract $274.29 from $347.20. When subtracting decimals, write the digits so that the decimal points are lined up, and then subtract in the same way that you subtract whole numbers.

**Example 1:** 347.20 − 274.29

Line up the decimal points.

```
        11
 2 14 6│ 1 10
 3 4 7 . 2 0
-2 7 4 . 2 9
 7 2 . 9 1
```

Mr. Umbro had $72.91 deducted from his earnings.

Sometimes it is helpful to write 0's to the right of a decimal before you subtract.

**Example 2:** 634.5 − 78.09

```
    12
 5 2 14 4 10
 6 3 4 . 5 0
 −  7 8 . 0 9
 5 5 6 . 4 1
```

**Example 3:** 20 − 9.58

```
   9   9
 1 10 10 10
 2 0 . 0 0
 −  9 . 5 8
 1 0 . 4 2
```

## EXERCISES

Subtract. Check your results.

| | | | |
|---|---|---|---|
| **1.** 15.2 − 2.3 | **2.** 36.1 − 9.8 | **3.** 24.04 − 17.39 | **4.** 46.21 − 18.36 | **5.** 17 − 4.29 |
| **6.** 46.3 − 27.49 | **7.** 94.7 − 38.59 | **8.** 62 − 7.84 | **9.** 392.5 − 269.6 | **10.** 500.8 − 241.9 |

**11.** $21.3 - 18.7$    **12.** $70.1 - 52.4$    **13.** $40.1 - 14.95$    **14.** $23 - 17.56$

| **15.** $9.834$ | **16.** $7.059$ | **17.** $8.15$ | **18.** $9.89$ | **19.** $403$ |
|---|---|---|---|---|
| $-6.04$ | $-1.06$ | $-4.652$ | $-7.021$ | $-198.7$ |

| **20.** $0.92$ | **21.** $0.131$ | **22.** $6.01$ | **23.** $7.4$ | **24.** $601$ |
|---|---|---|---|---|
| $-0.785$ | $-0.0412$ | $-4.902$ | $-1.235$ | $-76.31$ |

EXTRA PRACTICE page 474, set 5

# CALCULATOR NOTE

When you use a calculator to add and/or subtract with three or more numbers, the calculator will display a **subtotal** (a partial total up to that point) each time you press $+$ or $-$.

| ENTER | DISPLAY | |
|---|---|---|
| **25.99** | $25.99$ | |
| $+$ | $25.99$ | **subtotal** |
| **9.95** | $9.95$ | |
| $-$ | $35.94$ | **subtotal** $(25.99 + 9.95)$ |
| **14.98** | $14.98$ | |
| $+$ | $20.96$ | **subtotal** $(25.99 + 9.95 - 14.98)$ |
| **11.95** | $11.95$ | |
| $=$ | $32.91$ | **total** $(25.99 + 9.95 - 14.98 + 11.95)$ |

Use a calculator to find each total. Perform the operations from left to right.

**1.** $18.55 + 9.78 + 5.09$    **2.** $21.95 + 40.08 + 38.79$

**3.** $(17.25 - 9.87) + 16$    **4.** $(31.06 - 8.74) + 23.91$

John Lawlor/Click/Chicago Ltd.

**When you take away part of a group (or amount), you can use subtraction to find the number left.**

**Example 1:** 15 tennis players entered a tournament. 7 players have been eliminated. How many players are left in the tournament?

*Solution:* **15 − 7 = 8**

So 8 players are left in the tournament.

**When you compare two groups, you can use subtraction to find how many more (or less) there are in one group than in the other.**

**Example 2:** Matt made 15 free throws. Joe made 7 free throws. How many more free throws did Matt make?

*Solution:* **15 − 7 = 8**

So Matt made 8 more free throws than Joe.

**When you have part of a group missing, you can use subtraction to find how many more are needed.**

**Example 3:** Mary wants 15 sponsors for the walkathon. She has 7 sponsors. How many more does she need?

*Solution:* **15 − 7 = 8**

So Mary needs 8 more sponsors.

**When you separate a group on the basis of a certain quality to find how many have (or do not have) that quality, you can use subtraction.**

**Example 4:** Cecelia has 15 record albums. Of these, 7 are concert albums. How many are not concert albums?

*Solution:* **15 − 7 = 8**

So Cecelia has 8 albums that are not from concerts.

## EXERCISES

Each of the following problems can be solved by using subtraction. Write the subtraction. Solve.

1. There were 15 balloons in the air. After 2 hours, 9 had landed. How many were still in the air?

2. Neil planned to run 10 miles. When he passed Lucy's house, he knew he had run 6 miles. How much farther did he have to run?

3. Twelve contestants were competing in a look-alike contest. Three persons were eliminated in the first vote. How many were still in the contest?

4. Ellen has $67. Alice has $48. How much less money does Alice have?

5. Brenda can high jump 195 cm. The school record is 208 cm. To tie the record, how much higher will Brenda need to jump?

6. Milwaukee is 90 miles from Chicago. Along the way, Bill passed a sign that read "Milwaukee 37 miles." How far had Bill driven?

7. A turkey needs to roast for 3 hours. Baked potatoes take 1 hour. How long should the turkey cook before the potatoes are put in the oven?

8. A class raised $470 to buy a gift for the school. The gift costs $565. How much more money is needed?

9. A gas tank holds 76 liters. When it was last filled, it took 52 liters to fill it. How much gas (in liters) was in the tank before it was filled?

10. 53 bicycles are locked to the bike rack. Of these, 37 are ten-speeds. How many are not ten-speeds?

*EXTRA PRACTICE page 474, set 6*

Robert V. Eckert Jr.

**In a recent 26-mile marathon, the number of runners was listed in different ways:**

**Marathon records: 14,308 runners . . .**
**Newspaper: more than 14,000 runners . . .**
**Television: about 14,300 runners . . .**

Only the marathon records used the *exact* number. The others *rounded* that number. Rounded numbers are easier to say, record, and remember.

**When rounding to any place value, check the digit to the right of that place-value position, and**

**—round up if that digit is 5 or more.**

**—round down if that digit is less than 5.**

**Example 1:** Round 41,258 to the nearest hundred.

**Check the digit to the right of the hundreds place.**    **41,258**

**Since it is 5, round up.**    **41,300**

**Replace whole-number place values to the right of the hundreds place with 0's.**

**Example 2:** Round 67.49 to the nearest whole number. Rounding to the nearest whole number means rounding to the nearest one.

**Check the digit to the right of the ones place.**    **67.49**

**Since it is less than 5, round down.**    **67**

**Example 3:** Round 0.5974 to the nearest hundredth.

**Check the digit to the right of the hundredths place.**    **0.5974**

**Since it is more than 5, round up.**    **0.60**

**Example 4:** Round 2089 to its largest place value.

**Check the digit to the right of the thousands place.**    **2089**

**Since it is less than 5, round down.**    **2000**

## EXERCISES

Round to the nearest ten.

**1.** 683     **2.** 4491     **3.** 60,035     **4.** 6666     **5.** 9302

Round to the nearest hundred.

**6.** 1984     **7.** 2551     **8.** 958     **9.** 12,760     **10.** 59,827

Round to the nearest thousand.

**11.** 2524     **12.** 3468     **13.** 51,600     **14.** 8916     **15.** 40,612

Round to the nearest whole number.

**16.** 53.2     **17.** 49.6     **18.** 200.7     **19.** 35.5     **20.** 4.08

Round to the nearest tenth.

**21.** 48.62     **22.** 27.55     **23.** 2.96     **24.** 5.32     **25.** 8.08

Round to the nearest hundredth.

**26.** 0.157     **27.** 6.598     **28.** 0.105     **29.** 0.047     **30.** 8.104

Round to the largest place value.

**31.** 4536     **32.** 975     **33.** 59.86     **34.** 8.42     **35.** 607

*EXTRA PRACTICE page 475, set 7*

## SKILLS REVIEW

Subtract.

**36.**
$$\begin{array}{r} 4312 \\ -2694 \\ \hline \end{array}$$

**37.**
$$\begin{array}{r} 8092 \\ -6594 \\ \hline \end{array}$$

**38.**
$$\begin{array}{r} 3630 \\ -2943 \\ \hline \end{array}$$

**39.**
$$\begin{array}{r} 4003 \\ -2760 \\ \hline \end{array}$$

**40.**
$$\begin{array}{r} 18.3 \\ -13.9 \\ \hline \end{array}$$

**41.**
$$\begin{array}{r} 46 \\ -17.9 \\ \hline \end{array}$$

**42.**
$$\begin{array}{r} 54.34 \\ -29.9 \\ \hline \end{array}$$

**43.**
$$\begin{array}{r} 60.3 \\ -24.87 \\ \hline \end{array}$$

**ESTIMATING SUMS**

**Nathan spent $8.95 for an album, $1.75 for miniature golf, $3.50 for a movie ticket, and $4.35 for food. Estimate how much he spent in all.**

When estimating sums, you can round each number to any convenient place value. Then add mentally.

**Example 1:**

| 8.95 | 9 |
|---|---|
| 1.75 | 2 |
| 3.50 | 4 |
| +4.35 | +4 |
| | 19 |

**Example 2:** 2456+892

| 2000 | | 2500 |
|---|---|---|
| +1000 | or | + 900 |
| 3000 | | 3400 |

Nathan spent about $19 in all.

## EXERCISES

Estimate.

**1.**  33
  +56

**2.**  75
  +46

**3.**  81
  +95

**4.**  62
  +74

**5.**  77
  +74

**6.**  249
  +659

**7.**  750
  +590

**8.**  17.4
  + 9.5

**9.**  34.6
  +18.2

**10.**  86.3
  +24.9

**11.** 5.7+3.9+7.2

**12.** 8.3+6.4+4.9

**13.** 23.8+28.3+8.8

**14.** 48.95+94.9

**15.** 41.7+68.3

**16.** 129+57.1

**17.** 452+1109

**18.** 164+230

**19.** 2842+3481

Estimate to decide if each given answer is reasonable or not. Write *yes* or *no*.

**20.**  146
  +355
  501

**21.**  3456
  + 982
  5438

**22.**  2.95
  2.75
  +1.35
  10.05

**23.**  19.95
  +11.95
  31.90

**Jessica plans to buy a canoe. The catalog shows a list price of $379.95. The sale price is $209.50. Estimate the difference between the two prices.**

When estimating differences, you can round each number to any convenient place value. Then subtract mentally.

Jacqueline Durand

**Example:**

$$\begin{array}{rr} 379.95 & 400 \\ -209.50 & -200 \\ \hline & 200 \end{array}$$

The difference between the prices is about $200.

## *EXERCISES*

Estimate.

| | | | | |
|---|---|---|---|---|
| **1.** $\begin{array}{r} 8.4 \\ -3.9 \\ \hline \end{array}$ | **2.** $\begin{array}{r} 7.5 \\ -2.6 \\ \hline \end{array}$ | **3.** $\begin{array}{r} 28.4 \\ -8.9 \\ \hline \end{array}$ | **4.** $\begin{array}{r} 46.9 \\ -9.8 \\ \hline \end{array}$ | **5.** $\begin{array}{r} 360 \\ -180 \\ \hline \end{array}$ |
| **6.** $\begin{array}{r} 749 \\ -438 \\ \hline \end{array}$ | **7.** $\begin{array}{r} 2309 \\ -842 \\ \hline \end{array}$ | **8.** $\begin{array}{r} 1940 \\ -390 \\ \hline \end{array}$ | **9.** $\begin{array}{r} 17.75 \\ -8.60 \\ \hline \end{array}$ | **10.** $\begin{array}{r} 29 \\ -14.25 \\ \hline \end{array}$ |
| **11.** $\begin{array}{r} 50 \\ -26.30 \\ \hline \end{array}$ | **12.** $\begin{array}{r} 35 \\ -19.50 \\ \hline \end{array}$ | **13.** $\begin{array}{r} 256.9 \\ -118.4 \\ \hline \end{array}$ | **14.** $\begin{array}{r} 790 \\ -230.7 \\ \hline \end{array}$ | **15.** $\begin{array}{r} 918 \\ -372.4 \\ \hline \end{array}$ |

**16.** $100 - 46.95$

**17.** $1240 - 175$

**18.** $2350 - 1258$

**19.** $3491 - 1889$

Estimate to decide if each given answer is reasonable or not. Write *yes* or *no*.

| | | | |
|---|---|---|---|
| **20.** $\begin{array}{r} 83 \\ -49 \\ \hline 46 \end{array}$ | **21.** $\begin{array}{r} 29.5 \\ -8.15 \\ \hline 21.35 \end{array}$ | **22.** $\begin{array}{r} 48.9 \\ -29.4 \\ \hline 19.5 \end{array}$ | **23.** $\begin{array}{r} 6802 \\ -3221 \\ \hline 2681 \end{array}$ |

*EXTRA PRACTICE page 475, set 8*

J.A. Meyers/Jam Photography

The following steps are useful in solving a problem:

1. **Read the problem carefully. Decide what information is given and what you are to find.**

2. **Make a plan for solving the problem.**

3. **Do the computation.**

4. **Answer the question.**

5. **Check your answer with the information in the problem to see if the answer is reasonable.**

**Example:** Leslie bought a backpack for $25.95 and hiking boots for $39.95. How much did she spend?

**Read:**  *Given:*  Backpack costs $25.95.
Boots cost $39.95.

*To find:*  total bill

**Plan:**  Decide which operation (addition or subtraction) can be used to solve the problem. This problem involves combining two amounts, so you use addition.

**Compute:**

$$
\begin{array}{r}
{\scriptstyle 1\ \ 1\ \ 1}\phantom{0} \\
2\,5.9\,5 \\
+\,3\,9.9\,5 \\
\hline
6\,5.9\,0
\end{array}
$$

**Answer:**  Leslie spent $65.90.

**Check:**  In this case, estimate the sum.

$$
\begin{array}{r}
30 \\
+40 \\
\hline
70 \ \ \swarrow
\end{array}
$$

70 is a reasonable estimate for the addition.

## EXERCISES

1. The total repair bill after an accident was $955. Insurance paid only $725. How much did the owner have to pay?

2. Max earned $22,050 last year. He paid $5753 in taxes. What was his income after taxes?

3. A phone bill listed long-distance charges of $4.95 and $6.52. What is the total of these charges?

4. Suzanne bought wrapping paper for $2, ribbon for $0.79, tape for $0.49, and cards at $0.85 and $1.25. Tax was $0.32. How much did she pay for these items?

5. Jim bought a bicycle for $259. It was marked down from $315. How much was it marked down?

6. The Scanlons paid $475 in rent, $41.52 for electricity, $24.95 for phone service, and $20.16 for gas. What was the total for these expenses?

7. Laura cashed a check for $75.10. She deposited all but $15. How much did she deposit?

8. Matthew's savings account had $542.34 before his deposit of $25. What is his new balance?

9. An airline flight had reservations from 248 passengers but 27 of these were no-shows. How many passengers with reservations took the flight?

10. Bill's and Marguerite's dinners came to $19.50. They left a $3 tip. What was the total cost?

11. Emily spent the following amounts on a ski vacation: $249 for airfare, $231.25 for lodging, $95 for lift tickets, $125 for lessons, and $205 for food. How much did she spend in all?

12. Last year a real estate tax bill was $1392.44. This year the tax bill was $1444.29. By how much did the real estate taxes increase?

EXTRA PRACTICE page 475, set 9

## MATH NOTE

The sum of two numbers is 95. The difference of the same numbers is 27. What are the two numbers?

Many persons keep money in a checking account. Then when they need to pay a bill or want to give money to another person, they simply write a check. This check is an order to the bank to pay the amount of the check from that checking account.

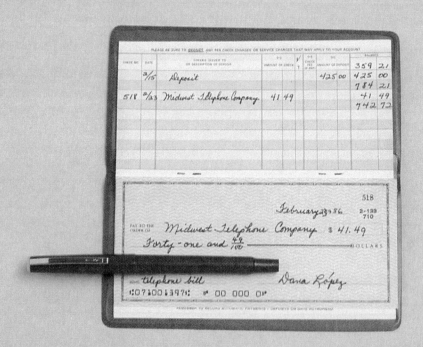

Write as you would on a check, using words and a fraction.

1. $25.00
2. $95.48
3. $73.85
4. $50.67
5. $136.08
6. $249.51
7. $468.18
8. $382.23

Write in place-value form. 1.1

**1.** twenty-five thousand, four hundred eight

**2.** five billion, three hundred million, eighteen thousand

**3.** seven million, thirty thousand, nine hundred one

Name the place value of each underlined digit.

**4.** 4̲30,625    **5.** 71,9̲04    **6.** 1̲4,697    **7.** 105̲,986,320

Compare. Write < or > for each ⬤.

**8.** 34⬤43    **9.** 903⬤930    **10.** 1659⬤1569

Arrange in order from least to greatest.

**11.** 195, 159, 915, 519    **12.** 1985, 1895, 5198, 5189

Add. 1.2

**13.**  58
      +47

**14.**  173
       +969

**15.**  2847
       + 989

**16.**  5504
       +4836

**17.** 395 + 68 + 208    **18.** 1607 + 198 + 3232

Write a decimal for each. 1.3

**19.** eighty-two thousandths    **20.** four tenths

**21.** fifty-nine and twenty-seven hundredths

Compare. Write <, =, or > for each ⬤.

**22.** 0.14⬤0.140    **23.** 3.29⬤3.92    **24.** 0.554⬤0.545

Arrange in order from greatest to least.

**25.** 3, 0.3, 3.3, 3.03    **26.** 16, 0.16, 0.016, 1.6

Add.

**27.** $\quad 9.7$
$\quad\ +5.4$

**28.** $\quad 10.3$
$\quad\ +\ 7.81$

**29.** $\quad 290.06$
$\quad\ +980.98$

**30.** $\quad 37$
$\quad +25.8$

**31.** $0.7+6.51+0.308$

**32.** $19.3+40.07+3.8$

**33.** $128+12.08+1.208$

**34.** $43.8+5.61+80.09$

Subtract.

**35.** $\quad 354$
$\quad -159$

**36.** $\quad 800$
$\quad -365$

**37.** $\quad 1285$
$\quad -1191$

**38.** $\quad 6503$
$\quad -4994$

**39.** $2900-561$

**40.** $32,040-6753$

Find each result.

**41.** $(37+10)-18$

**42.** $(73-48)+36$

Subtract.

**43.** $\quad 32.4$
$\quad -17.6$

**44.** $\quad 60.8$
$\quad -\ 8.9$

**45.** $\quad 36.06$
$\quad -19.87$

**46.** $\quad 40$
$\quad -23.8$

**47.** $148-84.05$

**48.** $22.5-1.79$

**49.** $30.5-15.84$

**50.** $924-835.79$

**51.** $56.4-30.8$

**52.** $20-16.39$

Round to the nearest ten.

**53.** 548

**54.** 37.3

**55.** 296.4

Round to the nearest hundred.

**56.** 873          **57.** 2439          **58.** 3061

Round to the nearest thousand.

**59.** 1258          **60.** 1443          **61.** 8578

Round to the nearest tenth.

**62.** 16.16          **63.** 3.54          **64.** 48.97

Round to the nearest hundredth.

**65.** 0.346          **66.** 4.087          **67.** 9.864

Round to the largest place value.

**68.** 75.3          **69.** 2261          **70.** 9.68

Estimate each sum.                                 1.10

**71.**   26.8
    +34.9

**72.**   781
    +524.7

**73.**   83.83
    +76.5

Estimate each difference.                          1.11

**74.**   84.3
    −27.3

**75.**   893
    −245.6

**76.**   92.3
    −34.68

Solve.                                          1.5,
1.8,
1.12

**77.** Gail bought a calculator for $15.95. Sales tax was $1.12. What was the total bill?

**78.** The bicycle path around the park is 15.4 km long. The running path through the park is 9.8 km long. How much longer is the bicycle path?

Write in place-value form.

**1.** seventy thousand, sixty-one

**2.** eight hundred nine

**3.** thirteen and nine tenths

**4.** forty and eighty-two hundredths

Name the place value of each underlined digit.

**5.** 1587.3          **6.** 209.38          **7.** 17.092          **8.** 60.58

Compare. Write <, =, or > for each ●.

**9.** 87●78          **10.** 0.2●0.20          **11.** 6.7●6.72          **12.** 10.2●3.58

Add.

**13.**   436          **14.**   607          **15.**   8.76          **16.**   10.3
   +985             +608             +3.9             +98.87

**17.** 364.2 + 48.07 + 6.778          **18.** 703 + 6.52 + 8.473

Subtract.

**19.**   519          **20.**   1841          **21.**   56.7          **22.**   81.09
   −372             − 676             −29.35             −13.7

**23.** 256 − 16.48          **24.** 352.72 − 173.483

Round to the largest place value.

**25.** 1990          **26.** 2.41          **27.** 35.4          **28.** 408.95

Estimate each sum or difference.

**29.**   49.3          **30.**   209.5          **31.**   58.3          **32.**   42.30
   +17.8             + 85.6             −30.8             −13.86

Solve.

**33.** Carl bought a down vest that sells for $49.95. He got a discount of $12.49. How much did he pay for the vest?

**34.** Jill earns $3.80 an hour. For working overtime she earns $1.90 more an hour. How much does she earn per hour for overtime work?

## PREVIEW TEST

Multiply.

**1.** $6 \times 7$     **2.** $9 \times 2$     **3.** $0 \times 9$     **4.** $1 \times 16$

**5.**  $\begin{array}{r} 12 \\ \times 3 \end{array}$     **6.**  $\begin{array}{r} 25 \\ \times 8 \end{array}$     **7.**  $\begin{array}{r} 122 \\ \times 5 \end{array}$     **8.**  $\begin{array}{r} 67 \\ \times 16 \end{array}$

**9.**  $\begin{array}{r} 72 \\ \times 58 \end{array}$     **10.**  $\begin{array}{r} 407 \\ \times 30 \end{array}$     **11.**  $\begin{array}{r} 345 \\ \times 205 \end{array}$     **12.**  $\begin{array}{r} 886 \\ \times 435 \end{array}$

**13.** $16 \times 10$     **14.** $30 \times 20$     **15.** $36 \times 100$     **16.** $240 \times 50$

Copy and complete by placing the decimal point in the product.

**17.**  $\begin{array}{r} 32 \\ \times 2.3 \\ \hline 96 \\ 64 \\ \hline 736 \end{array}$     **18.**  $\begin{array}{r} 6.7 \\ \times 5.4 \\ \hline 268 \\ 335 \\ \hline 3618 \end{array}$     **19.**  $\begin{array}{r} 3.21 \\ \times 0.8 \\ \hline 2568 \end{array}$     **20.**  $\begin{array}{r} 0.08 \\ \times 0.34 \\ \hline 32 \\ 24 \\ \hline 272 \end{array}$

Multiply.

**21.**  $\begin{array}{r} 67 \\ \times 0.3 \end{array}$     **22.**  $\begin{array}{r} 43 \\ \times 0.7 \end{array}$     **23.**  $\begin{array}{r} 89 \\ \times 3.8 \end{array}$     **24.**  $\begin{array}{r} 5.3 \\ \times 5 \end{array}$

**25.**  $\begin{array}{r} 2.3 \\ \times 0.8 \end{array}$     **26.**  $\begin{array}{r} 5.7 \\ \times 0.8 \end{array}$     **27.**  $\begin{array}{r} 16.2 \\ \times 9.3 \end{array}$     **28.**  $\begin{array}{r} 13.2 \\ \times 6.9 \end{array}$

**29.** $0.08 \times 10$     **30.** $24.9 \times 0.01$     **31.** $76 \times 0.001$     **32.** $2.3 \times 100$

Estimate.

**33.**  $\begin{array}{r} 58 \\ \times 12 \end{array}$     **34.**  $\begin{array}{r} 183 \\ \times 37 \end{array}$

Solve.

**35.** Chris gets $7.25 an hour. If she works 47 hours, how much does she earn?

**36.** A beekeeper has 6 rows of hives. If each row has 10 hives, how many hives are there in all?

37

# MULTIPLYING A 2-DIGIT NUMBER BY A 1-DIGIT NUMBER

P & L Hermann/Tom Stack & Associates

**At $82 an hour for a helicopter ride, what would the total cost be for a 3-hour trip?**

**Example 1:**  Multiply 82 and 3.

$$
\begin{array}{r}
8\ 2 \\
\times\ \ 3 \\
\hline
2\ 4\ 6
\end{array}
$$

$\longleftarrow 2 \times 3 = 6$

$\longleftarrow 80 \times 3 = 240$

The total cost would be $246.

**Example 2:**

$$
\begin{array}{r}
5 \\
4\ 7 \\
\times\ \ 8 \\
\hline
3\ 7\ 6
\end{array}
$$

$\longleftarrow 7 \times 8 = 56$   Carry 5 tens.

$\longleftarrow 40 \times 8 = 320$   $320 + 50 = 370$

**Example 3:**

$$
\begin{array}{r}
1 \\
7\ 2 \\
\times\ \ 7 \\
\hline
5\ 0\ 4
\end{array}
$$

$\longleftarrow 2 \times 7 = 14$   Carry 1 ten.

$\longleftarrow 70 \times 7 = 490$   $490 + 10 = 500$

**Example 4:**

$$
\begin{array}{r}
4 \\
6\ 5 \\
\times\ \ 8 \\
\hline
5\ 2\ 0
\end{array}
$$

# EXERCISES

Complete the multiplication.

| | | | |
|---|---|---|---|
| **1.** $\begin{array}{r} 1 \\ 72 \\ \times 8 \\ \hline 6 \end{array}$ | **2.** $\begin{array}{r} 3 \\ 45 \\ \times 7 \\ \hline 5 \end{array}$ | **3.** $\begin{array}{r} 5 \\ 19 \\ \times 6 \\ \hline 4 \end{array}$ | **4.** $\begin{array}{r} 2 \\ 24 \\ \times 7 \\ \hline 8 \end{array}$ |
| **5.** $\begin{array}{r} 3 \\ 54 \\ \times 8 \\ \hline 2 \end{array}$ | **6.** $\begin{array}{r} 4 \\ 69 \\ \times 5 \\ \hline 5 \end{array}$ | **7.** $\begin{array}{r} 1 \\ 32 \\ \times 9 \\ \hline 8 \end{array}$ | **8.** $\begin{array}{r} 2 \\ 84 \\ \times 6 \\ \hline 4 \end{array}$ |
| **9.** $\begin{array}{r} 3 \\ 26 \\ \times 5 \\ \hline 0 \end{array}$ | **10.** $\begin{array}{r} 2 \\ 65 \\ \times 4 \\ \hline 0 \end{array}$ | **11.** $\begin{array}{r} 2 \\ 77 \\ \times 4 \\ \hline 8 \end{array}$ | **12.** $\begin{array}{r} 4 \\ 67 \\ \times 6 \\ \hline 2 \end{array}$ |

Multiply.

| | | | |
|---|---|---|---|
| **13.** $\begin{array}{r} 32 \\ \times 4 \\ \hline \end{array}$ | **14.** $\begin{array}{r} 71 \\ \times 5 \\ \hline \end{array}$ | **15.** $\begin{array}{r} 19 \\ \times 1 \\ \hline \end{array}$ | **16.** $\begin{array}{r} 27 \\ \times 1 \\ \hline \end{array}$ |
| **17.** $\begin{array}{r} 83 \\ \times 3 \\ \hline \end{array}$ | **18.** $\begin{array}{r} 22 \\ \times 3 \\ \hline \end{array}$ | **19.** $\begin{array}{r} 30 \\ \times 5 \\ \hline \end{array}$ | **20.** $\begin{array}{r} 90 \\ \times 6 \\ \hline \end{array}$ |
| **21.** $\begin{array}{r} 12 \\ \times 3 \\ \hline \end{array}$ | **22.** $\begin{array}{r} 81 \\ \times 6 \\ \hline \end{array}$ | **23.** $\begin{array}{r} 45 \\ \times 6 \\ \hline \end{array}$ | **24.** $\begin{array}{r} 22 \\ \times 4 \\ \hline \end{array}$ |
| **25.** $\begin{array}{r} 82 \\ \times 9 \\ \hline \end{array}$ | **26.** $\begin{array}{r} 18 \\ \times 8 \\ \hline \end{array}$ | **27.** $\begin{array}{r} 87 \\ \times 6 \\ \hline \end{array}$ | **28.** $\begin{array}{r} 77 \\ \times 5 \\ \hline \end{array}$ |
| **29.** $\begin{array}{r} 43 \\ \times 4 \\ \hline \end{array}$ | **30.** $\begin{array}{r} 37 \\ \times 7 \\ \hline \end{array}$ | **31.** $\begin{array}{r} 72 \\ \times 6 \\ \hline \end{array}$ | **32.** $\begin{array}{r} 99 \\ \times 9 \\ \hline \end{array}$ |
| **33.** $\begin{array}{r} 39 \\ \times 4 \\ \hline \end{array}$ | **34.** $\begin{array}{r} 17 \\ \times 5 \\ \hline \end{array}$ | **35.** $\begin{array}{r} 84 \\ \times 4 \\ \hline \end{array}$ | **36.** $\begin{array}{r} 73 \\ \times 6 \\ \hline \end{array}$ |
| **37.** $\begin{array}{r} 79 \\ \times 9 \\ \hline \end{array}$ | **38.** $\begin{array}{r} 96 \\ \times 8 \\ \hline \end{array}$ | **39.** $\begin{array}{r} 88 \\ \times 7 \\ \hline \end{array}$ | **40.** $\begin{array}{r} 97 \\ \times 7 \\ \hline \end{array}$ |

*EXTRA PRACTICE page 476, set 10*

# MULTIPLYING WHOLE NUMBERS

M.T. O'Keefe/Tom Stack & Associates

**A newspaper uses 68 rolls of newsprint for each edition of the paper. How many rolls are needed for one week if 14 editions are printed?**

**Example 1:**  Multiply 68 and 14.

| Multiply by the number of ones. | Multiply by the number of tens. | Add. |
|---|---|---|
| 68 | 68 | 68 |
| ×14 | ×14 | ×14 |
| 272 | 272 | 272 |
| | 68 | 68 |
| | | 952 |

The newspaper would need 952 rolls of newsprint.

**Example 2:**   152
  ×35
  760
  456
  5320

**Example 3:**   203
  ×152
  406
  1015
  203
  30856

# EXERCISES

Complete the multiplication by adding.

| 1. | 47 | 2. | 85 | 3. | 90 | 4. | 70 |
|---|---|---|---|---|---|---|---|
| | ×39 | | ×17 | | ×36 | | ×43 |
| | 423 | | 595 | | 540 | | 210 |
| | 141 | | 85 | | 270 | | 280 |

Complete the multiplication.

| 5. | 26 | 6. | 37 | 7. | 46 | 8. | 57 |
|---|---|---|---|---|---|---|---|
| | ×81 | | ×63 | | ×30 | | ×20 |
| | 26 | | 111 | | 00 | | 00 |

Multiply.

| 9. | 36 | 10. | 18 | 11. | 75 | 12. | 86 | 13. | 77 |
|---|---|---|---|---|---|---|---|---|---|
| | ×54 | | ×42 | | ×35 | | ×62 | | ×43 |

| 14. | 91 | 15. | 83 | 16. | 80 | 17. | 69 | 18. | 83 |
|---|---|---|---|---|---|---|---|---|---|
| | ×19 | | ×64 | | ×37 | | ×45 | | ×28 |

| 19. | 79 | 20. | 32 | 21. | 127 | 22. | 803 | 23. | 954 |
|---|---|---|---|---|---|---|---|---|---|
| | ×44 | | ×16 | | ×5 | | ×6 | | ×14 |

| 24. | 887 | 25. | 123 | 26. | 670 | 27. | 541 | 28. | 242 |
|---|---|---|---|---|---|---|---|---|---|
| | ×32 | | ×44 | | ×21 | | ×136 | | ×107 |

EXTRA PRACTICE page 476, set 11

## SKILLS REVIEW

Add.

| 29. | 36 | 30. | 68 | 31. | 76 | 32. | 180 | 33. | 205 |
|---|---|---|---|---|---|---|---|---|---|
| | + 9 | | +13 | | +54 | | + 15 | | +118 |

| 34. | 16.8 | 35. | 15.65 | 36. | 6.24 | 37. | 4.095 | 38. | 12.9 |
|---|---|---|---|---|---|---|---|---|---|
| | + 2.5 | | + 3.2 | | +0.08 | | +1.3 | | + 6.03 |

When there are two or more groups with the same number of objects in each, you can use multiplication to find how many objects in all.

**Example 1:** Lynn bought 3 packages of buttons. Each package contained 4 buttons. What is the total number of buttons?

*Solution:*

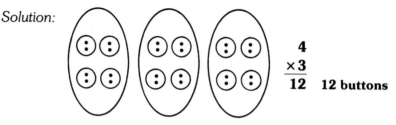

$$\begin{array}{r} 4 \\ \times 3 \\ \hline 12 \end{array}$$  12 buttons

**Example 2:** A classroom was set up with 5 rows of chairs and with 7 chairs in each row. How many chairs are in the classroom?

*Solution:*

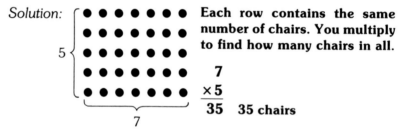

Each row contains the same number of chairs. You multiply to find how many chairs in all.

$$\begin{array}{r} 7 \\ \times 5 \\ \hline 35 \end{array}$$  35 chairs

When there are two or more equal amounts or measurements, you can use multiplication to find how much in all.

**Example 3:** Mike bought 4 concert tickets. If each ticket cost $6, how much did he spend?

*Solution:*

$$\begin{array}{r} 6 \\ \times 4 \\ \hline 24 \end{array}$$  $24

When you are given the length and width of a rectangle (in the same unit of measure), you can use multiplication to find the area (in square units).

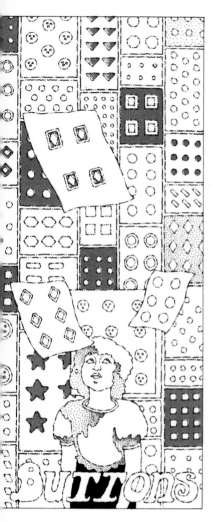

**Example 4:** A patio is 18 feet long and 12 feet wide. What is the area of the patio?

$$\begin{array}{r} 18 \\ \times\,12 \\ \hline 36 \\ 18\phantom{0} \\ \hline 216 \end{array}$$  **216 square feet**

12 feet

18 feet

## EXERCISES

Each of the following problems can be solved by using multiplication. Write the multiplication. Solve.

**1.**
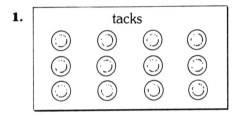

tacks

How many tacks are in 3 packages like this one?

**2.**
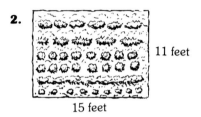

11 feet

15 feet

What is the area of the rectangular garden?

**3.** During the summer, Dave worked 9 weeks and earned $100 a week. How much did he earn during the summer?

**4.** A museum display has 6 rows with 4 tables in each row. How many tables are in the display?

**5.** A garden has 4 rows of sunflowers with 6 sunflower plants in each row. How many sunflower plants are in the garden?

**6.** Cans of fruit juice are sold in packages with 6 cans in a package. How many cans are in 5 packages?

**7.** Jim sold 15 tickets to the school play. Each ticket sells for $5. How much money did Jim take in?

**8.** A rectangular floor is 20 feet long and 16 feet wide. What is the area of the floor?

**9.** A small plane uses 11 gallons of fuel an hour. How many gallons would the plane use in 6 hours?

**10.** Sugar-free gum is packaged 7 sticks to a pack. How many sticks are in 4 packs of gum?

*EXTRA PRACTICE page 476, set 12*

J. Zimmerman/FPG

**For a fund-raising dinner for the rugby team, 80 tickets were sold. Each ticket cost \$20. How much money was taken in?**

**Example 1:**

$$
\begin{array}{r}
80 \longleftarrow \text{1 zero} \\
\times 20 \longleftarrow \text{1 zero} \\
\hline
00 \\
160 \\
\hline
1600 \longleftarrow \text{2 zeros}
\end{array}
$$

$(8 \times 2)$

\$1600 was taken in.

You can use a shortcut when you multiply numbers that have *final* 0 digits. First multiply by using only the digits that are not 0's. Then write as many final 0's in the product as there are in all the factors.

**Example 2:**  20  ×  6  =  120

1 zero               (2 × 6)  1 zero

**Example 3:**  500  ×  30  =  15000

2 zeros   1 zero   (5 × 3)  3 zeros

**Example 4:**  40  ×  50  =  2000

1 zero   1 zero   (4 × 5)  2 zeros

**Example 5:**   Estimate $582 \times 72$.

$$
\begin{array}{r}
582 \\
\times 72
\end{array}
$$
Round each number to its largest place value.
$$
\begin{array}{r}
600 \longleftarrow \text{2 zeros} \\
\times 70 \longleftarrow \text{1 zero} \\
\hline
42000 \longleftarrow \text{3 zeros}
\end{array}
$$

$(6 \times 7)$

## EXERCISES

Copy and complete by writing the correct number of final 0 digits for each product.

**1.** $8 \times 10 = 8$

**2.** $4 \times 50 = 20$

**3.** $20 \times 10 = 2$

**4.** $13 \times 100 = 13$

**5.** $90 \times 100 = 9$

**6.** $70 \times 400 = 28$

**7.** $3 \times 3000 = 9$

**8.** $40 \times 30 = 12$

**9.** $30 \times 200 = 6$

Multiply, using the shortcut.

**10.** $40 \times 10$

**11.** $700 \times 50$

**12.** $9 \times 200$

**13.** $90 \times 60$

**14.** $200 \times 70$

**15.** $800 \times 100$

Estimate each product.

**16.** $82 \times 29$

**17.** $18 \times 32$

**18.** $49 \times 50$

**19.** $11 \times 472$

**20.** $81 \times 573$

**21.** $79 \times 743$

**22.** $98 \times 43$

**23.** $817 \times 27$

**24.** $9171 \times 384$

EXTRA PRACTICE page 477, set 13

## CHECKPOINT

Multiply.

**1.** $\begin{array}{r} 67 \\ \times 7 \\ \hline \end{array}$

**2.** $\begin{array}{r} 25 \\ \times 12 \\ \hline \end{array}$

**3.** $\begin{array}{r} 34 \\ \times 56 \\ \hline \end{array}$

**4.** $\begin{array}{r} 108 \\ \times 26 \\ \hline \end{array}$

**5.** $\begin{array}{r} 483 \\ \times 105 \\ \hline \end{array}$

Estimate.

**6.** $\begin{array}{r} 37 \\ \times 29 \\ \hline \end{array}$

**7.** $\begin{array}{r} 183 \\ \times 31 \\ \hline \end{array}$

**8.** $\begin{array}{r} 688 \\ \times 212 \\ \hline \end{array}$

Solve.

**9.** Sally drove 35 miles an hour for 3 hours. How far did she drive?

**10.** There are 25 cards to a box. How many cards are in 5 boxes?

James P. Rowan

**With a roll of film, 36 pictures can be taken. How many pictures can be taken with 3 rolls of film?**

**Read:**   *Given:*   36 pictures per roll; 3 rolls

*To find:*   total number of pictures

**Plan:**   Which operation (addition, subtraction, or multiplication) can you use? This problem involves 3 groups with the same number of objects in each. So you can multiply.

**Compute:**
$$\begin{array}{r} 36 \\ \times 3 \\ \hline 108 \end{array}$$

**Answer:**   You can take 108 pictures.

**Check:**   Use an estimate to see if the answer seems reasonable.

$$\begin{array}{rr} 36 & 40 \\ \times 3 & \times 3 \\ \hline & 120 \end{array} \;\; \checkmark$$

So the answer of 108 pictures seems reasonable.

# EXERCISES

**1.**

steel-belted
radials
$55

What is the cost of 5 of these tires?

**2.**

pencils

How many pencils are in 6 packages like this one?

**3.** If you spend $54 a week for food, how much do you spend in a year (52 weeks)?

**4.** A salesperson sold 12 pumps at $80 each. What was the total amount of the sales?

**5.** A car gets 30 miles to the gallon. If the car has a 12-gallon tank, how far can it go on a tankful of gasoline?

**6.** Luis has to pay 4 installments of $65 each for a class ski trip. How much does the trip cost?

**7.** A farmer harvests about 42 bushels of wheat per acre. The farmer planted 280 acres of wheat. How many bushels of wheat can the farmer expect to harvest?

**8.** The National Football League has 28 teams. If each team has 44 players, how many football players are in the league?

**9.** Beth gives piano lessons for $15 an hour. If she gave lessons for 5 hours one day, how much money did she make?

**10.** Mark has to make a $57 installment payment every month for 24 months to buy a boat. How much does the boat cost?

**11.** A mail clerk shipped 234 packages one week, 87 the next week, and 176 the third week. How many packages were shipped in all?

**12.** A store manager recorded 895 boxes of shoes in stock. Last month the store sold 85 boxes of shoes. How many boxes of shoes are now in stock?

**13.** A truck's fuel tank holds 120 gallons. The truck gets 6 miles to the gallon when the truck is empty. How many miles can the empty truck go with a full tank?

**14.** When a truck has a full load, it gets 5 miles to the gallon. If the truck has a full load and a 115-gallon tank, how far can the truck go?

## PLACING DECIMAL POINTS IN PRODUCTS

Photo Network

**A truck is loaded with 69 boxes. Each box weighs 8.2 pounds. What is the total weight of the boxes?**

An estimate can be used to decide where to put the decimal point in the product.

**Example 1:**   estimate        exact product

$$
\begin{array}{r}
70 \\
\times 8 \\
\hline
560
\end{array}
\qquad
\begin{array}{r}
69 \\
\times 8.2 \\
\hline
13\ 8 \\
552 \\
\hline
565.8
\end{array}
$$

The boxes weigh 565.8 pounds.

Another way to place the decimal point in a product is to count the total number of digits after the decimal points in the factors. Then place the decimal point in the product so that there are the same number of digits after the decimal point.

**Example 2:**     $3.6$ ⟵ **1 digit after decimal point**
             $\times 2.4$ ⟵ **1 digit after decimal point**
$$
\begin{array}{r}
1\ 44 \\
7\ 2 \\
\hline
8.64
\end{array}
$$ ⟵ **1 + 1, or 2 digits after decimal point**

Sometimes 0's have to be inserted in the product in order to place the decimal point correctly.

**Example 3:**     $0.3$
             $\times 0.2$
$$
\overline{0.06} \quad 3 \times 2 = 6
$$

**Insert 0's
and place the
decimal point.**

## EXERCISES

Copy and complete by placing the decimal point in the product.

| | | | | | | | | | |
|---|---|---|---|---|---|---|---|---|---|
| **1.** | 68 | **2.** | 73 | **3.** | 5 | **4.** | 11 | **5.** | 312 |
| | ×0.1 | | ×0.1 | | ×0.1 | | ×0.1 | | ×0.01 |
| | 68 | | 73 | | 5 | | 11 | | 312 |

| | | | | | | | | | |
|---|---|---|---|---|---|---|---|---|---|
| **6.** | 918 | **7.** | 3421 | **8.** | 1021 | **9.** | 82 | **10.** | 954 |
| | ×0.01 | | ×0.01 | | ×0.01 | | ×0.3 | | ×0.7 |
| | 918 | | 3421 | | 1021 | | 246 | | 6678 |

| | | | | | | | | | |
|---|---|---|---|---|---|---|---|---|---|
| **11.** | 65 | **12.** | 74 | **13.** | 8.4 | **14.** | 9.9 | **15.** | 4.2 |
| | ×1.4 | | ×3.6 | | ×97 | | ×8.3 | | ×2.4 |
| | 260 | | 444 | | 588 | | 297 | | 168 |
| | 65 | | 222 | | 756 | | 792 | | 84 |
| | 910 | | 2664 | | 8148 | | 8217 | | 1008 |

| | | | | | | | | | |
|---|---|---|---|---|---|---|---|---|---|
| **16.** | 6.3 | **17.** | 5.5 | **18.** | 6.7 | **19.** | 0.7 | **20.** | 0.4 |
| | ×14 | | ×71 | | ×7.3 | | ×0.5 | | ×0.1 |
| | 252 | | 55 | | 201 | | 35 | | 4 |
| | 63 | | 385 | | 469 | | | | |
| | 882 | | 3905 | | 4891 | | | | |

| | | | | | | | | | |
|---|---|---|---|---|---|---|---|---|---|
| **21.** | 0.11 | **22.** | 0.01 | **23.** | 0.01 | **24.** | 0.02 | **25.** | 0.13 |
| | ×0.1 | | ×8 | | ×0.01 | | ×0.1 | | ×0.2 |
| | 11 | | 8 | | 1 | | 2 | | 26 |

---

## CALCULATOR NOTE

Check the answers to the exercises above by using a calculator.

**Example:**   $55 \times 2.65 = 145.75$

**Check:**  ENTER          DISPLAY

**55**  $\boxed{\times}$  **2.65**  $\boxed{=}$  $145.75$

49

| *MULTIPLYING DECIMALS* |

FPG

**What is the cost of 55 feet of cable if the cost per foot is $0.65?**

To find the cost, multiply 55 and 0.65 as you would whole numbers. Then place the decimal point in the product.

**Example 1:**

$$55 \longleftarrow \textbf{0 digits after decimal point}$$
$$\times 0.65 \longleftarrow \textbf{2 digits after decimal point}$$
$$\underline{2\ 75}$$
$$\underline{33\ 0}$$
$$35.75 \longleftarrow \textbf{0 + 2, or 2 digits after decimal point}$$

The total cost is $35.75.

**Example 2:**

$$3.4 \longleftarrow \textbf{1 digit after decimal point}$$
$$\times 2.9 \longleftarrow \textbf{1 digit after decimal point}$$
$$\underline{3\ 06}$$
$$\underline{6\ 8}$$
$$9.86 \longleftarrow \textbf{1 + 1, or 2 digits after decimal point}$$

**Example 3:**

$$1.5 \longleftarrow \textbf{1 digit after decimal point}$$
$$\times 0.04 \longleftarrow \textbf{2 digits after decimal point}$$
$$0\ 060 \longleftarrow \textbf{Insert 0's to place the decimal point correctly.}$$
$$\downarrow$$
$$0.060 \longleftarrow \textbf{3 digits after decimal point}$$
$$\downarrow$$
$$0.06 \qquad \textbf{Remember you can omit ending 0's without changing the value.}$$

## EXERCISES

Multiply.

| | | | |
|---|---|---|---|
| **1.** 8.6 ×4.3 | **2.** 7.2 ×35 | **3.** 5.3 ×3.9 | **4.** 4.5 ×14 |
| **5.** 9.1 ×8.6 | **6.** 0.07 ×0.12 | **7.** 0.06 ×0.5 | **8.** 0.09 ×0.3 |
| **9.** 0.78 ×0.65 | **10.** 9.3 ×0.4 | **11.** 0.24 ×0.06 | **12.** 0.84 ×0.6 |
| **13.** 0.59 ×0.5 | **14.** 0.54 ×0.49 | **15.** 6.6 ×0.9 | **16.** 8.6 ×4.8 |
| **17.** 12 ×0.44 | **18.** 38 ×0.56 | **19.** 3.8 ×0.12 | **20.** 0.81 ×0.3 |
| **21.** 0.14 ×8.6 | **22.** 0.01 ×0.04 | **23.** 0.05 ×0.04 | **24.** 7.6 ×0.23 |

**25.** 4.5 × 60

**26.** 3.8 × 4.9

**27.** 19 × 0.4

**28.** 11 × 0.11

**29.** 6.2 × 7.3

**30.** 0.99 × 8.4

**31.** 7.3 × 0.87

**32.** 0.45 × 0.56

**33.** 37 × 0.74

*EXTRA PRACTICE page 477, set 14*

## CALCULATOR NOTE

Use a calculator to find each product. Notice the placement of the decimal point in each product.

**1.** 5 × 10

**2.** 5 × 100

**3.** 5 × 1000

**4.** 34 × 10

**5.** 34 × 100

**6.** 34 × 1000

**7.** 126 × 0.1

**8.** 126 × 0.01

**9.** 126 × 0.001

**10.** 45 × 0.1

**11.** 45 × 0.01

**12.** 45 × 0.001

# MULTIPLYING DECIMALS BY MOVING THE DECIMAL POINT

Artstreet

**At a garage sale, Tim bought a box of old comic books. He paid $0.35 for each comic book. What was the total cost if the box contained 100 comic books?**

**Example:**   $0.35 \times 100 = 0\ 35. = 35$

The box cost $35.

**When multiplying by 10, 100, or 1000, count the number of 0's in 10, 100, or 1000 and move the decimal point in the other factor the same number of places to the right.**

| When you multiply by | the decimal point moves | Examples: |
|---|---|---|
| 10 | 1 place to the right | $0.06 \times 10 = 0.6$ |
| 100 | 2 places to the right | $4.9 \times 100 = 490$ |
| 1000 | 3 places to the right | $0.23 \times 1000 = 230$ |

**When multiplying by 0.1, 0.01 or 0.001, count the number of digits to the right of the decimal point in 0.1, 0.01, or 0.001 and move the decimal point in the other factor the same number of places to the left.**

| When you multiply by | the decimal point moves | Examples: |
|---|---|---|
| 0.1 | 1 place to the left | $4.9 \times 0.1 = 0.49$ |
| 0.01 | 2 places to the left | $3.6 \times 0.01 = 0.036$ |
| 0.001 | 3 places to the left | $44 \times 0.001 = 0.044$ |

# EXERCISES

Multiply.

1. $2.3 \times 10$      2. $56.6 \times 10$      3. $0.14 \times 10$

4. $0.08 \times 10$      5. $5.67 \times 100$      6. $34 \times 100$

7. $1.25 \times 100$      8. $0.076 \times 100$      9. $3.84 \times 1000$

10. $0.11 \times 1000$      11. $2.345 \times 1000$      12. $2.2 \times 1000$

13. $31.4 \times 0.1$      14. $5.6 \times 0.1$      15. $0.74 \times 0.1$

16. $0.3 \times 0.1$      17. $45.9 \times 0.01$      18. $6.7 \times 0.01$

19. $0.5 \times 0.01$      20. $6.5 \times 0.01$      21. $456 \times 0.001$

22. $34 \times 0.001$      23. $4 \times 0.001$      24. $0.5 \times 0.001$

25. $78 \times 0.1$      26. $5.6 \times 10$      27. $34.78 \times 0.01$

28. $0.5 \times 100$      29. $0.9 \times 0.001$      30. $3.4 \times 1000$

31. $12.12 \times 0.1$      32. $12.12 \times 10$      33. $63 \times 0.01$

34. $2.7 \times 100$      35. $0.3 \times 0.1$      36. $0.06 \times 1000$

37. $5.67 \times 10$      38. $3.08 \times 0.001$      39. $18.84 \times 100$

40. $18.84 \times 0.01$      41. $0.006 \times 100$      42. $2.4 \times 0.01$

Solve.

43. Elaine gave to charity 0.1 of the money she made by having a garage sale. She made $165. How much did she give to charity?

EXTRA PRACTICE page 477, set 15

## MATH NOTE

I bought some items at a store. All the items cost the same amount. I bought as many items as the cost in cents of each item. If I spent $2.25, how many items did I buy?

Christopher Morrow/Picture Group

**Some workers are paid by the number of pieces they work on or complete. How much would a worker be paid if 115 pieces were worked on at $1.35 a piece?**

Remember to multiply, add, and place the decimal point.

**Example:**

```
      1.35
   × 115
      6 75
     13 5
    135
   155.25
```

The worker would make $155.25.

## EXERCISES

Copy and complete by placing the decimal point in the product.

1.
```
   4.78
 ×0.49
 23422
```

2.
```
   12.34
 × 44.1
 544194
```

3.
```
   0.145
 ×0.132
  19140
```

4.
```
   99.9
 ×9.99
 998001
```

Multiply.

**5.** 6.48
×32

**6.** 9.37
×45

**7.** 0.104
×42

**8.** 0.309
×81

**9.** 12.6
×14

**10.** 15.8
×1.3

**11.** 562
×3.7

**12.** 8.75
×2.9

**13.** 4.16
×5.8

**14.** 2.08
×6.3

**15.** 7.16
×0.66

**16.** 7.09
×0.15

**17.** 47.3
×1.29

**18.** 36.8
×2.47

**19.** 145
×34.2

**20.** 3.16
×412

**21.** 901
×0.45

**22.** 706
×0.98

**23.** 621
×0.123

**24.** 809
×0.432

**25.** 0.645
×1.98

**26.** 0.721
×4.69

**27.** 0.383
×0.219

**28.** 0.476
×0.48

**29.** 12.63
×4.8

**30.** 156.9
×8.67

**31.** 16.807
×2.9

**32.** 0.206
×0.775

## SKILLS REVIEW

Subtract.

**33.** 36
− 9

**34.** 75
− 8

**35.** 76
−54

**36.** 168
− 24

**37.** 63
−59

**38.** 180
− 15

**39.** 205
−118

**40.** 300
− 36

**41.** 32.6
− 0.9

**42.** 25.16
− 8.72

**43.** 5.06
−2.2

**44.** 6.24
−0.08

**45.** 9.4
−6.03

**46.** 4.095
−1.3

**47.** 12.9
− 6.03

**48.** 0.57
−0.403

Bill Means

**What is the cost of 4 new tires at $64.95 a tire?**

**Read:**   *Given:*   buying 4 tires; cost $64.95 each

*To find:*   total cost

**Plan:**   Which operation can you use?

This problem involves 4 equal amounts.

So multiply.

**Compute:**   64.95

$\times 4$

259.8

**Answer:**   The total cost is $259.80.

**Check:**   Estimating would be a good way to check this answer.

60

$\times 4$

240   ✔

# EXERCISES

**1.**

Barko
dog food
$0.43 a can

How much would a dozen cans cost?

**2.**

pocket calculators
$8.97 each

How much would 4 calculators cost?

**3.** The operating costs for Glenda's car are $0.32 a mile. How much will it cost for a 412-mile trip?

**4.** A basketball team plays 41 home games, and a ticket for each game costs $6.75. What is the total cost of buying a ticket for each game?

**5.** A gallon of water weighs 8.34 pounds. How much would the water in a 215-gallon waterbed weigh?

**6.** How much does a computer center have to pay for 30 boxes of disks at $27.75 a box?

**7.** The YMCA swimming pool is 28.5 meters long. How many meters would a person swim in swimming 25 lengths of the pool?

**8.** A magazine subscription costs $0.80 an issue. If the magazine prints one issue a week, what is the cost for 52 weeks?

**9.** The Clarks have found that it costs them $0.42 a mile to operate the family automobile. If they drive 754.5 miles on vacation, how much are their auto expenses?

**10.** A section of highway 6.5 meters wide and 700 meters long needs repaving. What is the area of this section?

**11.** Steve gave the cashier $15 to pay for a meal costing $13.48. How much change did he get?

**12.** A truck is carrying 34 boxes that weigh 26.3 pounds each. What is the total weight of the boxes?

**13.** The long-distance phone rate between two cities is $0.35 per minute. What is the cost of a 20-minute call?

**14.** The charge for the first three minutes of a telephone call was $1.20. The charge for the next minute was $0.30. What was the total charge for the four-minute call?

EXTRA PRACTICE page 478, set 16

Photos by Ed Hoppe Photography

**1.** An airplane descended 525 feet per minute for 15 minutes. How far had the plane descended after 15 minutes?

**2.** A theater has 30 rows of seats. Each row has 15 seats. How many seats are in the theater?

**3.** How much did a movie star earn if the star was paid $1000 a day for 50 days?

**4.** Jill is credited with 0.625 vacation days per pay period. If she is paid 24 times a year, how many vacation days is she credited with a year?

**5.** Mr. Clark's medicine costs $23.45 a month. How much does he pay for medicine in a year?

**6.** What is the area of a rectangular floor if the floor is 14 feet wide and 21 feet long?

**7.** A person blinks about 25 times each minute. How many times does a person blink in an hour?

**8.** The human heart beats about 70 times a minute. How many times does it beat in an hour?

9. If a light plane uses 11.4 gallons of gasoline an hour, how many gallons are used in 3.5 hours?

10. How much would 3 records cost if each record cost $6.79?

11. A government agency wrote 525 memos in one day. If the same number of memos are written each day, how many memos are written in 20 days?

12. Bess worked 15.5 hours last week. She is paid $2.10 an hour. How much money did Bess earn last week?

13. A new car cost $8829 last year. This year the owner sold it for $6270. How much did the car lose in value?

14. The average American family spends about 10.5 hours a day doing housework. How many hours is that a week?

15. A waitress made $10.35 in tips during the morning and $18.20 in tips during the afternoon. How much did the waitress make in tips in all?

16. The average American teenager spends about 0.08 hours a day doing housework. How many hours is that a week?

The charge for a dial-direct call varies, depending on the time of day and the day of the week that the call is made. Calls made during business hours—8 to 5, Monday through Friday—are more costly than calls made at other times. Some calls have to be made during business hours. Other calls, however, can be made during times when the rates are lower. Rate tables like the one below can be found in the front of most telephone books or can be obtained from the telephone company.

Eric Futran/Marilyn Gartman Photo Agency

| Dial-direct | Weekday | | Evening | | Night & weekend | |
|---|---|---|---|---|---|---|
| Sample rates **Chicago** to: | First minute | Each additional minute or fraction thereof | First minute | Each additional minute or fraction thereof | First minute | Each additional minute or fraction thereof |
| **Bloomington** | $ .37 | $ .26 | $ .28 | $ .20 | $ .23 | $ .16 |
| **Centralia** | .40 | .31 | .30 | .24 | .24 | .19 |
| **Decatur** | .39 | .29 | .30 | .22 | .24 | .18 |
| **Joliet** | .27 | .17 | .21 | .13 | .17 | .11 |
| **Springfield** | .39 | .29 | .30 | .22 | .24 | .18 |

Use the table to find the cost of each call made from Chicago.

1. a 5-minute call to Decatur at 6 P.M. Friday; Saturday

2. a 15-minute call to Centralia at noon on Tuesday; Sunday

3. a 36-minute call to Joliet at 3:30 A.M. Tuesday

4. a 20-minute call to Bloomington at 10 A.M. Monday; Saturday

5. a 5-minute call to Springfield at 4:55 P.M. Thursday; at 5:05 P.M. Thursday

One of the duties of a payroll clerk is to compute each employee's gross income (income before taxes and other deductions). The total number of hours worked each week multiplied by the employee's pay per hour equals his or her gross income. Accuracy is extremely important in this profession. Many payroll clerks use computers to keep track of employee salary information and to compute the payroll.

James H. Pickerell

Complete the following pay sheet.

| Name | M | T | W | Th | F | Total hours | Pay per hour | Gross income |
|---|---|---|---|---|---|---|---|---|
| Burn, Jack | 7 | 7.5 | 5 | 7 | 6 | 32.5 | $4.50 | |
| Campos, Alejo | 6 | 8 | 6 | 7 | 7 | | $4.50 | |
| Friel, Francis | 8 | 8 | 8.5 | 7.7 | 8 | | $6.75 | |
| Horton, Peter | 8 | 8 | 8 | 8 | 8 | | $8.25 | |
| Newman, Al | 6 | 7 | 7 | 6 | 7 | | $3.25 | |
| Peterson, Karen | 5.5 | 5 | 6 | 5 | 5 | | $6.50 | |
| Small, Beth | 7 | 7 | 7 | 7 | 7 | | $4.50 | |
| Taylor, Tom | 8 | 8 | 7.5 | 8 | 8 | | $7.70 | |
| Will, Martin | 7 | 8 | 8 | 7 | 6 | | $3.50 | |
| Yarrow, Clare | 7 | 7 | 5.5 | 8 | 8 | | $6.00 | |

Multiply.

| | | | |
|---|---|---|---|
| **1.**   4 <br> $\times 2$ | **2.**   3 <br> $\times 5$ | **3.**   5 <br> $\times 2$ | **4.**   9 <br> $\times 8$    2.1 |
| **5.**   12 <br> $\times 3$ | **6.**   50 <br> $\times 8$ | **7.**   64 <br> $\times 4$ | **8.**   32 <br> $\times 8$ |
| **9.**   54 <br> $\times 33$ | **10.**   45 <br> $\times 23$ | **11.**   96 <br> $\times 54$ | **12.**   95 <br> $\times 84$    2.2 |
| **13.**   120 <br> $\times 16$ | **14.**   212 <br> $\times 60$ | **15.**   106 <br> $\times 67$ | **16.**   500 <br> $\times 36$ |
| **17.** 146 <br> $\times 3$ | **18.** 160 <br> $\times 7$ | **19.** 205 <br> $\times 3$ | **20.** 115 <br> $\times 4$ |
| **21.**   405 <br> $\times 234$ | **22.**   765 <br> $\times 134$ | **23.**   123 <br> $\times 100$ | **24.**   243 <br> $\times 191$ |

**25.** $24 \times 10$      **26.** $70 \times 30$      **27.** $36 \times 100$    2.4

**28.** $50 \times 20$      **29.** $11 \times 1000$      **30.** $20 \times 60$

Estimate each product.

| | | | |
|---|---|---|---|
| **31.**   59 <br> $\times 32$ | **32.**   72 <br> $\times 68$ | **33.**   58 <br> $\times 39$ | **34.**   42 <br> $\times 21$ |
| **35.**   629 <br> $\times 38$ | **36.**   212 <br> $\times 161$ | **37.**   582 <br> $\times 270$ | **38.**   8753 <br> $\times 421$ |

Copy and complete by placing the decimal point in the product.    2.6

| | | | |
|---|---|---|---|
| **39.**   42 <br> $\times 0.1$ <br> 42 | **40.**   217 <br> $\times 0.02$ <br> 434 | **41.**   0.8 <br> $\times 0.6$ <br> 48 | **42.**   0.22 <br> $\times 0.3$ <br> 66 |

**43.**
$$\begin{array}{r} 5.16 \\ \times 0.8 \\ \hline 4128 \end{array}$$

**44.**
$$\begin{array}{r} 19.8 \\ \times 6.25 \\ \hline 990 \\ 396 \\ 1188 \\ \hline 123750 \end{array}$$

**45.**
$$\begin{array}{r} 76 \\ \times 1.5 \\ \hline 380 \\ 76 \\ \hline 1140 \end{array}$$

**46.**
$$\begin{array}{r} 2.3 \\ \times 6.1 \\ \hline 23 \\ 138 \\ \hline 1403 \end{array}$$

Multiply.

**47.**
$$\begin{array}{r} 0.3 \\ \times 0.2 \end{array}$$

**48.**
$$\begin{array}{r} 66 \\ \times 0.12 \end{array}$$

**49.**
$$\begin{array}{r} 3.4 \\ \times 0.8 \end{array}$$

**50.**
$$\begin{array}{r} 59 \\ \times 2.3 \end{array}$$
  2.7

**51.**
$$\begin{array}{r} 0.08 \\ \times 0.16 \end{array}$$

**52.**
$$\begin{array}{r} 0.07 \\ \times 0.5 \end{array}$$

**53.**
$$\begin{array}{r} 6.7 \\ \times 3.4 \end{array}$$

**54.**
$$\begin{array}{r} 6.3 \\ \times 0.12 \end{array}$$

**55.**
$$\begin{array}{r} 0.25 \\ \times 0.6 \end{array}$$

**56.**
$$\begin{array}{r} 0.56 \\ \times 0.25 \end{array}$$

**57.**
$$\begin{array}{r} 7.9 \\ \times 0.34 \end{array}$$

**58.**
$$\begin{array}{r} 5.4 \\ \times 3.7 \end{array}$$

**59.** $2.6 \times 10$

**60.** $14.3 \times 0.01$
  2.8

**61.** $4.2 \times 0.1$

**62.** $0.9 \times 10$

**63.** $1.27 \times 100$

**64.** $387 \times 0.001$

**65.**
$$\begin{array}{r} 9.12 \\ \times 23 \end{array}$$

**66.**
$$\begin{array}{r} 5.107 \\ \times 38 \end{array}$$

**67.**
$$\begin{array}{r} 512 \\ \times 0.231 \end{array}$$

**68.**
$$\begin{array}{r} 48.7 \\ \times 3.86 \end{array}$$
  2.9

**69.**
$$\begin{array}{r} 8.15 \\ \times 0.5 \end{array}$$

**70.**
$$\begin{array}{r} 8.16 \\ \times 4.03 \end{array}$$

**71.**
$$\begin{array}{r} 123.6 \\ \times 5.9 \end{array}$$

**72.**
$$\begin{array}{r} 24.36 \\ \times 9.28 \end{array}$$

Solve.

**73.** The cafeteria has 22 tables with 6 chairs at each table. How many chairs are in the cafeteria?
  2.3

**74.** Peter pays his car insurance in 4 installments. If each installment payment is $92, how much does Peter pay for car insurance?
  2.5

**75.** The average person drinks 4.9 pints of milk a week. How much is that in a year (52 weeks)?
  2.10

Multiply.

**1.** $8 \times 8$ **2.** $4 \times 5$ **3.** $7 \times 0$ **4.** $3 \times 1$

**5.** $\begin{array}{r} 56 \\ \times 4 \\ \hline \end{array}$ **6.** $\begin{array}{r} 90 \\ \times 8 \\ \hline \end{array}$ **7.** $\begin{array}{r} 178 \\ \times 3 \\ \hline \end{array}$ **8.** $\begin{array}{r} 43 \\ \times 12 \\ \hline \end{array}$

**9.** $\begin{array}{r} 32 \\ \times 45 \\ \hline \end{array}$ **10.** $\begin{array}{r} 178 \\ \times 34 \\ \hline \end{array}$ **11.** $\begin{array}{r} 507 \\ \times 334 \\ \hline \end{array}$ **12.** $\begin{array}{r} 765 \\ \times 408 \\ \hline \end{array}$

**13.** $30 \times 20$ **14.** $50 \times 20$ **15.** $46 \times 100$ **16.** $14 \times 50$

Copy and complete by placing the decimal point in the product.

**17.** $\begin{array}{r} 65 \\ \times 0.4 \\ \hline 260 \end{array}$ **18.** $\begin{array}{r} 8.3 \\ \times 2.5 \\ \hline 415 \\ 166 \\ \hline 2075 \end{array}$ **19.** $\begin{array}{r} 4.08 \\ \times 1.12 \\ \hline 816 \\ 408 \\ 408 \\ \hline 45696 \end{array}$ **20.** $\begin{array}{r} 0.06 \\ \times 0.07 \\ \hline 42 \end{array}$

Multiply.

**21.** $\begin{array}{r} 56 \\ \times 0.4 \\ \hline \end{array}$ **22.** $\begin{array}{r} 26 \\ \times 0.5 \\ \hline \end{array}$ **23.** $\begin{array}{r} 76 \\ \times 5.4 \\ \hline \end{array}$ **24.** $\begin{array}{r} 0.12 \\ \times 0.5 \\ \hline \end{array}$

**25.** $\begin{array}{r} 1.3 \\ \times 3.4 \\ \hline \end{array}$ **26.** $\begin{array}{r} 0.65 \\ \times 8.3 \\ \hline \end{array}$ **27.** $\begin{array}{r} 704 \\ \times 3.54 \\ \hline \end{array}$ **28.** $\begin{array}{r} 0.765 \\ \times 4.56 \\ \hline \end{array}$

**29.** $0.46 \times 1000$ **30.** $0.08 \times 10$ **31.** $42 \times 0.01$ **32.** $7.8 \times 0.1$

Estimate.

**33.** $\begin{array}{r} 106 \\ \times 88 \\ \hline \end{array}$ **34.** $\begin{array}{r} 122 \\ \times 392 \\ \hline \end{array}$

Solve.

**35.** A worker earns $7.50 an hour. How much does the worker earn in a 40-hour week?

**36.** A case of canned goods holds 24 cans. How many cans are in 12 cases?

**PREVIEW TEST**

Divide and check. Write any remainder as a whole number.

**1.** $7\overline{)55}$        **2.** $9\overline{)379}$        **3.** $4\overline{)5031}$

**4.** $26\overline{)229}$        **5.** $63\overline{)2346}$        **6.** $73\overline{)28056}$

**7.** $315\overline{)6571}$        **8.** $240\overline{)69156}$        **9.** $399\overline{)60567}$

Divide until the remainder is 0.

**10.** $8\overline{)1.89}$        **11.** $36\overline{)190.8}$        **12.** $154\overline{)446.6}$

**13.** $78\overline{)7.644}$        **14.** $58.1 \div 10$        **15.** $6.05 \div 100$

**16.** $821 \div 1000$        **17.** $14.43 \div 1000$        **18.** $65.3 \div 100$

**19.** $0.09\overline{)36}$        **20.** $3.5\overline{)231}$        **21.** $0.54\overline{)972}$

**22.** $0.58\overline{)36.54}$        **23.** $0.42\overline{)12.642}$        **24.** $0.63\overline{)157.5}$

**25.** $1.5\overline{)0.6}$        **26.** $0.47\overline{)34.31}$        **27.** $3.6\overline{)14.616}$

Divide. Round the quotient to the nearest tenth.

**28.** $1.4\overline{)31}$        **29.** $5.3\overline{)39}$        **30.** $0.23\overline{)0.66}$

Solve.

**31.** The Glee Club wants to earn $500. If the club has a car wash and earns $3 per car, how many cars must be washed to reach the goal?

**32.** 25 shirts are being placed on 3 display racks with the same number of shirts on each rack. How many shirts is that on each rack? How many shirts will be left over?

Stowe Ski Area

One morning the ski school had 112 skiers sign up for group lessons. If each group had 8 skiers, how many groups were formed?

**Example 1:** Find $112 \div 8$.

$$
\begin{array}{r}
14 \\
8\overline{)112} \\
8 \\
\hline
32 \\
32 \\
\hline
0
\end{array}
$$

$1 \times 8 \longrightarrow$

$4 \times 8 \longrightarrow$

Think: $8\overline{)11}$ → 1

Think: $8\overline{)32}$ → 4

Check:

$$
\begin{array}{r}
14 \quad \text{quotient} \\
\times 8 \quad \text{divisor} \\
\hline
112 \quad \text{dividend} \checkmark
\end{array}
$$

14 groups were formed.

**Example 2:** Find $4222 \div 6$.

$$
\begin{array}{r}
703 \text{ R4} \\
6\overline{)4222} \\
42 \\
\hline
02 \\
0 \\
\hline
22 \\
18 \\
\hline
4
\end{array}
$$

Think: $6\overline{)42}$ → 7

Think: $6\overline{)2}$ → 0

Think: $6\overline{)22}$ → 3

Check:

$$
\begin{array}{r}
703 \quad \text{quotient} \\
\times 6 \quad \text{divisor} \\
\hline
4218 \\
+ \quad 4 \quad \text{remainder} \\
\hline
4222 \quad \text{dividend} \checkmark
\end{array}
$$

Short division can be used when dividing by a one-digit number.

**Example 3:** Find $1986 \div 4$.

**short division**

$$
\begin{array}{r}
4\ 9\ 6 \text{ R2} \\
4\overline{)1\ 9_3 8_2 6}
\end{array}
$$

Write the remainder before the next digit. (Of course, first you must mentally multiply and subtract to find the remainder.)

**long divison**

$$
\begin{array}{r}
496 \text{ R2} \\
4\overline{)1986} \\
16 \\
\hline
38 \\
36 \\
\hline
26 \\
24 \\
\hline
2
\end{array}
$$

Check:

$$
\begin{array}{r}
496 \quad \text{quotient} \\
\times 4 \quad \text{divisor} \\
\hline
1984 \\
+ \quad 2 \quad \text{remainder} \\
\hline
1986 \quad \text{dividend} \checkmark
\end{array}
$$

# EXERCISES

Divide and check.

**1.** $42 \div 6$          **2.** $64 \div 8$

**3.** $49 \div 7$          **4.** $56 \div 7$

**5.** $45 \div 5$          **6.** $72 \div 8$

**7.** $48 \div 6$          **8.** $63 \div 7$

**9.** $36 \div 9$          **10.** $54 \div 6$

**11.** $5\overline{)38}$  **12.** $8\overline{)51}$  **13.** $9\overline{)85}$  **14.** $6\overline{)37}$  **15.** $7\overline{)32}$

**16.** $2\overline{)148}$  **17.** $5\overline{)258}$  **18.** $4\overline{)72}$  **19.** $3\overline{)81}$  **20.** $4\overline{)66}$

**21.** $8\overline{)146}$  **22.** $6\overline{)258}$  **23.** $4\overline{)97}$  **24.** $7\overline{)134}$  **25.** $8\overline{)285}$

**26.** $3\overline{)607}$  **27.** $4\overline{)804}$  **28.** $5\overline{)504}$  **29.** $9\overline{)907}$  **30.** $6\overline{)3571}$

**31.** $4\overline{)2946}$  **32.** $3\overline{)1604}$  **33.** $5\overline{)2209}$  **34.** $8\overline{)4816}$  **35.** $7\overline{)2821}$

**36.** $9\overline{)7256}$  **37.** $2\overline{)1615}$  **38.** $6\overline{)2520}$  **39.** $5\overline{)3650}$  **40.** $8\overline{)7007}$

**41.** $3\overline{)3945}$  **42.** $5\overline{)5620}$  **43.** $4\overline{)8259}$  **44.** $2\overline{)6164}$  **45.** $6\overline{)21361}$

**46.** $7\overline{)29356}$  **47.** $5\overline{)46249}$  **48.** $9\overline{)71181}$  **49.** $8\overline{)54246}$  **50.** $4\overline{)33208}$

**51.** $6\overline{)44041}$  **52.** $3\overline{)23408}$  **53.** $2\overline{)15462}$  **54.** $8\overline{)70048}$  **55.** $6\overline{)50028}$

EXTRA PRACTICE page 478, set 17

## SKILLS REVIEW

Multiply.

**56.** $\begin{array}{r} 631 \\ \times 46 \\ \hline \end{array}$  **57.** $\begin{array}{r} 335 \\ \times 31 \\ \hline \end{array}$  **58.** $\begin{array}{r} 102 \\ \times 89 \\ \hline \end{array}$  **59.** $\begin{array}{r} 494 \\ \times 19 \\ \hline \end{array}$  **60.** $\begin{array}{r} 340 \\ \times 19 \\ \hline \end{array}$

Kenji Kerins

**Rosa wants to save $645 for a stereo. She can save $15 each week. How many weeks must she save?**

**Example 1:**  Find $645 \div 15$.

```
      43                    4        Check:
  15)645    Think:  15)64
      60                   3            43   quotient
      45    Think:  15)45             ×15   divisor
      45                              215
       0                               43
                                      645   dividend ✔
```

Rosa must save for 43 weeks.

**Example 2:**  Find $3354 \div 16$.

```
    209 R10                   2       Check:
  16)3354    Think:  16)33
      32                     0           209   quotient
      15                                 ×16   divisor
       0     Think:  16)15              1254
      154                    9           209
      144    Think:  16)154             3344
       10                              +  10   remainder
                                        3354   dividend ✔
```

## EXERCISES

Divide and check.

**1.** $23\overline{)184}$  **2.** $36\overline{)144}$  **3.** $19\overline{)114}$  **4.** $28\overline{)196}$  **5.** $41\overline{)328}$

**6.** $45\overline{)367}$  **7.** $52\overline{)486}$  **8.** $34\overline{)227}$  **9.** $26\overline{)206}$  **10.** $64\overline{)484}$

**11.** $50\overline{)3860}$  **12.** $46\overline{)1288}$  **13.** $37\overline{)1961}$  **14.** $41\overline{)1690}$  **15.** $24\overline{)1240}$

**16.** $79\overline{)6575}$  **17.** $66\overline{)2178}$  **18.** $52\overline{)2600}$  **19.** $48\overline{)2880}$  **20.** $36\overline{)2268}$

**21.** $33\overline{)1980}$  **22.** $45\overline{)3630}$  **23.** $29\overline{)1580}$  **24.** $92\overline{)3870}$  **25.** $85\overline{)3065}$

**26.** $42\overline{)8652}$  **27.** $37\overline{)14911}$  **28.** $26\overline{)5954}$  **29.** $45\overline{)10665}$  **30.** $52\overline{)31408}$

**31.** $34\overline{)16660}$  **32.** $28\overline{)14840}$  **33.** $16\overline{)14208}$  **34.** $25\overline{)16350}$  **35.** $36\overline{)19980}$

*EXTRA PRACTICE page 478, set 18*

---

## CALCULATOR NOTE

When you use a calculator to divide, the calculator will display the quotient after the $=$ is entered.

**Example:** Find $166 \div 12$.

| ENTER | DISPLAY | |
|---|---|---|
| **166** | *166* | dividend |
| $\div$ | *166* | |
| **12** | *12* | divisor |
| $=$ | *13.833333* | quotient |

The calculator will display a decimal as part of the quotient. You can use the calculator to find the remainder.

| ENTER | DISPLAY | |
|---|---|---|
| **13** | *13* | whole-number part of quotient |
| $\times$ | *13* | |
| **12** | *12* | divisor |
| $=$ | *156* | |
| **M+** | *156* | Pressing $\boxed{M+}$ puts 156 in the calculator's memory. |
| **166** | *166* | dividend |
| $-$ | *166* | |
| **RM** | *156* | Pressing $\boxed{RM}$ recalls 156 from the calculator's memory. |
| $=$ | *10* | remainder |

Use a calculator as shown here to check your work for exercises 6–10.

When a collection of objects is separated into groups with the *same number* of objects in each, you can use division to find the number of groups or the number of objects in each group.

**Example 1:** 38 oranges are to be placed in bags, with 4 oranges in each bag. How many bags can be filled?

*Solution:* Divide 38 by 4.

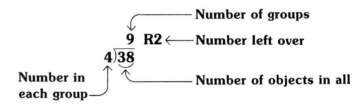

So 9 bags can be filled, and 2 oranges will be left over.

**Example 2:** 36 books are being placed in 4 stacks, with the same number of books in each stack. How many books will there be in each stack?

*Solution:* Divide 36 by 4.

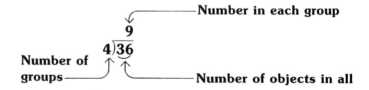

So there will be 9 books in each stack, and no books will be left over.

Division can be used to solve problems in which you are asked to compare two numbers or amounts. Such problems usually ask you to find an average. Or they ask you to find how much per hour, per person, per gallon, and so on.

**Example 3:** Gene earned $36 for 9 hours of work. How much did he earn per hour?

*Solution:* Divide 36 by 9.

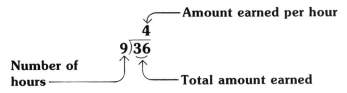

Amount earned per hour

Number of hours ─── Total amount earned

So Gene earned $4 per hour. (Or we can say his average earnings were $4 an hour.)

## EXERCISES

Each of the following problems can be solved by using division. Write the division. Solve.

**1.**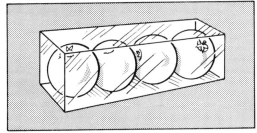

How many trays like this one can be filled from a basket of 84 tomatoes?

**2.**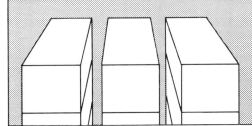

There are 24 boxes in all. How many are there in each stack?

**3.** 56 whole wheat rolls are being packed in bags, with 6 rolls in each bag. How many bags can be filled? How many rolls will be left over?

**4.** Each drinking glass holds 8 ounces. How many 8-ounce servings can be poured from a 64-ounce carton?

**5.** 216 people signed up to ride a river raft. If 18 people ride the raft at one time, how many trips will the raft make?

**6.** How many cars are needed to carry 60 band members if 4 band members ride in each car?

**7.** A bus traveled 270 miles in 6 hours. How many miles is that per hour?

**8.** 35 students must earn $3150 for a class trip. How much is that per student?

*EXTRA PRACTICE page 479, set 19*

## DIVIDING A DECIMAL BY A WHOLE NUMBER

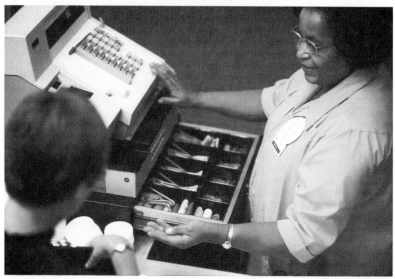

Tom Campbell/FPG

**A restaurant bill totaled $23.75. If 5 persons paid an equal share of the bill, how much did each person pay?**

**Example 1:** Find $23.75 \div 5$.

**When dividing a decimal by a whole number, write the decimal point in the quotient above the decimal point in the dividend.**

$$5\overline{)23.75}$$

**Then divide as with whole numbers.**

```
    4.75        Check:
5)23.75
  20              4.75
   3 7           × 5
   3 5          23.75  ✔
     25
     25
      0
```

Each person paid $4.75.

Sometimes 0's are needed as placeholders in the quotient.

**Example 2:** Find $0.375 \div 15$.

**Write the decimal point in the quotient.**
**Write 0 as a placeholder after the decimal point.**

$$
\begin{array}{r}
0.025 \\
15\overline{)0.375} \\
\underline{30}\phantom{5} \\
75 \\
\underline{75} \\
0
\end{array}
$$

Check:

$$
\begin{array}{r}
0.025 \\
\times 15 \\
\hline
125 \\
25\phantom{5} \\
\hline
0.375 \quad \checkmark
\end{array}
$$

## EXERCISES

Copy and place the decimal point correctly in each quotient. In some cases, you must insert one or more 0's.

1. $4\overline{)9.6}$ → 24
2. $6\overline{)1.26}$ → 21
3. $8\overline{)0.664}$ → 83
4. $5\overline{)5.25}$ → 105

5. $12\overline{)38.4}$ → 32
6. $25\overline{)16.25}$ → 65
7. $36\overline{)15.12}$ → 42
8. $18\overline{)50.04}$ → 278

Divide and check.

9. $7\overline{)0.49}$
10. $9\overline{)0.72}$
11. $5\overline{)3.5}$
12. $8\overline{)4.8}$

13. $9\overline{)1.08}$
14. $6\overline{)1.98}$
15. $8\overline{)0.232}$
16. $5\overline{)0.415}$

17. $2\overline{)9.04}$
18. $3\overline{)25.53}$
19. $6\overline{)38.28}$
20. $4\overline{)0.984}$

21. $12\overline{)7.56}$
22. $25\overline{)20.25}$
23. $36\overline{)226.8}$
24. $16\overline{)142.4}$

25. $22\overline{)16.94}$
26. $54\overline{)47.52}$
27. $41\overline{)3.526}$
28. $62\overline{)4.712}$

29. $52\overline{)72.28}$
30. $64\overline{)97.28}$
31. $83\overline{)171.81}$
32. $71\overline{)215.84}$

33. $46\overline{)4.416}$
34. $38\overline{)2.128}$
35. $29\overline{)1.392}$
36. $35\overline{)1.295}$

*EXTRA PRACTICE page 479, set 20*

Everett C. Johnson/Leo de Wys Inc.

When you use division to solve a problem, sometimes the result of the computation is not the answer to the question.

**Example 1:** 278 students plan to go on a field trip. Each bus holds 48 students. How many buses are needed?

**Read:** *Given:* 278 students

48 students per bus

*To find:* How many buses are needed?

**Plan:** Which operation can be used? Divide 278 by 48.

**Compute:**

$$
\begin{array}{r}
5 \;\; R38 \\
48\overline{)278} \\
240 \\
\hline
38
\end{array}
$$

**Answer:** 5 buses will not be enough. 5 R38 buses makes no sense. So in this case, the next larger whole number is the answer. 6 buses are needed.

**Check:**

$$
\begin{array}{r}
48 \\
\times 5 \\
\hline
240 \\
+ \;\; 38 \\
\hline
278 \;\; \checkmark
\end{array}
$$

Sometimes the remainder in a division computation is the answer to the question.

**Example 2:** John has 101 photos from his camping trip. If 6 pictures fit on each page of the photo album, how many pictures are left over for a partly filled page?

**Read:** *Given:* 101 pictures

6 pictures per page

*To find:* How many pictures will be left over for a partly filled page?

**Plan:** Which operation can be used? Divide 101 by 6.

**Compute:**

$$
\begin{array}{r}
16 \ \ \text{R5} \\
6\overline{)101} \\
\underline{6} \ \ \ \ \\
41 \\
\underline{36} \\
5
\end{array}
$$

**Answer:** The remainder tells how many pictures are left over. 5 pictures will be on the partly filled page.

**Check:**

$$
\begin{array}{r}
16 \\
\times 6 \\
\hline
96 \\
+ \ 5 \\
\hline
101 \ \ \checkmark
\end{array}
$$

## EXERCISES

Be sure to read the problems below carefully. Make sure you answer the question asked.

**1.** A batch of sourdough makes 50 rolls. How many rolls will remain if bags of 12 rolls each are packaged from a batch?

**2.** If 20 people can sit in each row of seats, how many rows of seats can be completely filled by 270 people?

**3.** A spool contains 200 feet of twine. How many pieces, each 3 feet long, can be cut from the spool? How much twine will be left over?

**4.** In a tennis tournament the winner received $50,000. The runner-up's share was $28,700. How much more was the winner's share?

**5.** One section in a stadium has 37 rows of 58 seats each. How many seats are in that section?

**6.** Mr. Kapche spent $47.04 for materials to insulate 12 basement windows. How much did it cost per window?

**7.** 853 people were seated at a banquet. Each table was set for 8 people. How many tables were needed if as few tables as possible were used?

**8.** Minerva must pay back $2251.20 in 24 equal payments. How much is each payment?

*EXTRA PRACTICE page 479, set 21*

## DIVIDING BY A 3-DIGIT NUMBER

H. Armstrong Roberts

**The distance around a running track is 352 feet. How many times around the track equals 1 mile? (1 mile = 5280 feet)**

**Example 1:** Find $5280 \div 352$.

```
        15
  352)5280     Think:  352)528         Check:
      352                                 15
      1760     Think:  352)1760         ×352
      1760                                30
         0                                75
                                          45
                                        5280  ✔
```

15 times around the track equals 1 mile.

Sometimes you may have to write 0's in the dividend so that you can continue dividing.

**Example 2:** Find $82.6 \div 236$.

```
       0.35
  236)82.60
      70 8 ⤸——— Write 0 in the dividend       Check:
      11 80       and continue dividing.       0.35
      11 80                                    ×2 36
          0                                    2 10
                                               10 5
                                               70
                                               82.60  ✔
```

**Example 3:** Find $1.4 \div 112$.

```
       0.0125
  112)1.4000
      1 12 ⤸——— Write 0's in the            Check:
       280        dividend and divide.       0.0125
       224                                   ×112
       560                                    250
       560                                    125
         0                                   1 25
                                             1.4000  ✔
```

## EXERCISES

Divide and check. In some cases, you may have to write 0's in the dividend so that you can continue dividing.

1. $180\overline{)1440}$     2. $270\overline{)1890}$     3. $365\overline{)4380}$     4. $241\overline{)3856}$

5. $144\overline{)468}$     6. $510\overline{)433.5}$     7. $449\overline{)1032.7}$     8. $253\overline{)455.4}$

9. $826\overline{)2271.5}$     10. $128\overline{)108.8}$     11. $231\overline{)78.54}$     12. $223\overline{)75.82}$

13. $411\overline{)2260.5}$     14. $508\overline{)2336.8}$     15. $704\overline{)14.784}$     16. $915\overline{)28.365}$

17. $911\overline{)983.88}$     18. $142\overline{)427.42}$     19. $581\overline{)592.62}$     20. $613\overline{)643.65}$

21. $185\overline{)5.18}$     22. $354\overline{)17.7}$     23. $271\overline{)16.26}$     24. $857\overline{)77.13}$

25. $198\overline{)603.9}$     26. $555\overline{)1121.1}$     27. $612\overline{)134.64}$     28. $424\overline{)267.12}$

29. $322\overline{)267.26}$     30. $504\overline{)549.36}$     31. $405\overline{)834.3}$     32. $370\overline{)765.9}$

EXTRA PRACTICE page 480, set 22

## CHECKPOINT

Divide. Write any remainder as a whole number.

1. $8\overline{)16368}$     2. $25\overline{)13255}$     3. $106\overline{)4590}$

Divide until the remainder is 0.

4. $6\overline{)30.18}$     5. $39\overline{)0.975}$     6. $144\overline{)90}$

7. 5000 trees are being planted in rows of 75 each. How many trees will be left over?

## 3.7 | DIVIDING BY 10, 100, AND 1000

When you divide by 10, 100, or 1000, you can move the decimal point *left* one place for each zero in the divisor.

**Example 1:** $19.49 \div 10 = 1.9\,49 = 1.949$

1 zero     1 place left

**Example 2:** $1.25 \div 100 = 0.01\,25 = 0.0125$

2 zeros     2 places left

**Example 3:** $401 \div 1000 = 0.401 = 0.401$

3 zeros     3 places left

## EXERCISES

Divide.

**1.** $24.1 \div 10$      **2.** $449 \div 10$      **3.** $0.29 \div 10$

**4.** $178 \div 100$      **5.** $46.8 \div 100$      **6.** $2.75 \div 100$

**7.** $3.4 \div 1000$      **8.** $5150 \div 1000$      **9.** $0.4 \div 1000$

**10.** $38.9 \div 10$      **11.** $11.4 \div 1000$      **12.** $6.4 \div 100$

**13.** $0.89 \div 100$      **14.** $4.6 \div 10$      **15.** $2.1 \div 1000$

**16.** $2.04 \div 100$      **17.** $0.05 \div 1000$      **18.** $0.8 \div 10$

**19.** $0.8 \div 1000$      **20.** $9.04 \div 10$      **21.** $371.6 \div 100$

**22.** $100\overline{)1.16}$      **23.** $10\overline{)6}$      **24.** $1000\overline{)7}$

**25.** $1000\overline{)65}$      **26.** $100\overline{)125}$      **27.** $10\overline{)23}$

**28.** $10\overline{)75}$      **29.** $100\overline{)87}$      **30.** $1000\overline{)940}$

EXTRA PRACTICE page 480, set 23

You probably know that light bulbs have watt ratings. A 100-watt bulb is brighter and uses more electrical power than a 60-watt bulb.

All electric appliances have watt ratings. Some typical examples are

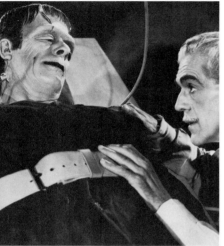

Lambert Studios

| clock | 2 watts | radio | 71 watts |
|---|---|---|---|
| hair dryer | 1000 watts | television (bw) | 55 watts |
| iron | 1100 watts | television (color) | 200 watts |
| microwave oven | 1500 watts | vacuum cleaner | 630 watts |

Watt ratings can be changed to kilowatts; just divide by 1000. (1000 watts = 1 kilowatt)

**Example 1:**   Change 1100 watts to kilowatts.

**1100 watts = 1.100 kilowatts**

A kilowatt-hour is the unit used to measure electrical power. One kilowatt-hour is the electrical power used by a 1000-watt appliance in 1 hour.

**Example 2:**   Find the kilowatt-hours used when a 100-watt light bulb is lit for 24 hours. To find the number of kilowatt-hours, multiply the number of kilowatts by the number of hours used.

**100 watts = 0.1 kw**   **First change the watt rating to kilowatts.**

**0.1 × 24 = 2.4 kwh**   **Then multiply kilowatts by the number of hours used.**

Find the kilowatt-hours of power used in each case.

1. By a 1500-watt microwave oven that is used 7 hours during a month

2. By a 200-watt color TV that is used for 35 hours during a week

3. By a 1000-watt hair dryer that is used for 3.5 hours during a month

Mary E. Messenger

**Last month Susan worked the following number of hours each week: 14.25, 12, 19.25, and 15.5. How many hours did she average per week?**

**Read:**   *Given:*   hours worked each week:   14.25, 12, 19.25, 15.5

  *To find:*   average number of hours worked per week

**Plan:**   First add to find the total number of hours worked. Then divide to find the average number of hours per week for the 4 weeks.

**Compute:**
```
  14.25
  12
  19.25
+ 15.5            15.25
  61.00        4)61.00
```

**Answer:**   She worked an average of 15.25 hours per week.

**Check:**   First check the addition by rounding each number to the same place value.

Then check the division.

```
  10          15.25
  10           × 4
  20          61.00  ✔
+ 20
  60  ✔
```

# EXERCISES

1. 6 servings cost $1.44. What is the cost per serving?

2. 32 ounces cost $1.28. What is the cost per ounce?

3. The total for the restaurant check was $31.40. If 4 persons paid equal amounts, what was each person's share?

4. For the matinee show, 863 adult tickets and 249 children's tickets were sold. How many tickets were sold in all?

5. Electric bills for 3 summer months were $35.95, $49.82, and $40.26. What was the average monthly bill?

6. Natalie bought 6 record albums. The total amount was $53.04. What was the average cost of one album?

7. Miss Sclafani earned $23,685.75 last year. Her company computes employee salaries on a 261-day work year. How much did she earn per day?

8. Mr. Tanaka plans to repay his car loan in 36 equal payments. The amount borrowed and the finance charge total $6435. What is the amount of each payment?

9. Pedro baby-sat 4.5 hours Friday night and 6.75 hours Saturday. How many hours did he baby-sit in all?

10. A high-school district's state aid was $5,250,200. There are 5000 students in the district. How much does state aid pay per student in that district?

11. What is each person's average bowling score?

12. If one tire costs $69.50, how much will 4 tires cost?

|  | Game | | |
| Player | 1 | 2 | 3 |
| --- | --- | --- | --- |
| Bob | 156 | 163 | 137 |
| Bill | 173 | 151 | 159 |
| Jim | 159 | 172 | 152 |
| Joe | 161 | 149 | 170 |

# DIVIDING A WHOLE NUMBER BY A DECIMAL

Multiplying a divisor and a dividend by the same nonzero number does not change the quotient.

For example,

Multiply 3 and 21 by 2.        Multiply 3 and 21 by 10.

$$3\overline{)21} \quad 6\overline{)42} \qquad 3\overline{)21} \quad 30\overline{)210}$$

with quotient 7 for each.

This idea is very useful when dividing by a decimal.

**Example 1:**  Find $343 \div 9.8$.

**Multiply the divisor by 10 to make it a whole number.**

$$9.8\,\overline{)343}$$

**Also multiply the dividend by 10, so that the quotient is not changed.**

$$9.8\,\overline{)343.0}$$

**Write the decimal point in the quotient.**

$$9.8\,\overline{)343.0}$$

**Then divide.**

```
        3 5.
9.8 )343.0
      294
       49 0
       49 0
          0
```

**Check:**

```
    3 5
  ×9.8
   28 0
  315
  343.0  ✔
```

Use the original divisor when checking.

**Example 2:**  Find $5 \div 0.25$.

**Multiply the divisor and the dividend by 100. Write the decimal point in the quotient.**

$$0.25\,\overline{)5.00}$$

**Then divide.**

```
       20.
0.25 )5.00
      5 0
       00
```

**Check:**

```
     20
  ×0.25
   1 00
   4 0
   5.00  ✔
```

## EXERCISES

Should you multiply both divisor and dividend by 10, 100, or 1000 to find each quotient?

**1.** $0.8\overline{)64}$     **2.** $0.07\overline{)49}$     **3.** $1.2\overline{)156}$     **4.** $0.15\overline{)195}$

**5.** $2.5\overline{)75}$     **6.** $0.25\overline{)75}$     **7.** $0.025\overline{)75}$     **8.** $6.1\overline{)122}$

Divide and check.

**9.** $840 \div 0.03$     **10.** $1 \div 0.05$     **11.** $5128 \div 0.8$     **12.** $3910 \div 0.5$

**13.** $0.6\overline{)894}$     **14.** $0.9\overline{)1080}$     **15.** $0.03\overline{)1404}$     **16.** $0.06\overline{)2502}$

**17.** $0.27\overline{)9612}$     **18.** $0.015\overline{)900}$     **19.** $4.7\overline{)1645}$     **20.** $0.045\overline{)180}$

**21.** $0.12\overline{)228}$     **22.** $0.42\overline{)966}$     **23.** $3.5\overline{)1225}$     **24.** $2.1\overline{)1092}$

**25.** $0.29\overline{)812}$     **26.** $0.75\overline{)1350}$     **27.** $0.81\overline{)1782}$     **28.** $0.93\overline{)2976}$

**29.** $1.13\overline{)3842}$     **30.** $2.05\overline{)6765}$     **31.** $0.335\overline{)4355}$     **32.** $0.125\overline{)6625}$

*EXTRA PRACTICE page 480, set 24*

---

## MATH NOTE

Division A and Division B have the same dividend and the same quotient. Find the dividend and the quotient.

Division A:

Division B:

$$15\overline{)\blacksquare}\ \ \blacktriangle\ \text{R12}$$

Dr. John D. Cunningham

Joyce earned \$19.53, working 4.5 hours. How much did she earn per hour?

**Example 1:** Find $19.53 \div 4.5$.

Multiply the divisor and the dividend by 10. Write the decimal point in the quotient.

$$4.5\,)\overline{19.5\,3}$$

Then divide.

```
          4.34
4.5 )19.5 30
     18 0
      1 5 3
      1 3 5
        1 80
        1 80
           0
```

Check:

```
   4.34
  ×4.5
  2 170
  17 36
  19.530  ✓
```

Joyce earned \$4.34 per hour.

**Example 2:** Find $20.3 \div 0.05$.

Multiply the divisor and the dividend by 100. Write the decimal point in the quotient.

$$0.05\,)\overline{20.30}$$

Then divide.

```
        4 06.
0.05 )20.30
      20
       0 30
         30
          0
```

Check:

```
    406
  ×0.05
  20.30  ✓
```

# EXERCISES

Complete.

**1.** $0.25 \times \boxed{?} = 25$

**2.** $0.09 \times \boxed{?} = 9$

**3.** $2.04 \times \boxed{?} = 204$

**4.** $3.6 \times \boxed{?} = 36$

**5.** $0.8 \times \boxed{?} = 8$

**6.** $16.5 \times \boxed{?} = 165$

Copy each division. Then show the new positions of the decimal points after you multiply the divisor and the dividend by 10, 100, or 1000.

**Example:**  $0.17\overline{)6.8}$  $\longrightarrow$  $0.17\overline{)6.80}$

**7.** $0.6\overline{)82.8}$  **8.** $0.8\overline{)50.88}$  **9.** $0.04\overline{)1.97}$  **10.** $0.09\overline{)0.2124}$

**11.** $0.56\overline{)7.504}$  **12.** $7.1\overline{)49.7}$  **13.** $0.55\overline{)19.8}$  **14.** $0.32\overline{)75.2}$

Divide and check.

**15.** $0.3\overline{)19.02}$  **16.** $0.8\overline{)44.24}$  **17.** $0.06\overline{)14.4}$  **18.** $0.05\overline{)11.9}$

**19.** $0.06\overline{)2.142}$  **20.** $0.08\overline{)51.04}$  **21.** $0.6\overline{)3.96}$  **22.** $0.7\overline{)65.8}$

**23.** $1.6\overline{)6.88}$  **24.** $6.5\overline{)34.45}$  **25.** $0.44\overline{)134.2}$  **26.** $0.33\overline{)68.97}$

**27.** $0.42\overline{)1.302}$  **28.** $0.52\overline{)1.508}$  **29.** $0.82\overline{)45.92}$  **30.** $0.73\overline{)33.58}$

**31.** $5.6\overline{)0.1624}$  **32.** $2.8\overline{)0.1008}$  **33.** $3.5\overline{)14.07}$  **34.** $4.8\overline{)14.832}$

**35.** $0.008\overline{)0.424}$  **36.** $0.006\overline{)0.534}$  **37.** $0.015\overline{)0.072}$  **38.** $0.024\overline{)0.2064}$

**39.** $1.25\overline{)4.625}$  **40.** $20.5\overline{)10.045}$  **41.** $11.5\overline{)6.21}$  **42.** $10.8\overline{)3.348}$

EXTRA PRACTICE page 481, set 25

*SKILLS REVIEW*

Multiply.

**43.**   $\begin{array}{r} 4.5 \\ \times 3.7 \\ \hline \end{array}$  **44.**   $\begin{array}{r} 0.52 \\ \times 4.1 \\ \hline \end{array}$  **45.**   $\begin{array}{r} 0.015 \\ \times 0.29 \\ \hline \end{array}$  **46.**   $\begin{array}{r} 10.34 \\ \times 0.16 \\ \hline \end{array}$

**47.**   $\begin{array}{r} 4.01 \\ \times 2.23 \\ \hline \end{array}$  **48.**   $\begin{array}{r} 194.9 \\ \times 0.34 \\ \hline \end{array}$  **49.**   $\begin{array}{r} 1.98 \\ \times 3.5 \\ \hline \end{array}$  **50.**   $\begin{array}{r} 4.85 \\ \times 3.2 \\ \hline \end{array}$

A 64-ounce container of fresh orange juice costs $2.29. What is the cost per ounce to the nearest cent?

**Example 1:** Find $2.29 \div 64$. Round the quotient to the nearest hundredth.

$$\begin{array}{r} 0.035 \approx 0.04 \\ 64\overline{)2.290} \\ \underline{1\ 92} \\ 370 \\ \underline{320} \\ 50 \end{array}$$

≈ means *is approximately equal to.*

First find the quotient to the thousandths place. Then round to the nearest hundredth.

The cost is about $0.04 per ounce.

**Example 2:** Find $289 \div 8.8$. Round the quotient to the nearest whole number.

$$\begin{array}{r} 3\ 2.8 \approx 33 \\ 8.8\,\overline{)289.0\ 0} \\ 264 \\ 25\ 0 \\ 17\ 6 \\ 7\ 4\ 0 \\ 7\ 0\ 4 \\ 3\ 6 \end{array}$$

Find the quotient to the tenths place. Then round to the nearest one.

## EXERCISES

Round each quotient to the nearest whole number.

1. $\overset{33.5}{0.2\overline{)6.7}}$

2. $\overset{37.8}{0.6\overline{)22.68}}$

3. $\overset{60.6}{0.15\overline{)9.09}}$

4. $\overset{32.4}{4.6\overline{)149.04}}$

Round each quotient to the nearest tenth.

5. $\overset{19.28}{47\overline{)906.16}}$

6. $\overset{33.57}{0.2\overline{)6.714}}$

7. $\overset{3.32}{4.6\overline{)15.272}}$

8. $\overset{5.06}{7.2\overline{)36.432}}$

Round each quotient to the nearest hundredth.

**9.** $\overset{3.632}{75\overline{)272.4}}$    **10.** $\overset{0.164}{4\overline{)0.656}}$    **11.** $\overset{8.894}{0.85\overline{)7.5599}}$    **12.** $\overset{1.005}{6.2\overline{)6.231}}$

Divide. Round the quotient to the nearest whole number.

**13.** $23\overline{)818.8}$    **14.** $58\overline{)1358.9}$    **15.** $0.4\overline{)2.96}$    **16.** $0.08\overline{)3.5}$    **17.** $3.6\overline{)301.32}$

Divide. Round the quotient to the nearest tenth.

**18.** $30\overline{)1.8}$    **19.** $3.2\overline{)8.5}$    **20.** $4.1\overline{)7.2}$    **21.** $0.65\overline{)19}$    **22.** $0.51\overline{)12}$

Divide. Round the quotient to the nearest hundredth.

**23.** $75\overline{)272}$    **24.** $6\overline{)0.174}$    **25.** $3.4\overline{)6.82}$    **26.** $5.8\overline{)26.62}$    **27.** $0.42\overline{)0.802}$

*EXTRA PRACTICE page 481, set 26*

## CALCULATOR NOTE

Sometimes when you divide, the digits in the quotient form a pattern with one or more digits repeating without end.

**Example 1:** Find $2 \div 3$.

ENTER                DISPLAY

2 ÷ 3 =      **This quotient is called *a repeating decimal.***

You can write a repeating decimal by including a bar over the digit or digits that repeat.

**Example 2:** $0.6666666 = 0.\overline{6}$          **Example 3:** $0.4545454 = 0.\overline{45}$

Use a calculator to find each quotient. First write the quotient displayed by the calculator. Then write it again, using a bar as in the examples above.

**1.** $2 \div 11$    **2.** $5 \div 6$    **3.** $4 \div 9$    **4.** $1 \div 15$    **5.** $5 \div 18$

Camerique

A container of shampoo costs **$3.29** for **8.5 ounces.** How much does the shampoo cost per ounce to the nearest cent?

**Read:** *Given:* total cost $3.29

8.5 ounces

*To find:* cost per ounce

**Plan:** Which operation can be used? Divide 3.29 by 8.5 to thousandths. Then round to the nearest hundredth.

**Compute:**

$$
\begin{array}{r}
0.387 \approx 0.39 \\
8.5\overline{)3.2\,900} \\
2\,5\,5 \\
\overline{\phantom{0}7\,40} \\
6\,80 \\
\overline{\phantom{00}600} \\
595 \\
\overline{\phantom{000}5}
\end{array}
$$

**Answer:** The shampoo cost about $0.39 per ounce.

**Check:** An exact check may not be possible when you round the quotient.

$$
\begin{array}{r}
0.39 \\
\times 8.5 \\
\hline
195 \\
3\,12\phantom{0} \\
\hline
3.315
\end{array}
$$

0.39  rounded quotient

3.315 is close to the dividend 3.29, so it checks. ✔

# EXERCISES

**1.** How many lengths of balsa wood 2.7 centimeters long can be cut from a piece of balsa 18.9 centimeters long?

2. A shipment of 8 tennis rackets cost $412.27. What is the average cost of each racket to the nearest cent?

3. Mrs. Figueroa earned $422 in a week. She worked 40 hours. How much did she earn per hour?

4. After she makes the down payment, Teresa will owe $2898 on her new motorcycle. She plans to pay $126 a month. How many months will she make payments?

5. Nora bought 3 plants at $5.99 each. How much did the plants cost?

6. A baseball player's batting average is found by dividing the number of hits by the number of times at bat. Find the batting averages for each player in the table below. (Divide to ten-thousandths. Round to the nearest thousandth.)

| Player | Times at bat | Hits |
| --- | --- | --- |
| Bill Buckner | 657 | 201 |
| Mike Schmidt | 514 | 144 |
| Reggie Jackson | 530 | 146 |
| Robin Yount | 635 | 210 |
| Keith Hernandez | 579 | 173 |

7. While on vacation the Roths drove 1507 miles and bought 102 gallons of gasoline. Find the average miles per gallon for their trip to the nearest tenth.

8. The regular price for a warm-up suit was $34.95. During a sale, Nick paid $20.97. How much was the item marked down?

9. A certain stock paid $2028.80 in dividends for 634 shares. How much did each share earn?

10. Laura drove 333 miles and her car used 9.8 gallons of gasoline. How many miles per gallon did the car average? Round the answer to the nearest whole number.

*EXTRA PRACTICE page 481, set 27*

***Unit price*** is the cost per unit of measure, such as gram, kilogram, ounce, or pound. When the same product is packaged in different sizes, a consumer can compare the unit prices of both sizes. The size with the lower unit price is the *better buy.*

**Example:** Find the unit price of each item. Compare the unit prices. Choose the better buy.

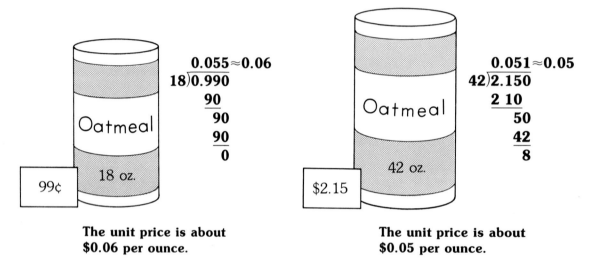

$$18\overline{)0.990} \quad 0.055 \approx 0.06$$

The unit price is about
$0.06 per ounce.

$$42\overline{)2.150} \quad 0.051 \approx 0.05$$

The unit price is about
$0.05 per ounce.

So the 42-ounce container is the better buy.

For each product, find the unit price to the nearest cent for each size. Decide which size is the better buy.

**1.** applesauce:  8 ounces for 45¢ or 15 ounces for 67¢

**2.** peanut butter:  18 ounces for $1.64 or 28 ounces for $2.66

**3.** flour:  2 pounds for 60¢ or 5 pounds for 98¢

**4.** tomato sauce:  15 ounces for 60¢ or 8 ounces for 32¢

**5.** toothpaste:  4.6 ounces for $1.27 or 6.4 ounces for $1.59

**6.** laundry soap:  20 ounces for $1.15 or 49 ounces for $2.39

Use the division below to answer the following:                                3.1

$$\begin{array}{r} 5 \text{ R}11 \\ 49\overline{)256} \end{array}$$

**1.** What number is the **divisor?**

**2.** What number is the **dividend?**

**3.** What number is the **quotient?**

**4.** What number is the **remainder?**

Divide and check. Write any remainder as a whole number.

**5.** $8\overline{)976}$                **6.** $7\overline{)3292}$                **7.** $5\overline{)2349}$

**8.** $32\overline{)835}$               **9.** $79\overline{)24095}$             **10.** $46\overline{)30857}$          3.2

**11.** $301\overline{)7290}$           **12.** $148\overline{)13334}$           **13.** $208\overline{)8944}$         3.6

Divide until the remainder is 0. Check.

**14.** $6\overline{)21.42}$            **15.** $55\overline{)1.65}$             **16.** $48\overline{)156.288}$        3.4

**17.** $252\overline{)8568}$          **18.** $115\overline{)16.445}$          **19.** $125\overline{)378.125}$       3.6

**20.** $23.8 \div 100$          **21.** $129 \div 10$             **22.** $0.15 \div 1000$         3.7

**23.** $198.5 \div 100$         **24.** $4.9 \div 1000$           **25.** $2.23 \div 10$

**26.** $0.6\overline{)246}$            **27.** $3.8\overline{)57}$              **28.** $0.24\overline{)144}$         3.9

**29.** $0.08\overline{)28.8}$          **30.** $1.5\overline{)3.12}$            **31.** $0.71\overline{)3.976}$       3.10

**32.** $0.25\overline{)0.7}$           **33.** $7.5\overline{)0.18}$            **34.** $1.25\overline{)0.3}$

Divide. Round the quotient to the nearest whole number.

3.11

**35.** $32\overline{)55}$

**36.** $4.1\overline{)153}$

**37.** $0.19\overline{)42.9}$

Divide. Round the quotient to the nearest tenth.

**38.** $0.6\overline{)2.14}$

**39.** $0.65\overline{)1.9}$

**40.** $7\overline{)1.75}$

Divide. Round the quotient to the nearest hundredth.

**41.** $9\overline{)11.583}$

**42.** $0.3\overline{)8.99}$

**43.** $0.09\overline{)3.5}$

Solve.

**44.** 224 people were expected at a luncheon. Each table was set for 8 people. How many tables were needed if as few tables as possible were used?

3.3

**45.** If a typist can type 55 words per minute, how long would it take to type a 2200-word report?

**46.** There are 24 pictures on a roll of film. One summer Hank took 275 pictures. How many pictures were left on the last roll?

3.5

**47.** A machine can make 450 parts an hour. How many hours will it take to fill an order for 2700 parts?

**48.** 4 people split the cost of a pizza equally. If the pizza cost $9.60, how much did each person pay?

**49.** Floor tiles are sold in cartons of 45 tiles each. If a carton costs $38.25, what is the cost per tile?

**50.** Phyllis spent $3.90, $4.75, and $3.80 for lunch on three different days. What was the average amount she spent each day?

3.8

**51.** Mrs. Garza paid $13.56 for a turkey that weighed 15.2 pounds. What was the cost per pound to the nearest cent?

3.12

**52.** Michael worked for 4.5 hours and made $19.35. How much did he earn per hour?

# CHAPTER TEST

Divide and check. Write any remainder as a whole number.

**1.** $4\overline{)71}$

**2.** $7\overline{)224}$

**3.** $6\overline{)3704}$

**4.** $23\overline{)170}$

**5.** $78\overline{)3510}$

**6.** $52\overline{)15970}$

**7.** $125\overline{)7875}$

**8.** $144\overline{)44352}$

**9.** $250\overline{)30750}$

Divide until the remainder is 0.

**10.** $9\overline{)21.6}$

**11.** $12\overline{)24.72}$

**12.** $62\overline{)251.72}$

**13.** $105\overline{)451.5}$

**14.** $48.9 \div 100$

**15.** $25.07 \div 10$

**16.** $729 \div 1000$

**17.** $8.53 \div 100$

**18.** $29.01 \div 1000$

**19.** $1.5\overline{)48}$

**20.** $0.08\overline{)12}$

**21.** $0.28\overline{)1036}$

**22.** $3.5\overline{)21}$

**23.** $0.32\overline{)307.2}$

**24.** $0.07\overline{)2.275}$

**25.** $0.36\overline{)191.52}$

**26.** $1.25\overline{)0.05}$

**27.** $0.72\overline{)26.208}$

Divide. Round the quotient to the nearest hundredth.

**28.** $9\overline{)12.25}$

**29.** $0.16\overline{)4.02}$

**30.** $2.4\overline{)49}$

Solve.

**31.** The total labor charge for repairing a car is $123.50. If the hourly labor charge is $19, how many hours of labor are charged for?

**32.** Alicia saves $12 each month from her baby-sitting money. How many months will it take her to save $108?

**33.** How many 16-ounce packages of nuts can be made from 200 ounces of nuts?

# CUMULATIVE REVIEW

Name the place value of each underlined digit.

**1.** 40.3̲12

**2.** 69̲5

**3.** 1̲285

**4.** 52.08̲

**5.** 6.7̲13

**6.** 43.527̲

Compare. Write <, =, or > for each ●.

**7.** 1208 ● 1280

**8.** 629 ● 93

**9.** 40.9 ● 40.90

**10.** 17.71 ● 177.1

**11.** 532 ● 325

**12.** 1.708 ● 1.9

Add.

**13.**  82
      +59

**14.**   713
       +298

**15.**   1290
       +  857

**16.**   3076
       +7265

**17.**  6.39
      +8.8

**18.**   23.05
       +40.98

**19.**   423
       +  89.7

**20.** $3.6 + 0.87 + 18$

Subtract.

**21.**   1100
       −  829

**22.**   20,315
       − 13,463

**23.**   70,716
       − 40,820

**24.** $40,149 − 22,350$

**25.**  4.26
      −1.98

**26.**   12.03
       −  3.17

**27.**   126.37
       −  70.9

**28.** $56.9 − 39.07$

Round to the nearest hundred.

**29.** 1264

**30.** 5492

**31.** 854

**32.** 980

**33.** 739

Round to the largest place value.

**34.** 19.6      **35.** 25      **36.** 436      **37.** 8299      **38.** 0.47

Estimate.

**39.**
$$\begin{array}{r} 230 \\ +180 \\ \hline \end{array}$$
**40.**
$$\begin{array}{r} 591 \\ -129 \\ \hline \end{array}$$
**41.**
$$\begin{array}{r} 86 \\ +75 \\ \hline \end{array}$$
**42.**
$$\begin{array}{r} 44 \\ +52 \\ \hline \end{array}$$
**43.**
$$\begin{array}{r} 1985 \\ -708 \\ \hline \end{array}$$

Solve.

**44.** Louis had $1567.89 withheld for taxes from his wages last year. But only $1479.90 should have been withheld. How much money was his tax refund?

**45.** Expenses for Jennifer's ski trip were $199 for airfare, $90 for lift tickets, $225 for lodging, $105 for lessons, and $110 for meals. How much did she spend in all?

Multiply.

**46.**
$$\begin{array}{r} 65 \\ \times 9 \\ \hline \end{array}$$
**47.**
$$\begin{array}{r} 84 \\ \times 6 \\ \hline \end{array}$$
**48.**
$$\begin{array}{r} 35 \\ \times 54 \\ \hline \end{array}$$
**49.**
$$\begin{array}{r} 106 \\ \times 49 \\ \hline \end{array}$$

Estimate each product.

**50.** $53 \times 65$      **51.** $84 \times 28$      **52.** $471 \times 19$      **53.** $541 \times 11$

Multiply.

**54.**
$$\begin{array}{r} 0.65 \\ \times 9 \\ \hline \end{array}$$
**55.**
$$\begin{array}{r} 2.3 \\ \times 0.8 \\ \hline \end{array}$$
**56.**
$$\begin{array}{r} 7.3 \\ \times 2.5 \\ \hline \end{array}$$
**57.**
$$\begin{array}{r} 0.89 \\ \times 3.1 \\ \hline \end{array}$$

**58.**
$$\begin{array}{r} 4.9 \\ \times 0.64 \\ \hline \end{array}$$
**59.**
$$\begin{array}{r} 0.23 \\ \times 0.51 \\ \hline \end{array}$$
**60.** $6.07 \times 10$      **61.** $17.3 \times 0.01$

**62.** $3.5 \times 100$

**63.** $16.3 \\ \underline{\times 3.2}$

**64.** $9.73 \\ \underline{\times 0.22}$

**65.** $0.66 \\ \underline{\times 80.1}$

**66.** $8.6 \\ \underline{\times 4.07}$

**67.** $7.1 \\ \underline{\times 0.34}$

**68.** $20.8 \\ \underline{\times 4.7}$

**69.** $5.24 \\ \underline{\times 0.85}$

Solve.

**70.** If carpeting sells for $21 per square yard, how much would 28 square yards cost?

**71.** Lori baby-sat for 5 hours one evening. If she charged $1.75 per hour, how much did she earn?

Divide.

**72.** $3\overline{)825}$

**73.** $8\overline{)2848}$

**74.** $6\overline{)1602}$

**75.** $28\overline{)8624}$

**76.** $42\overline{)19320}$

**77.** $50\overline{)20300}$

**78.** $75\overline{)12.6}$

**79.** $36\overline{)86.04}$

**80.** $350\overline{)12600}$

**81.** $4.3 \div 10$

**82.** $64 \div 1000$

**83.** $125.9 \div 100$

**84.** $0.6\overline{)108}$

**85.** $0.25\overline{)125}$

**86.** $0.006\overline{)0.528}$

**87.** $0.52\overline{)1.404}$

**88.** $3.6\overline{)29.88}$

**89.** $0.48\overline{)2.592}$

**90.** $0.65\overline{)474.5}$

**91.** $0.29\overline{)1168.7}$

Divide. Round the quotient to the nearest hundredth.

**92.** $75\overline{)373}$

**93.** $4\overline{)0.696}$

**94.** $0.52\overline{)0.992}$

**95.** $0.35\overline{)7.7476}$

Solve.

**96.** A car wash charges $2.25 per wash. If $171 was collected in an afternoon, how many cars used the car wash?

**97.** 1 gallon of paint covers 400 square feet. How many gallons are needed to cover 1450 square feet?

1. Write a fraction for the shaded part of the figure.

2. Find a fraction equivalent to $\frac{3}{4}$ by multiplying the numerator and the denominator by 6.

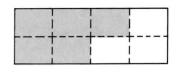

Reduce to lowest terms.

3. $\frac{4}{12}$

4. $\frac{8}{20}$

5. $\frac{12}{30}$

Express as a decimal.

6. $\frac{7}{100}$

7. $\frac{4}{5}$

8. $\frac{9}{20}$

Express as a fraction. Reduce to lowest terms.

9. 0.6

10. 0.75

11. 0.08

Change each pair of fractions to equivalent fractions with a common denominator.

12. $\frac{3}{4}, \frac{1}{8}$

13. $\frac{5}{6}, \frac{1}{4}$

14. $\frac{3}{7}, \frac{1}{2}$

Add. Simplify.

15. $\frac{7}{9} + \frac{1}{9}$

16. $\frac{4}{15} + \frac{7}{15}$

17. $\frac{5}{12} + \frac{1}{12}$

18. $\frac{1}{4} + \frac{3}{8}$

19. $\frac{1}{6} + \frac{3}{4}$

20. $\frac{3}{5} + \frac{2}{3}$

21. $\frac{3}{4} + \frac{5}{6}$

22. $1\frac{2}{3} + 2\frac{4}{5}$

23. $4\frac{1}{6} + 3\frac{1}{2}$

24. Express $\frac{47}{6}$ as a mixed number.

25. Express $3\frac{2}{5}$ as a fraction.

Solve.

26. A sheet of plastic $\frac{1}{8}$ inch thick is glued to a sheet of plywood $\frac{3}{8}$ inch thick. What is the total thickness?

27. Hank bought $2\frac{1}{3}$ yards of burlap and $3\frac{1}{4}$ yards of felt. How much material did he buy in all?

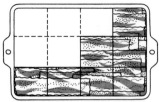

**Notice that the pieces must be *exactly* the same size.**

Fractions are used to stand for the following:

1. PART OF A WHOLE

$\frac{5}{12}$ of the lasagna (5 out of the 12 pieces) has been eaten.

$\frac{7}{12}$ of the lasagna (7 out of the 12 pieces) remains.

2. PART OF A GROUP

$\frac{3}{8}$ of the drinks (3 out of the 8 drinks) are tomato juice.

$\frac{5}{8}$ of the drinks (5 out of the 8 drinks) are milk.

3. DIVISION

numerator ———→ $\frac{3}{4}$ means 4)$\overline{3}$ or 3 ÷ 4.
denominator ———→

Remember, 0 can never be the divisor in a division problem. Therefore, 0 can never be the denominator in a fraction.

**Example 1:** Express $6 \div 5$, 9)$\overline{1}$, and $7 \div 1$ as fractions.

| Division | Fraction |
|----------|----------|
| $6 \div 5$ | $\frac{6}{5}$ |
| 9)$\overline{1}$ | $\frac{1}{9}$ |
| $7 \div 1$ | $\frac{7}{1}$ |

Any whole number may be expressed as a fraction with a denominator of 1. Here's why.

Notice that $9 \div 1 = 9$ and $9 \div 1 = \frac{9}{1}$. So $9 = \frac{9}{1}$.

**98**

**Example 2:**   Express 5, 8, and 10 as fractions.

$5 = \dfrac{5}{1}$      $8 = \dfrac{8}{1}$      $10 = \dfrac{10}{1}$

## EXERCISES

Write a fraction for the shaded part of each figure.

**1.**    **2.**    **3.**    **4.**    **5.**

Write a fraction for the shaded part of each group.

**6.**    **7.**    **8.**    **9.**

Write a fraction for the part of the figure that is in each color.

**10.** red          **11.** black

**12.** gray         **13.** white

Write a fraction for the part of the flag that is in each color.

**14.** red

**15.** white

**16.** black

Write a fraction for the part of the group of mice in each color.

**17.** black

**18.** white

**19.** gray

Express as fractions.

**20.** $5 \div 9$          **21.** $5\overline{)4}$          **22.** $7 \div 3$          **23.** $9\overline{)8}$

**24.** $1 \div 9$          **25.** $8\overline{)1}$          **26.** 6          **27.** 15

The pictures below show what remains of two cheese wheels, both the same size.

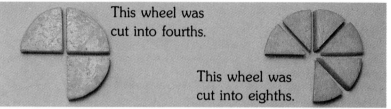

This wheel was cut into fourths.

This wheel was cut into eighths.

Ed Hoppe Photography

Notice that $\frac{3}{4}$ and $\frac{6}{8}$ stand for the same amount. That is, $\frac{3}{4} = \frac{6}{8}$.

If you multiply both the numerator and the denominator of $\frac{3}{4}$ by 2, the result is $\frac{6}{8}$.

$$\frac{3}{4} = \frac{3 \times 2}{4 \times 2} = \frac{6}{8}$$

If you divide both the numerator and the denominator of $\frac{6}{8}$ by 2, the result is $\frac{3}{4}$.

$$\frac{6}{8} = \frac{6 \div 2}{8 \div 2} = \frac{3}{4}$$

We say $\frac{3}{4}$ and $\frac{6}{8}$ are **equivalent fractions.**

**To find a fraction equivalent to a given fraction, multiply or divide the numerator and the denominator by the same nonzero number.**

**Example 1:** Find a fraction equivalent to $\frac{8}{12}$ by dividing the numerator and the denominator by the number in red.

$$\frac{8}{12}, \quad 4 \qquad \frac{8}{12} = \frac{8 \div 4}{12 \div 4} = \frac{2}{3}$$

**Example 2:** Find two fractions equivalent to $\frac{5}{6}$ by multiplying the numerator and the denominator by the numbers in red.

$$\frac{5}{6}, \quad 3 \qquad \frac{5}{6} = \frac{5 \times 3}{6 \times 3} = \frac{15}{18} \qquad\qquad \frac{5}{6}, \quad 10 \qquad \frac{5}{6} = \frac{5 \times 10}{6 \times 10} = \frac{50}{60}$$

# EXERCISES

Copy and complete the following:

**1.** $\dfrac{18}{20} = \dfrac{18 \div 2}{20 \div 2} = \dfrac{9}{\boxed{?}}$

**2.** $\dfrac{24}{30} = \dfrac{24 \div 6}{30 \div 6} = \dfrac{\boxed{?}}{5}$

**3.** $\dfrac{4}{12} = \dfrac{4 \div \boxed{?}}{12 \div 4} = \dfrac{1}{3}$

**4.** $\dfrac{15}{20} = \dfrac{15 \div 5}{20 \div \boxed{?}} = \dfrac{3}{4}$

**5.** $\dfrac{10}{60} = \dfrac{10 \div 10}{60 \div 10} = \dfrac{\boxed{?}}{6}$

**6.** $\dfrac{22}{24} = \dfrac{22 \div 2}{24 \div 2} = \dfrac{11}{\boxed{?}}$

**7.** $\dfrac{24}{32} = \dfrac{24 \div \boxed{?}}{32 \div 8} = \dfrac{3}{4}$

**8.** $\dfrac{42}{48} = \dfrac{42 \div 6}{48 \div \boxed{?}} = \dfrac{7}{8}$

**9.** $\dfrac{24}{36} = \dfrac{24 \div 12}{36 \div 12} = \dfrac{\boxed{?}}{3}$

**10.** $\dfrac{15}{60} = \dfrac{15 \div 15}{60 \div 15} = \dfrac{1}{\boxed{?}}$

Find a fraction equivalent to the given fraction by dividing the numerator and the denominator by the number in red.

**11.** $\dfrac{6}{10},\ 2$

**12.** $\dfrac{15}{18},\ 3$

**13.** $\dfrac{4}{16},\ 4$

**14.** $\dfrac{5}{15},\ 5$

**15.** $\dfrac{16}{24},\ 8$

**16.** $\dfrac{12}{18},\ 6$

**17.** $\dfrac{15}{27},\ 3$

**18.** $\dfrac{30}{80},\ 10$

**19.** $\dfrac{24}{36},\ 12$

Find a fraction equivalent to the given fraction by multiplying the numerator and the denominator by the number in red.

**20.** $\dfrac{1}{2},\ 4$

**21.** $\dfrac{2}{3},\ 5$

**22.** $\dfrac{3}{4},\ 6$

**23.** $\dfrac{3}{7},\ 8$

**24.** $\dfrac{1}{4},\ 9$

**25.** $\dfrac{4}{5},\ 3$

**26.** $\dfrac{1}{3},\ 10$

**27.** $\dfrac{5}{6},\ 4$

**28.** $\dfrac{7}{8},\ 2$

For each fraction in exercises 29–34, choose two equivalent fractions from the following list:

$$\dfrac{1}{2},\ \dfrac{4}{8},\ \dfrac{1}{3},\ \dfrac{2}{6},\ \dfrac{6}{8},\ \dfrac{9}{12},\ \dfrac{2}{20},\ \dfrac{5}{50}$$

**29.** $\dfrac{3}{4}$

**30.** $\dfrac{2}{4}$

**31.** $\dfrac{4}{12}$

**32.** $\dfrac{1}{10}$

**33.** $\dfrac{12}{24}$

**34.** $\dfrac{10}{100}$

*EXTRA PRACTICE page 482, set 28*

Historical Pictures Service

**At a party, 12 out of 18 people are in costume. What part of the group is in costume?**

We can say that $\frac{12}{18}$ of the group is in costume. But the fraction $\frac{12}{18}$ can be changed to a *simpler* equivalent fraction.

**Example 1:** Simplify $\frac{12}{18}$.

We can divide both the numerator and the denominator of $\frac{12}{18}$ by 2.

$$\frac{12}{18}=\frac{12\div2}{18\div2}=\frac{6}{9} \longleftarrow \textbf{ can be simplified further}$$

We can divide both the numerator and the denominator of $\frac{6}{9}$ by 3.

$$\frac{6}{9}=\frac{6\div3}{9\div3}=\frac{2}{3}$$ **The only whole number that will divide both 2 and 3 is 1. We say $\frac{2}{3}$ is in lowest terms.**

**A fraction is *reduced to lowest terms* if 1 is the only whole number that divides both the numerator and the denominator.**

**Example 2:** Reduce $\frac{12}{18}$ to lowest terms.

In Example 1, we reduced $\frac{12}{18}$ to lowest terms in two steps. Here's a way to do it in one step.

$$\frac{12}{18}=\frac{12\div6}{18\div6}=\frac{2}{3}$$

**Example 3:** Reduce $\frac{20}{40}$ to lowest terms.

| In three steps: | In two steps: | In one step: |
|---|---|---|
| $\frac{20}{40}=\frac{20\div2}{40\div2}=\frac{10}{20}$ | $\frac{20}{40}=\frac{20\div5}{40\div5}=\frac{4}{8}$ | $\frac{20}{40}=\frac{20\div20}{40\div20}=\frac{1}{2}$ |
| $\frac{10}{20}=\frac{10\div2}{20\div2}=\frac{5}{10}$ | $\frac{4}{8}=\frac{4\div4}{8\div4}=\frac{1}{2}$ | |
| $\frac{5}{10}=\frac{5\div5}{10\div5}=\frac{1}{2}$ | | |

# EXERCISES

Reduce to lowest terms.

1. $\frac{3}{6}$  2. $\frac{4}{10}$  3. $\frac{6}{9}$  4. $\frac{8}{24}$  5. $\frac{2}{12}$

6. $\frac{3}{9}$  7. $\frac{10}{80}$  8. $\frac{8}{12}$  9. $\frac{4}{8}$  10. $\frac{10}{12}$

11. $\frac{5}{25}$  12. $\frac{6}{10}$  13. $\frac{3}{12}$  14. $\frac{12}{15}$  15. $\frac{8}{10}$

16. $\frac{9}{15}$  17. $\frac{9}{12}$  18. $\frac{4}{12}$  19. $\frac{15}{45}$  20. $\frac{3}{21}$

21. $\frac{4}{32}$  22. $\frac{3}{24}$  23. $\frac{14}{16}$  24. $\frac{3}{15}$  25. $\frac{10}{100}$

26. $\frac{4}{24}$  27. $\frac{5}{15}$  28. $\frac{9}{21}$  29. $\frac{2}{14}$  30. $\frac{10}{15}$

31. $\frac{6}{18}$  32. $\frac{4}{20}$  33. $\frac{6}{24}$  34. $\frac{15}{18}$  35. $\frac{15}{25}$

36. $\frac{6}{33}$  37. $\frac{15}{24}$  38. $\frac{10}{16}$  39. $\frac{12}{32}$  40. $\frac{2}{26}$

41. $\frac{15}{100}$  42. $\frac{9}{27}$  43. $\frac{5}{30}$  44. $\frac{12}{18}$  45. $\frac{8}{28}$

46. $\frac{21}{36}$  47. $\frac{14}{30}$  48. $\frac{12}{60}$  49. $\frac{15}{90}$  50. $\frac{24}{42}$

51. $\frac{16}{32}$  52. $\frac{45}{80}$  53. $\frac{36}{45}$  54. $\frac{24}{64}$  55. $\frac{21}{66}$

56. $\frac{18}{81}$  57. $\frac{60}{85}$  58. $\frac{39}{48}$  59. $\frac{84}{90}$  60. $\frac{57}{90}$

Solve.

61. In a class, 9 out of 27 students are in the Pep Club. What is $\frac{9}{27}$ in lowest terms?

62. In another class, 5 out of 30 students have their driver's license. What is $\frac{5}{30}$ in lowest terms?

63. In a hockey game, a player made 2 shots out of 12. What is $\frac{2}{12}$ in lowest terms?

64. On a test, a student got 20 out of 25 questions correct. What is $\frac{20}{25}$ in lowest terms?

*EXTRA PRACTICE page 482, set 29*

Karen Phillips

**At a high-school variety show, 75 out of 100 fans used student passes. As a fraction, seventy-five hundredths is written $\frac{75}{100}$. How is it written as a decimal?**

Fractions with a denominator of 10, 100, or 1000 are easily changed to decimals.

$$\frac{8}{10}=0.8 \qquad \frac{23}{100}=0.23 \qquad \frac{368}{1000}=0.368$$

Be sure to use zero as a placeholder if necessary.

$$\frac{7}{100}=0.07 \qquad \frac{13}{1000}=0.013 \qquad \frac{9}{1000}=0.009$$

**Example 1:** Change $\frac{75}{100}$ to a decimal.

$$\frac{75}{100}=0.75$$

To change a fraction to a decimal, you can divide.

**Example 2:** Change $\frac{2}{5}$ to a decimal.

$$\frac{2}{5} \longrightarrow 5\overline{)\begin{array}{l} 0.4 \\ 2.0 \\ \underline{2\ 0} \\ \phantom{2}0 \end{array}} \qquad \frac{2}{5}=0.4$$

**Example 3:** Change $\frac{2}{3}$ to a decimal.

$$\frac{2}{3} \longrightarrow 3\overline{)\begin{array}{l} 0.666\cdots \\ 2.000 \\ \underline{1\ 8} \\ \phantom{1}20 \\ \underline{\phantom{1}18} \\ \phantom{11}20 \\ \underline{\phantom{11}18} \\ \phantom{111}2 \end{array}}$$

The division can be continued without end.

Fractions like $\frac{2}{3}$ are equal to **repeating decimals**. We write

$$\frac{2}{3}=0.666\cdots \text{ or } \frac{2}{3}=0.\overline{6}.$$

The bar shows that the digit 6 repeats.

**Example 4:** Change 0.15 to a fraction in lowest terms.

$$0.15=\frac{15}{100}=\frac{3}{20}$$

# EXERCISES

Change to a decimal.

1. $\frac{9}{10}$          2. $\frac{33}{100}$          3. $\frac{673}{1000}$          4. $\frac{4}{10}$

5. $\frac{75}{100}$          6. $\frac{125}{1000}$          7. $\frac{1}{10}$          8. $\frac{3}{100}$

9. $\frac{27}{1000}$          10. $\frac{6}{1000}$          11. $\frac{3}{10}$          12. $\frac{71}{100}$

13. $\frac{8}{10}$          14. $\frac{250}{1000}$          15. $\frac{47}{100}$          16. $\frac{1}{4}$

17. $\frac{2}{5}$          18. $\frac{1}{2}$          19. $\frac{3}{4}$          20. $\frac{1}{8}$

21. $\frac{3}{20}$          22. $\frac{3}{5}$          23. $\frac{1}{5}$          24. $\frac{1}{3}$

25. $\frac{5}{8}$          26. $\frac{1}{20}$          27. $\frac{11}{25}$          28. $\frac{1}{9}$

29. $\frac{1}{6}$          30. $\frac{19}{20}$          31. $\frac{2}{9}$          32. $\frac{13}{50}$

Change to a fraction in lowest terms.

33. 0.9          34. 0.31          35. 0.4          36. 0.25          37. 0.125

38. 0.2          39. 0.60          40. 0.08          41. 0.15          42. 0.06

43. 0.30          44. 0.04          45. 0.075          46. 0.250          47. 0.625

*EXTRA PRACTICE page 482, set 30*

## SKILLS REVIEW

Add.

48.     639          49.     708          50.     5416          51.     6349
      + 57                +596              +  897                +5872

52. $69 + 204 + 56$          53. $597 + 38 + 126$

54. $3764 + 983$          55. $7824 + 6987$

James Tallon

The gas tank of Ellen's camper holds 25 gallons of gasoline. During one week, the camper used 10 gallons of gasoline. Write a fraction for the part of the gasoline used. Write a fraction for the part of the gasoline remaining.

**Read:**   *Given:*   holds 25 gallons; used 10 gallons

*To find:*   fractions for the part of the gasoline used and for the part of the gasoline remaining

**Plan:**   To find a fraction for the part of the gasoline used, write the number of gallons used over the total number of gallons the tank holds. Then reduce the fraction to lowest terms.

To find a fraction for the part of the gasoline remaining, first find the number of gallons remaining. Then write that number over the total number of gallons the tank holds and reduce the fraction to lowest terms.

**Compute:**   *Part of the gasoline used:*

$$\frac{10}{25} = \frac{2}{5}$$

*Part of the gasoline remaining:*

$$25 - 10 = 15$$

$$\frac{15}{25} = \frac{3}{5}$$

**Answer:**   The camper used $\frac{2}{5}$ of the gasoline, and $\frac{3}{5}$ remains.

**Check:**   Does 10 out of 25 equal $\frac{2}{5}$?   ✔

Does 15 out of 25 equal $\frac{3}{5}$?   ✔

# EXERCISES

1. Fred bought a dozen eggs. When he arrived home, 2 of the eggs were broken. Write a fraction for the part of the eggs that were broken. Write a fraction for the part of the eggs that were not broken.

2. In an election 240 people voted, but only 80 voted for Ms. Garza. Write a fraction for the part of the people that voted for Ms. Garza. Write a fraction for the part of the people that did not vote for Ms. Garza.

3. The county highway department checked 15 road signs and found that 5 needed repair. Write a fraction for the part of the road signs that needed repair.

4. An assembly line produced 5 white cars, 3 black cars, and 2 blue cars. Write a fraction for the part of the cars that were white. Write a fraction for the part of the cars that were black.

5. After the football game, Joe had $0.75 left. Ken had $0.60 left. Write a fraction for the part of a dollar each boy had left.

6. The Fox Valley High School football team played 10 games and won 8. Write a decimal for the part of their games that they won.

7. The girls' soccer team played 8 home games and lost 2. Write a decimal for the part of their games that they lost.

8. The student council arranged 9 dances for the coming year. Gwen volunteered to work at 3 of the dances. Maria volunteered to work at 2. Write a fraction for the part of the dances for which each girl volunteered.

9. In a survey, 24 out of 36 students bought lunch at school. Write a fraction for the part of the students that bought lunch at school. Write a fraction for the part of the students that did not buy lunch at school.

10. A telephone salesperson made 200 calls, and 12 calls resulted in sales. Write a fraction for the part of the calls that resulted in sales.

11. A basketball player made 22 free throws out of 50 attempted shots. Write a fraction for the part of the free throws made.

12. The water tank in Jim's camper holds 100 gallons of water. On a trip, Jim used 65 gallons of water. Write a fraction for the part of the water Jim used. Write a fraction for the part of the water Jim did not use.

Jack L. Riesland/Berg & Associates

In industrial arts class, Jean glued a sheet of wood $\frac{5}{16}$ inch thick to a sheet of plastic $\frac{3}{16}$ inch thick. What was the thickness of the wood and the plastic when they were glued together?

$\longleftarrow \frac{3}{16}$ inch plastic

$\longleftarrow \frac{5}{16}$ inch wood

**Example 1:** Find the thickness of the plastic and the wood together.

$$\begin{array}{r} \frac{3}{16} \\ +\frac{5}{16} \\ \hline \frac{8}{16} = \frac{1}{2} \end{array}$$

Fractions with the same denominator (a common denominator) are called **like fractions.**

The thickness of the plastic and the wood together is $\frac{1}{2}$ inch.

**When adding like fractions, add only the numerators. Keep the same denominator.**

**Example 2:** Add $\frac{4}{9}$ and $\frac{3}{9}$.

$$\begin{array}{r} \frac{4}{9} \\ +\frac{3}{9} \\ \hline \frac{7}{9} \end{array}$$

**Example 3:** Add $\frac{3}{12}$ and $\frac{6}{12}$.

$$\begin{array}{r} \frac{3}{12} \\ +\frac{6}{12} \\ \hline \frac{9}{12} = \frac{3}{4} \end{array}$$

Note that the fraction was simplified by reducing to lowest terms.

# EXERCISES

Add. Reduce to lowest terms.

1. $\frac{2}{8}$ $+\frac{3}{8}$

2. $\frac{4}{9}$ $+\frac{1}{9}$

3. $\frac{3}{5}$ $+\frac{1}{5}$

4. $\frac{5}{12}$ $+\frac{6}{12}$

5. $\frac{1}{8}$ $+\frac{6}{8}$

6. $\frac{4}{6}$ $+\frac{1}{6}$

7. $\frac{3}{7}$ $+\frac{2}{7}$

8. $\frac{2}{12}$ $+\frac{3}{12}$

9. $\frac{6}{10}$ $+\frac{2}{10}$

10. $\frac{1}{6}$ $+\frac{3}{6}$

11. $\frac{2}{9}$ $+\frac{4}{9}$

12. $\frac{2}{10}$ $+\frac{3}{10}$

13. $\frac{4}{12}$ $+\frac{4}{12}$

14. $\frac{9}{25}$ $+\frac{3}{25}$

15. $\frac{6}{21}$ $+\frac{1}{21}$

16. $\frac{3}{36}$ $+\frac{6}{36}$

17. $\frac{3}{20}$ $+\frac{2}{20}$

18. $\frac{8}{15}$ $+\frac{2}{15}$

19. $\frac{1}{14}$ $+\frac{1}{14}$

20. $\frac{8}{30}$ $+\frac{2}{30}$

21. $\frac{6}{15}$ $+\frac{4}{15}$

22. $\frac{3}{18}$ $+\frac{12}{18}$

23. $\frac{2}{14}$ $+\frac{5}{14}$

24. $\frac{10}{30}$ $+\frac{5}{30}$

25. $\frac{8}{24}$ $+\frac{4}{24}$

26. $\frac{5}{16}$ $+\frac{7}{16}$

27. $\frac{5}{18}$ $+\frac{3}{18}$

28. $\frac{21}{50}$ $+\frac{4}{50}$

29. $\frac{12}{20}$ $+\frac{3}{20}$

30. $\frac{10}{60}$ $+\frac{10}{60}$

31. $\frac{4}{25}$ $+\frac{11}{25}$

32. $\frac{5}{32}$ $+\frac{5}{32}$

33. $\frac{41}{64}$ $+\frac{7}{64}$

34. $\frac{7}{100}$ $+\frac{3}{100}$

35. $\frac{87}{1000}$ $+\frac{13}{1000}$

Solve.

36. A panel of wood that is $\frac{5}{8}$ inch thick is glued to a sheet of plastic that is $\frac{1}{8}$ inch thick. What is the total thickness?

37. A layer of glass $\frac{5}{16}$ inch thick is laid over a sheet of metal $\frac{1}{16}$ inch thick. What is the total thickness?

EXTRA PRACTICE page 483, set 31

Ed Hoppe Photography

**Mike has two drill bits. One is a $\frac{1}{4}$-inch bit, and the other is a $\frac{3}{8}$-inch bit. Which is larger?**

Sometimes we need to change fractions to equivalent fractions with a common denominator.

**Example 1:** Change $\frac{1}{4}$ and $\frac{3}{8}$ to equivalent fractions having a common denominator.

Multiply both the numerator and the denominator of $\frac{3}{8}$ by 2, 3, 4, and so on. Then do the same with $\frac{1}{4}$. Continue until you find fractions with a common denominator.

Equivalent fractions for $\frac{3}{8}$: $\frac{3}{8}, \frac{6}{16}, \frac{9}{24}, \frac{12}{32}, \cdots$

Equivalent fractions for $\frac{1}{4}$: $\frac{1}{4}, \frac{2}{8}, \frac{3}{12}, \frac{4}{16}, \frac{5}{20}, \frac{6}{24} \cdots$

Notice that there is more than one pair of fractions with a common denominator. Often we use the **least common denominator.** In this case, the least common denominator is 8.

Since $\frac{3}{8}$ inch is more than $\frac{2}{8}$ inch, the $\frac{3}{8}$-inch bit is larger than the $\frac{1}{4}$-inch bit.

**Example 2:** Change $\frac{5}{6}$ and $\frac{2}{9}$ to equivalent fractions with a common denominator.

Equivalent fractions for $\frac{5}{6}$: $\frac{5}{6}, \frac{10}{12}, \frac{15}{18}, \frac{20}{24}, \cdots$

Equivalent fractions for $\frac{2}{9}$: $\frac{2}{9}, \frac{4}{18} \cdots$

$$\frac{5}{6} = \frac{15}{18} \text{ and } \frac{2}{9} = \frac{4}{18}$$

**Example 3:** Change $\frac{3}{4}$ and $\frac{4}{5}$ to equivalent fractions with a common denominator.

Equivalent fractions for $\frac{3}{4}$: $\frac{3}{4}, \frac{6}{8}, \frac{9}{12}, \frac{12}{16}, \boxed{\frac{15}{20}}$ · · ·

Equivalent fractions for $\frac{4}{5}$: $\frac{4}{5}, \frac{8}{10}, \frac{12}{15}, \boxed{\frac{16}{20}}$ · · ·

$$\frac{3}{4} = \frac{15}{20} \text{ and } \frac{4}{5} = \frac{16}{20}$$

## EXERCISES

Change each pair of fractions to equivalent fractions with a common denominator.

**1.** $\frac{1}{6}, \frac{3}{4}$  **2.** $\frac{1}{3}, \frac{1}{4}$  **3.** $\frac{2}{9}, \frac{1}{3}$  **4.** $\frac{2}{3}, \frac{5}{6}$

**5.** $\frac{3}{4}, \frac{2}{3}$  **6.** $\frac{3}{4}, \frac{5}{8}$  **7.** $\frac{1}{6}, \frac{2}{3}$  **8.** $\frac{5}{8}, \frac{1}{4}$

**9.** $\frac{2}{5}, \frac{2}{3}$  **10.** $\frac{1}{2}, \frac{1}{6}$  **11.** $\frac{2}{3}, \frac{5}{9}$  **12.** $\frac{3}{7}, \frac{1}{2}$

**13.** $\frac{1}{8}, \frac{1}{3}$  **14.** $\frac{4}{5}, \frac{9}{10}$  **15.** $\frac{3}{5}, \frac{5}{6}$  **16.** $\frac{1}{7}, \frac{3}{8}$

**17.** $\frac{5}{6}, \frac{7}{12}$  **18.** $\frac{2}{7}, \frac{5}{6}$  **19.** $\frac{3}{5}, \frac{11}{15}$  **20.** $\frac{5}{12}, \frac{1}{24}$

**21.** $\frac{7}{10}, \frac{4}{15}$  **22.** $\frac{5}{8}, \frac{5}{12}$  **23.** $\frac{7}{9}, \frac{1}{15}$  **24.** $\frac{7}{12}, \frac{1}{18}$

**25.** $\frac{9}{10}, \frac{7}{15}$  **26.** $\frac{7}{9}, \frac{8}{15}$  **27.** $\frac{5}{12}, \frac{1}{36}$  **28.** $\frac{11}{20}, \frac{13}{30}$

*EXTRA PRACTICE page 483, set 32*

## SKILLS REVIEW

Add.

**29.**    56.39
    $+\ 7.82$

**30.**    697.3
    $+\ 58.95$

**31.**    26.39
    142.5
    $+\ \ \ 0.963$

**32.**    36
    25.8
    $+\ 1.19$

**33.** $2.6 + 13.85 + 0.42$

**34.** $0.16 + 7 + 3.9$

**35.** $4.256 + 0.8 + 25.17$

**36.** $46 + 0.18 + 3.5$

Connie and P.C. Peri

**Adela bought $\frac{1}{2}$ pound of pecans and $\frac{1}{4}$ pound of cashews. What was the total weight of the nuts Adela bought?**

To find the answer, you must add $\frac{1}{2}$ and $\frac{1}{4}$. When you add fractions that do not have the same denominator, you must change the fractions so that they have a common denominator. Then add and reduce the sum to lowest terms if possible.

**Example 1:**
**Fractions with different denominators are called unlike fractions.**

$$\frac{1}{2} = \frac{2}{4}$$
$$+\frac{1}{4} = \frac{1}{4}$$
$$\frac{3}{4}$$

a common denominator for $\frac{1}{2}$ and $\frac{1}{4}$

The total weight of the nuts was $\frac{3}{4}$ pound.

**Example 2:**  Add $\frac{3}{8}$ and $\frac{1}{4}$.

A common denominator for $\frac{3}{8}$ and $\frac{1}{4}$ is 16.

$$\frac{3}{8} = \frac{6}{16}$$
$$+\frac{1}{4} = \frac{4}{16}$$
$$\frac{10}{16} = \frac{5}{8}$$

**Note that the answer was simplified by reducing to lowest terms.**

You may arrive at the same answer, using the *least common denominator*.

**Example 3:**  Add $\frac{3}{8}$ and $\frac{1}{4}$.

The least common denominator for $\frac{3}{8}$ and $\frac{1}{4}$ is 8.

$$\frac{3}{8} = \frac{3}{8}$$
$$+\frac{1}{4} = \frac{2}{8}$$
$$\frac{5}{8}$$

# EXERCISES

Add. Reduce to lowest terms.

1. $\frac{1}{2}$
   $+\frac{1}{3}$

2. $\frac{1}{6}$
   $+\frac{1}{4}$

3. $\frac{1}{4}$
   $+\frac{1}{3}$

4. $\frac{5}{8}$
   $+\frac{1}{4}$

5. $\frac{2}{3}$
   $+\frac{1}{9}$

6. $\frac{3}{10}$
   $+\frac{2}{5}$

7. $\frac{1}{5}$
   $+\frac{1}{4}$

8. $\frac{1}{12}$
   $+\frac{1}{3}$

9. $\frac{2}{3}$
   $+\frac{2}{9}$

10. $\frac{1}{4}$
    $+\frac{1}{8}$

11. $\frac{3}{8}$
    $+\frac{1}{4}$

12. $\frac{1}{3}$
    $+\frac{1}{6}$

13. $\frac{3}{8}$
    $+\frac{1}{6}$

14. $\frac{3}{4}$
    $+\frac{1}{5}$

15. $\frac{3}{8}$
    $+\frac{1}{3}$

16. $\frac{1}{2}$
    $+\frac{1}{7}$

17. $\frac{1}{4}$
    $+\frac{3}{10}$

18. $\frac{1}{2}$
    $+\frac{1}{7}$

19. $\frac{5}{8}$
    $+\frac{2}{9}$

20. $\frac{2}{9}$
    $+\frac{1}{6}$

21. $\frac{3}{5}$
    $+\frac{2}{7}$

22. $\frac{2}{9}$
    $+\frac{1}{5}$

23. $\frac{2}{9}$
    $+\frac{5}{18}$

24. $\frac{3}{10}$
    $+\frac{1}{2}$

EXTRA PRACTICE page 483, set 33

## CHECKPOINT

Find a fraction equivalent to the given fraction by multiplying the numerator and denominator by the number in red.

1. $\frac{7}{8}$, 3

2. $\frac{9}{10}$, 5

3. $\frac{5}{6}$, 6

4. $\frac{4}{5}$, 7

Reduce to lowest terms.

5. $\frac{6}{24}$

6. $\frac{10}{15}$

7. $\frac{12}{36}$

8. $\frac{15}{25}$

Add. Reduce to lowest terms.

9. $\frac{3}{10}$
   $+\frac{5}{10}$

10. $\frac{4}{15}$
    $+\frac{2}{15}$

11. $\frac{1}{5}$
    $+\frac{1}{10}$

12. $\frac{1}{5}$
    $+\frac{1}{3}$

113

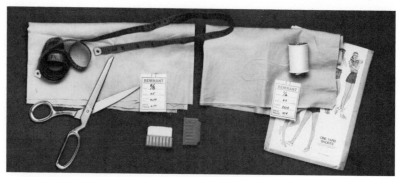

Ed Hoppe Photography

**Sharon had $\frac{1}{4}$ yard of cotton fabric. She bought another $\frac{5}{8}$ yard. How much fabric does Sharon have now?**

**Read:**  *Given:*  had $\frac{1}{4}$ yard; bought $\frac{5}{8}$ yard

*To find:*  total amount of fabric that Sharon has

**Plan:**  Add $\frac{1}{4}$ and $\frac{5}{8}$.

**Compute:**
$$\frac{1}{4} = \frac{2}{8}$$
$$+\frac{5}{8} = \frac{5}{8}$$
$$\overline{\phantom{+\frac{5}{8}=}\;\frac{7}{8}}$$

**Answer:**  Sharon has $\frac{7}{8}$ yard of fabric.

**Check:**

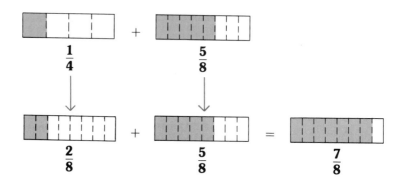

## EXERCISES

1. A recipe calls for $\frac{1}{2}$ cup of milk and $\frac{1}{3}$ cup of water. What is the total amount of milk and water?

2. A piece of wood $\frac{3}{8}$ inch thick is glued to a piece of wood $\frac{1}{4}$ inch thick. What is the total thickness of the two pieces of wood?

3. A sheet of wood that is $\frac{1}{2}$ inch thick has a sheet of glass that is $\frac{3}{32}$ inch thick laid on top of it. What is the combined thickness of the wood and the glass?

4. Carpet tile $\frac{5}{16}$ inch thick is laid over a sheet of plywood $\frac{1}{2}$ inch thick. What is the total thickness of the tile and the plywood?

5. If $\frac{1}{2}$ cup of water is mixed with $\frac{1}{8}$ cup of lemon juice, how much liquid is in the mixture?

6. In home economics class, Chang added $\frac{1}{4}$ teaspoon of salt to the soup. After tasting it, he added another $\frac{1}{4}$ teaspoon of salt. How much salt did Chang add in all?

7. Tina jogged $\frac{1}{2}$ mile, then walked $\frac{3}{8}$ mile farther. What was the total distance Tina traveled?

8. If $\frac{1}{4}$ quart of orange juice is mixed with $\frac{1}{3}$ quart of grapefruit juice, how much juice is in the mixture?

9. Safety glass is made from two pieces of glass fused together. If each piece of glass is $\frac{1}{16}$ inch thick, what is the total thickness of the glass?

10. Two washers are placed on a bolt. One washer is $\frac{1}{8}$ inch thick. The other washer is $\frac{1}{16}$ inch thick. What is the thickness of the two washers together?

11. A plastic coating $\frac{1}{32}$ inch thick is applied to a sheet of cardboard that is $\frac{1}{16}$ inch thick. What is the combined thickness of the coating and the cardboard?

*EXTRA PRACTICE page 484, set 34*

Talladega/Worldwide Photography

**A stock car went around the entire track 3 times. Then it went another $\frac{3}{4}$ of the way around before having a blowout. How many times did the car go around the track?**

The answer is a **mixed number,** $3\frac{3}{4}$. $3\frac{3}{4}$ means $3 + \frac{3}{4}$.

Sometimes it is helpful to write the result of a division problem as a mixed number.

**Example 1:** Express the quotient as a mixed number.

$$5\overline{)39} \longrightarrow \begin{array}{r} 7 \\ 5\overline{)39} \\ \underline{35} \\ 4 \end{array} \longrightarrow 7\frac{4}{5} \begin{array}{l} \leftarrow \textbf{remainder} \\ \leftarrow \textbf{divisor} \end{array}$$

In an **improper fraction,** the numerator is greater than or equal to the denominator. Improper fractions can be written as mixed numbers or as whole numbers.

**Example 2:** Write $\frac{12}{6}$ as a mixed number or as a whole number.

$$\frac{12}{6} \text{ means } 6\overline{)12}. \longrightarrow \begin{array}{r} 2 \\ 6\overline{)12} \\ \underline{12} \\ 0 \end{array} \longrightarrow 2$$

**Example 3:** Write $\frac{15}{6}$ as a mixed number or as a whole number.

$$\frac{15}{6} \text{ means } 6\overline{)15}. \longrightarrow \begin{array}{r} 2 \\ 6\overline{)15} \\ \underline{12} \\ 3 \end{array} \longrightarrow 2\frac{3}{6}$$

Sometimes the fraction part of a mixed number can be reduced to lowest terms.

$$2\frac{3}{6} = 2\frac{1}{2}$$

Expressing a mixed number as a fraction is a 4-step process.

**Example 4:** Express $6\frac{2}{3}$ as a fraction.

| Multiply the denominator and the whole number. | Add the product to the numerator. | Write the sum over the denominator. | Check by changing $\frac{20}{3}$ to a mixed number. |
|---|---|---|---|

$6\frac{2}{3}$ $\qquad$ $6\frac{2}{3}$ $\qquad\qquad$ $18 + 2 = 20$ $\qquad\qquad$ $\dfrac{20}{3}$ $\qquad\qquad$ $6\frac{2}{3}$

$\qquad\qquad 6 \times 3 = 18 \qquad\qquad\qquad 6\frac{2}{3}$ $\qquad\qquad\qquad\qquad\qquad 3\overline{)20}$

$\qquad\qquad\qquad\qquad\qquad\qquad\qquad\qquad\qquad\qquad\qquad\qquad\qquad \dfrac{18}{2}$

## EXERCISES

Express as a mixed number or as a whole number. Simplify.

**1.** $8\overline{)25}$ $\qquad$ **2.** $64 \div 9$ $\qquad$ **3.** $7\overline{)39}$ $\qquad$ **4.** $41 \div 6$

**5.** $47 \div 5$ $\qquad$ **6.** $10\overline{)31}$ $\qquad$ **7.** $18 \div 4$ $\qquad$ **8.** $9\overline{)48}$

**9.** $6\overline{)45}$ $\qquad$ **10.** $70 \div 8$ $\qquad$ **11.** $12\overline{)146}$ $\qquad$ **12.** $105 \div 10$

**13.** $15\overline{)48}$ $\qquad$ **14.** $38 \div 11$ $\qquad$ **15.** $20\overline{)465}$ $\qquad$ **16.** $75 \div 35$

Express as a mixed number. Simplify.

**17.** $\frac{15}{7}$ $\qquad$ **18.** $\frac{29}{9}$ $\qquad$ **19.** $\frac{38}{6}$ $\qquad$ **20.** $\frac{26}{4}$

**21.** $\frac{43}{10}$ $\qquad$ **22.** $\frac{60}{8}$ $\qquad$ **23.** $\frac{72}{5}$ $\qquad$ **24.** $\frac{34}{3}$

**25.** $\frac{49}{6}$ $\qquad$ **26.** $\frac{45}{7}$ $\qquad$ **27.** $\frac{84}{9}$ $\qquad$ **28.** $\frac{61}{2}$

**29.** $\frac{92}{8}$ $\qquad$ **30.** $\frac{75}{10}$ $\qquad$ **31.** $\frac{80}{15}$ $\qquad$ **32.** $\frac{126}{8}$

Express as a fraction.

**33.** $1\frac{3}{4}$ $\qquad$ **34.** $2\frac{2}{3}$ $\qquad$ **35.** $6\frac{1}{2}$ $\qquad$ **36.** $4\frac{3}{5}$ $\qquad$ **37.** $7\frac{2}{7}$

**38.** $8\frac{1}{9}$ $\qquad$ **39.** $10\frac{2}{3}$ $\qquad$ **40.** $1\frac{7}{8}$ $\qquad$ **41.** $12\frac{1}{2}$ $\qquad$ **42.** $9\frac{3}{8}$

*EXTRA PRACTICE page 484, set 35*

H. Armstrong Roberts

**The normal rainfall in Albuquerque, New Mexico, in October is $\frac{8}{10}$ inch. In November, the normal rainfall is $\frac{3}{10}$ inch. What is the total normal rainfall for the two months of October and November?**

**Example 1:** Add $\frac{8}{10}$ and $\frac{3}{10}$.

$$\frac{8}{10}$$
$$+\frac{3}{10}$$
$$\frac{11}{10}=1\frac{1}{10} \leftarrow$$ **When the sum of two fractions is an improper fraction, simplify the sum by expressing it as a mixed number.**

The total normal rainfall for October and November is $1\frac{1}{10}$ inches.

If the fractions being added do not have a common denominator, change the fractions to equivalent fractions with a common denominator and add.

**Example 2:** Add $\frac{5}{6}$ and $\frac{3}{4}$.

$$\frac{5}{6}=\frac{10}{12}$$
$$+\frac{3}{4}=\frac{9}{12}$$
$$\frac{19}{12}=1\frac{7}{12}$$

Sometimes the fraction in the mixed number will have to be reduced to lowest terms.

**Example 3:** Add $\frac{5}{6}$ and $\frac{2}{3}$.

$$\frac{5}{6}=\frac{5}{6}$$
$$+\frac{2}{3}=\frac{4}{6}$$
$$\frac{9}{6}=1\frac{3}{6}=1\frac{1}{2}$$

# EXERCISES

Add. Simplify.

1. $\frac{6}{7}$
   $+\frac{5}{7}$

2. $\frac{3}{5}$
   $+\frac{4}{5}$

3. $\frac{5}{8}$
   $+\frac{7}{8}$

4. $\frac{5}{9}$
   $+\frac{5}{6}$

5. $\frac{2}{5}$
   $+\frac{5}{6}$

6. $\frac{5}{6}$
   $+\frac{5}{6}$

7. $\frac{7}{9}$
   $+\frac{5}{9}$

8. $\frac{3}{4}$
   $+\frac{1}{2}$

9. $\frac{2}{3}$
   $+\frac{5}{9}$

10. $\frac{3}{8}$
    $+\frac{3}{4}$

11. $\frac{7}{8}$
    $+\frac{3}{16}$

12. $\frac{5}{8}$
    $+\frac{1}{2}$

13. $\frac{3}{4}$
    $+\frac{5}{6}$

14. $\frac{1}{3}$
    $+\frac{7}{9}$

15. $\frac{5}{6}$
    $+\frac{1}{3}$

16. $\frac{5}{12}$
    $+\frac{2}{3}$

17. $\frac{2}{3}$
    $+\frac{5}{6}$

18. $\frac{5}{6}$
    $+\frac{3}{10}$

19. $\frac{2}{3}$
    $+\frac{7}{12}$

20. $\frac{9}{10}$
    $+\frac{3}{5}$

21. $\frac{5}{6}$
    $+\frac{11}{12}$

22. $\frac{7}{12}$
    $+\frac{4}{9}$

23. $\frac{7}{12}$
    $+\frac{5}{6}$

24. $\frac{5}{6}$
    $+\frac{3}{8}$

25. $\frac{3}{4}$
    $+\frac{5}{8}$

26. $\frac{7}{12}$
    $+\frac{3}{4}$

27. $\frac{3}{4}$
    $+\frac{7}{10}$

28. $\frac{5}{8}$
    $+\frac{7}{12}$

29. $\frac{7}{8}$
    $+\frac{5}{6}$

30. $\frac{5}{8}$
    $+\frac{3}{5}$

31. $\frac{7}{8}$
    $+\frac{5}{12}$

32. $\frac{4}{5}$
    $+\frac{6}{7}$

33. $\frac{5}{6}$
    $+\frac{4}{9}$

34. $\frac{7}{9}$
    $+\frac{3}{4}$

35. $\frac{7}{9}$
    $+\frac{5}{8}$

Solve.

36. Jan is making an apron that requires $\frac{7}{8}$ yard of fabric and potholders that require $\frac{1}{2}$ yard of fabric. How much fabric will she use?

37. A piece of plasterboard $\frac{1}{2}$ inch thick is nailed to a panel $\frac{3}{4}$ inch thick. What is the total thickness?

EXTRA PRACTICE page 484, set 36

# 4.12 | ADDING MIXED NUMBERS

Joseph A. Di Chello, Jr.

**Alexander caught two fish. One weighs $2\frac{3}{8}$ pounds and the other weighs $3\frac{1}{8}$ pounds. How much do the two fish weigh together?**

**Example 1:** Find the total weight of the two fish.

$$2\frac{3}{8}$$
$$+3\frac{1}{8}$$
$$\overline{5\frac{4}{8}=5\frac{1}{2}}$$

The total weight of the two fish is $5\frac{1}{2}$ pounds.

**When adding mixed numbers, add the fractions first. Then add the whole numbers.**

If the denominators of the fractions are different, change the fractions to a common denominator and add.

**Example 2:**
$$5\frac{5}{12}=5\frac{5}{12}$$
$$+6\frac{1}{3}=6\frac{4}{12}$$
$$\overline{11\frac{9}{12}=11\frac{3}{4}}$$

Sometimes, the sum of the fractions is an improper fraction. Then simplify by changing the improper fraction to a mixed number and adding again, as below.

**Example 3:**
$$6\frac{3}{4}=6\frac{9}{12}$$
$$+4\frac{2}{3}=4\frac{8}{12}$$

add

$$10\frac{17}{12}=10+1\frac{5}{12}=11\frac{5}{12}$$

Change to a
mixed number.

# EXERCISES

Add. Simplify.

1. $6\frac{1}{8}$
$+3\frac{6}{8}$

2. $4\frac{2}{9}$
$+5\frac{5}{9}$

3. $8\frac{3}{10}$
$+3\frac{4}{10}$

4. $9\frac{5}{12}$
$+1\frac{2}{12}$

5. $8\frac{6}{7}$
$+3\frac{5}{7}$

6. $5\frac{7}{10}$
$+2\frac{4}{10}$

7. $5\frac{1}{2}$
$+2\frac{1}{3}$

8. $4\frac{1}{6}$
$+3\frac{1}{4}$

9. $3\frac{1}{5}$
$+6\frac{1}{2}$

10. $8\frac{1}{4}$
$+3\frac{2}{5}$

11. $1\frac{1}{3}$
$+2\frac{3}{8}$

12. $7\frac{1}{6}$
$+4\frac{1}{6}$

13. $8\frac{5}{12}$
$+4\frac{1}{4}$

14. $14\frac{5}{6}$
$+\ 7\frac{5}{6}$

15. $2\frac{2}{3}$
$+5\frac{4}{5}$

16. $8\frac{1}{3}$
$+1\frac{5}{6}$

17. $2\frac{1}{3}$
$+7\frac{1}{6}$

18. $2\frac{3}{4}$
$+4\frac{4}{5}$

19. $6\frac{3}{4}$
$+9\frac{2}{3}$

20. $1\frac{3}{5}$
$+5\frac{3}{4}$

21. $9\frac{1}{2}$
$+1\frac{3}{4}$

22. $4\frac{1}{4}$
$+2\frac{5}{12}$

23. $10\frac{1}{2}$
$+12\frac{1}{6}$

24. $3\frac{1}{3}$
$+3\frac{1}{6}$

25. $7\frac{6}{7}$
$+5\frac{4}{5}$

26. $4\frac{4}{5}$
$+3\frac{7}{10}$

27. $13\frac{3}{4}$
$+\ 1\frac{7}{8}$

28. $2\frac{2}{9}$
$+7\frac{5}{6}$

29. $9\frac{7}{12}$
$+3\frac{3}{4}$

30. $11\frac{7}{8}$
$+\ 4\frac{7}{9}$

31. $3\frac{3}{4}$
$+6\frac{5}{12}$

32. $18\frac{5}{6}$
$+12\frac{3}{10}$

33. $15\frac{1}{2}$
$+\ 9\frac{5}{7}$

34. $14\frac{1}{6}$
$+10\frac{5}{8}$

35. $12\frac{3}{10}$
$+\ 9\frac{3}{8}$

Solve.

36. During April $3\frac{3}{4}$ inches of rain fell. During May $2\frac{1}{8}$ inches of rain fell. What was the total rainfall for both months?

37. A sewing pattern requires $2\frac{1}{2}$ yards of fabric for a jacket and $1\frac{5}{8}$ yards for a skirt. How many yards are required in all?

EXTRA PRACTICE page 485, set 37

FPG

**The course for a bicycle race was laid out in two sections. The first section was $16\frac{1}{3}$ miles long. The second section was $18\frac{3}{4}$ miles long. What was the total length of the racecourse?**

**Read:** *Given:* First section was $16\frac{1}{3}$ miles;

second section was $18\frac{3}{4}$ miles.

*To find:* total length of the racecourse

**Plan:** Add $16\frac{1}{3}$ and $18\frac{3}{4}$.

**Compute:**

$$16\frac{1}{3} = 16\frac{4}{12}$$
$$+18\frac{3}{4} = 18\frac{9}{12}$$
$$34\frac{13}{12} = 35\frac{1}{12}$$

**Answer:** The total length of the racecourse was $35\frac{1}{12}$ miles.

**Check:** Does $35\frac{1}{12}$ miles seem to be a reasonable answer? ✔

# EXERCISES

1. Fred worked $6\frac{1}{4}$ hours on Saturday and $3\frac{1}{2}$ hours on Monday. How many hours did Fred work both days?

2. Anita bought $3\frac{1}{4}$ yards of cotton fabric and $2\frac{1}{2}$ yards of wool fabric. How many yards of fabric did Anita buy in all?

3. A sheet of fiberglass $\frac{1}{8}$ inch thick is glued to a sheet of wood $\frac{5}{8}$ inch thick. What is the total thickness of the two pieces when they are glued together?

4. Ed jogged $3\frac{2}{3}$ miles and walked $1\frac{1}{4}$ miles. How many miles did he travel in all?

5. A truck weighing $4\frac{1}{2}$ tons is used to carry a $9\frac{1}{2}$-ton machine. What is the combined weight of the truck and the machine?

6. Louise cut a board into two pieces. One piece was $3\frac{1}{16}$ inches long. The other was $4\frac{3}{8}$ inches long. How long was the board before Louise cut it?

7. Chicago had $2\frac{5}{8}$ inches of snow in January and $4\frac{3}{4}$ inches of snow in February. How many inches of snow fell in January and February together?

8. Hal is $3\frac{1}{4}$ inches taller than Diane. Tim is $2\frac{5}{8}$ inches taller than Hal. Tim is how much taller than Diane?

9. A truck is loaded with $2\frac{1}{8}$ tons of cement blocks and $5\frac{3}{4}$ tons of bricks. What is the total weight that the truck is carrying?

10. Lisa bought a mixture of $\frac{1}{4}$ pound of peanuts and $\frac{1}{2}$ pound of walnuts. What was the total weight of her purchase?

11. A stock closed at the price of $17\frac{3}{4}$ on Monday. By the end of the next day, it had increased by $2\frac{1}{2}$. What was its price at the end of Tuesday?

EXTRA PRACTICE page 485, set 38

Besides preparing food, a restaurant chef must also develop new recipes, order food, and train new employees. Here are some problems a chef might have to solve.

Freda Leinwand

1. If a recipe calls for $1\frac{1}{2}$ cups of water and $\frac{1}{4}$ cup of juice, how much liquid is that?

2. If a chef spends $1\frac{3}{4}$ hours preparing the food and $\frac{1}{2}$ hour arranging it to be served, what is the total time spent on the meal?

3. If a recipe calls for $\frac{1}{4}$ teaspoon of a certain spice and $\frac{1}{8}$ teaspoon of another spice, what is the total amount of spices called for?

4. If a part-time employee worked $6\frac{3}{4}$ hours on Monday and $7\frac{1}{2}$ hours on Tuesday, what is the total number of hours the employee worked both days?

# CHAPTER REVIEW

Write a fraction for the shaded part of each figure.

**1.**  **2.**  **3.**  **4.**

Write a fraction for the shaded part of each group.

**5.** **6.** **7.** **8.**

Find a fraction equivalent to the given fraction by multiplying the numerator and the denominator by the number in red.

**9.** $\frac{2}{3}$, 6 **10.** $\frac{5}{6}$, 10 **11.** $\frac{7}{8}$, 4 **12.** $\frac{8}{9}$, 12

**13.** $\frac{3}{8}$, 9 **14.** $\frac{3}{4}$, 5 **15.** $\frac{4}{9}$, 7 **16.** $\frac{7}{10}$, 8

Find a fraction equivalent to the given fraction by dividing the numerator and the denominator by the number in red.

**17.** $\frac{8}{12}$, 4 **18.** $\frac{3}{6}$, 3 **19.** $\frac{10}{15}$, 5 **20.** $\frac{2}{10}$, 2

**21.** $\frac{6}{9}$, 3 **22.** $\frac{12}{18}$, 6 **23.** $\frac{8}{16}$, 8 **24.** $\frac{18}{27}$, 9

Reduce to lowest terms.

**25.** $\frac{8}{12}$ **26.** $\frac{6}{18}$ **27.** $\frac{9}{27}$ **28.** $\frac{12}{16}$

**29.** $\frac{5}{20}$ **30.** $\frac{16}{32}$ **31.** $\frac{16}{24}$ **32.** $\frac{15}{45}$

Change to a decimal.

**33.** $\frac{9}{10}$ **34.** $\frac{35}{100}$ **35.** $\frac{15}{1000}$ **36.** $\frac{8}{1000}$

**37.** $\frac{4}{5}$ **38.** $\frac{7}{8}$ **39.** $\frac{13}{20}$ **40.** $\frac{14}{25}$

Change to a fraction in lowest terms.

**41.** 0.8       **42.** 0.45       **43.** 0.025       **44.** 0.06

**45.** 0.75       **46.** 0.90       **47.** 0.005       **48.** 0.065

Add. Reduce to lowest terms.       4.6

**49.** $\dfrac{1}{6}$   $+\dfrac{4}{6}$       **50.** $\dfrac{3}{8}$   $+\dfrac{2}{8}$       **51.** $\dfrac{4}{9}$   $+\dfrac{1}{9}$       **52.** $\dfrac{3}{10}$   $+\dfrac{4}{10}$

**53.** $\dfrac{1}{8}$   $+\dfrac{5}{8}$       **54.** $\dfrac{5}{12}$   $+\dfrac{1}{12}$       **55.** $\dfrac{2}{15}$   $+\dfrac{4}{15}$       **56.** $\dfrac{11}{20}$   $+\dfrac{7}{20}$

Change each pair of fractions to equivalent fractions with a common       4.7
denominator.

**57.** $\dfrac{2}{3}, \dfrac{1}{6}$       **58.** $\dfrac{3}{4}, \dfrac{3}{8}$       **59.** $\dfrac{1}{6}, \dfrac{5}{8}$       **60.** $\dfrac{4}{9}, \dfrac{1}{27}$

**61.** $\dfrac{3}{4}, \dfrac{2}{3}$       **62.** $\dfrac{5}{6}, \dfrac{4}{9}$       **63.** $\dfrac{3}{5}, \dfrac{4}{15}$       **64.** $\dfrac{5}{12}, \dfrac{7}{18}$

Add. Reduce to lowest terms.       4.8

**65.** $\dfrac{1}{6}$   $+\dfrac{3}{4}$       **66.** $\dfrac{2}{3}$   $+\dfrac{1}{5}$       **67.** $\dfrac{5}{8}$   $+\dfrac{1}{4}$       **68.** $\dfrac{1}{6}$   $+\dfrac{1}{3}$

**69.** $\dfrac{3}{10}$   $+\dfrac{2}{5}$       **70.** $\dfrac{4}{9}$   $+\dfrac{1}{3}$       **71.** $\dfrac{2}{3}$   $+\dfrac{1}{4}$       **72.** $\dfrac{5}{8}$   $+\dfrac{1}{3}$

Express as a mixed number. Simplify.       4.10

**73.** $32 \div 5$       **74.** $68 \div 8$       **75.** $\dfrac{16}{9}$       **76.** $\dfrac{27}{5}$

**77.** $\dfrac{34}{7}$       **78.** $\dfrac{40}{6}$       **79.** $\dfrac{34}{4}$       **80.** $\dfrac{25}{10}$

Express as a fraction.

**81.** $2\frac{1}{3}$

**82.** $5\frac{3}{4}$

**83.** $7\frac{1}{2}$

**84.** $6\frac{3}{5}$

**85.** $9\frac{3}{8}$

**86.** $10\frac{5}{6}$

**87.** $4\frac{2}{5}$

**88.** $8\frac{2}{3}$

Add. Simplify.

**89.** $\frac{5}{6}$ $+\frac{3}{4}$

**90.** $\frac{2}{3}$ $+\frac{5}{8}$

**91.** $\frac{7}{12}$ $+\frac{5}{6}$

**92.** $\frac{3}{5}$ $+\frac{5}{6}$     4.11

**93.** $\frac{6}{15}$ $+\frac{4}{5}$

**94.** $\frac{8}{9}$ $+\frac{7}{18}$

**95.** $5\frac{1}{8}$ $+7\frac{2}{8}$

**96.** $9\frac{1}{4}$ $+3\frac{2}{3}$     4.12

**97.** $6\frac{1}{4}$ $+4\frac{1}{6}$

**98.** $8\frac{3}{8}$ $+5\frac{5}{6}$

**99.** $2\frac{1}{9}$ $+4\frac{2}{3}$

**100.** $10\frac{3}{4}$ $+ 1\frac{1}{8}$

Solve.

**101.** A soccer team played 16 games and won 12. Write a fraction for the part of the games won.     4.5

**102.** In a poll, 18 out of 30 students had part-time jobs. Write a fraction for the part of the students who had part-time jobs.

**103.** A student ran $\frac{1}{3}$ mile and walked $\frac{1}{4}$ mile. What was the total distance she traveled?     4.9

**104.** Ted bought $\frac{1}{4}$ yard of wool and $\frac{2}{3}$ yard of flannel. What was the total amount of fabric that Ted bought?

**105.** A $9\frac{1}{2}$-foot board is placed end to end with a $6\frac{3}{4}$-foot board. How long are the two boards together?     4.13

**106.** Leah worked $6\frac{1}{2}$ hours one day and $5\frac{3}{4}$ hours the next day. What was the total number of hours Leah worked?

**1.** Write a fraction for the shaded part of the figure.

**2.** Find a fraction equivalent to $\frac{7}{8}$ by multiplying the numerator and the denominator by 9.

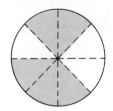

Reduce to lowest terms.

**3.** $\frac{8}{12}$

**4.** $\frac{10}{35}$

**5.** $\frac{24}{36}$

Express as a decimal.

**6.** $\frac{9}{100}$

**7.** $\frac{2}{5}$

**8.** $\frac{3}{8}$

Express as a fraction. Reduce to lowest terms.

**9.** 0.13

**10.** 0.85

**11.** 0.06

Change each pair of fractions to equivalent fractions with a common denominator.

**12.** $\frac{3}{4}, \frac{2}{9}$

**13.** $\frac{5}{6}, \frac{3}{8}$

**14.** $\frac{7}{12}, \frac{5}{6}$

Add. Simplify.

**15.** $\frac{5}{8} + \frac{2}{8}$

**16.** $\frac{5}{12} + \frac{6}{12}$

**17.** $\frac{1}{3} + \frac{1}{6}$

**18.** $\frac{3}{8} + \frac{1}{6}$

**19.** $\frac{3}{4} + \frac{2}{5}$

**20.** $\frac{3}{4} + \frac{5}{8}$

**21.** $2\frac{5}{6} + 3\frac{2}{3}$

**22.** $1\frac{4}{9} + 4\frac{5}{6}$

**23.** Express $\frac{41}{5}$ as a mixed number.

**24.** Express $4\frac{2}{3}$ as a fraction.

Solve.

**25.** A town received $1\frac{1}{2}$ inches of snow on Monday and $2\frac{3}{4}$ inches on Tuesday. What was the total snowfall for both days?

**26.** A board $\frac{5}{8}$ inch thick is nailed to a board $\frac{1}{4}$ inch thick. How thick are the two boards together?

Which symbol, $>$ or $<$, should replace each ●?

**1.** $\frac{1}{2}$ ● $\frac{3}{4}$

**2.** $\frac{5}{8}$ ● $\frac{7}{8}$

Determine if each statement is true or false by changing each fraction or mixed number to its decimal equivalent.

**3.** $1\frac{4}{5} < 1\frac{2}{3}$

**4.** $2\frac{3}{4} > 2\frac{1}{2}$

Subtract. Simplify each answer.

**5.** $\frac{2}{3}$ $-\frac{1}{3}$

**6.** $\frac{4}{5}$ $-\frac{1}{5}$

**7.** $\frac{7}{8}$ $-\frac{3}{8}$

**8.** $\frac{5}{6}$ $-\frac{1}{6}$

**9.** $\frac{9}{10}$ $-\frac{1}{2}$

**10.** $\frac{1}{2}$ $-\frac{1}{3}$

**11.** $3\frac{3}{4}$ $-1\frac{1}{4}$

**12.** $2\frac{2}{5}$ $-1\frac{1}{10}$

**13.** $10$ $-3\frac{1}{6}$

**14.** $4$ $-2\frac{5}{8}$

**15.** $6\frac{1}{2}$ $-3\frac{7}{8}$

**16.** $5\frac{1}{4}$ $-3\frac{7}{12}$

**17.** $6\frac{2}{3}$ $-3\frac{1}{8}$

**18.** $5\frac{4}{5}$ $-2\frac{1}{4}$

**19.** $3\frac{1}{3}$ $-1\frac{2}{5}$

Find each answer.

**20.** $\frac{5}{8} - \frac{1}{4}$

**21.** $1\frac{1}{2} + 2\frac{3}{4}$

**22.** $1\frac{1}{2} + 2\frac{1}{6} + 5\frac{2}{3}$

Complete.

**23.** 1 ft = ____ in.

**24.** 2 gal = ____ qt

**25.** 1 lb = ____ oz

**26.** 3 pt = ____ c

Solve.

**27.** Which has a larger opening, a $\frac{9}{32}$-inch wrench or a $\frac{1}{4}$-inch wrench?

**28.** A piece of ribbon is 36 inches long. If $22\frac{1}{2}$ inches are cut off, how much ribbon is left?

Ed Hoppe Photography

$\frac{3}{8}$ inch

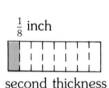

first thickness

$\frac{1}{8}$ inch

second thickness

**Judy wants to build a glider. She can order balsa wood either $\frac{3}{8}$ inch thick or $\frac{1}{8}$ inch thick. Which thickness is greater?**

The pictures show that $\frac{3}{8}$ inch is more than $\frac{1}{8}$ inch. The first thickness is greater.

**To compare two fractions that have a common denominator, compare the numerators.**

**Example 1:** Compare $\frac{7}{12}$ and $\frac{11}{12}$.

$7 < 11$, so $\frac{7}{12} < \frac{11}{12}$.

**To compare two fractions that have different denominators, change the fractions so that they have a common denominator. Then compare the numerators.**

**Example 2:** Compare $\frac{3}{4}$ and $\frac{5}{8}$.

$$\frac{3}{4} = \frac{6}{8}, \quad \frac{5}{8}$$

$6 > 5$, so $\frac{6}{8} > \frac{5}{8}$.

Then $\frac{3}{4} > \frac{5}{8}$.

**To compare two mixed numbers with the same whole-number part, just compare the fraction parts.**

**Example 3:** Compare $6\frac{3}{5}$ and $6\frac{1}{3}$.

First compare $\frac{3}{5}$ and $\frac{1}{3}$. Change $\frac{3}{5}$ and $\frac{1}{3}$ to equivalent fractions with a common denominator.

$$\frac{3}{5} = \frac{9}{15} \longleftarrow$$
$$\frac{1}{3} = \frac{5}{15} \longleftarrow \qquad 9 > 5$$

So $\frac{3}{5} > \frac{1}{3}$.

Then $6\frac{3}{5} > 6\frac{1}{3}$.

## EXERCISES

Which symbol, $>$ or $<$, should replace each ●?

1. $\frac{3}{8}$ ● $\frac{1}{8}$  2. $\frac{1}{4}$ ● $\frac{3}{4}$  3. $\frac{2}{5}$ ● $\frac{3}{5}$  4. $\frac{5}{8}$ ● $\frac{3}{8}$  5. $\frac{1}{6}$ ● $\frac{5}{6}$

6. $\frac{4}{5}$ ● $\frac{2}{5}$  7. $1\frac{3}{5}$ ● $1\frac{2}{5}$  8. $3\frac{7}{8}$ ● $3\frac{3}{8}$  9. $6\frac{7}{12}$ ● $6\frac{11}{12}$  10. $15\frac{9}{10}$ ● $15\frac{7}{10}$

11. $\frac{1}{5}$ ● $\frac{1}{4}$  12. $3\frac{5}{12}$ ● $3\frac{1}{3}$  13. $1\frac{5}{8}$ ● $1\frac{3}{4}$  14. $\frac{5}{8}$ ● $\frac{7}{16}$  15. $\frac{2}{3}$ ● $\frac{8}{9}$

16. $\frac{1}{4}$ ● $\frac{3}{16}$  17. $\frac{7}{8}$ ● $\frac{5}{12}$  18. $\frac{4}{5}$ ● $\frac{5}{8}$  19. $4\frac{1}{2}$ ● $4\frac{2}{3}$  20. $7\frac{3}{8}$ ● $6\frac{15}{16}$

Fractions can be compared by using **cross products**.

**Examples:**  a. $\overset{\frown}{\underset{16 \quad 16}{\frac{2}{4} \quad \frac{4}{8}}}$   b. $\overset{\frown}{\underset{2 \quad 3}{\frac{1}{3} \quad \frac{1}{2}}}$   c. $\overset{\frown}{\underset{16 \quad 15}{\frac{4}{5} \quad \frac{3}{4}}}$   **Multiply as shown by the arrows.**

$\qquad\qquad\qquad =\qquad\qquad\qquad < \qquad\qquad\qquad >$

Use cross products to determine which symbol, $>$, $<$, or $=$, should replace each ●.

21. $\frac{3}{4}$ ● $\frac{5}{6}$   22. $\frac{6}{8}$ ● $\frac{3}{4}$   23. $\frac{9}{10}$ ● $\frac{1}{2}$   24. $\frac{4}{5}$ ● $\frac{7}{8}$

25. $\frac{6}{10}$ ● $\frac{3}{5}$   26. $\frac{4}{5}$ ● $\frac{3}{8}$   27. $\frac{5}{8}$ ● $\frac{2}{3}$   28. $\frac{4}{20}$ ● $\frac{1}{5}$

Ed Hoppe Photography

**Tina is comparing two similar recipes for macaroni and cheese. The first requires $\frac{1}{4}$ cup of cheese, and the second requires $\frac{3}{8}$ cup. Which amount is greater?**

Two fractions can be compared by changing each to an equivalent decimal.

**Example 1:** Compare $\frac{1}{4}$ and $\frac{3}{8}$.

$$\frac{1}{4} \longrightarrow \begin{array}{r} 0.25 \\ 4\overline{)1.00} \\ \underline{8}\phantom{0} \\ 20 \\ \underline{20} \\ 0 \end{array} \qquad \frac{3}{8} \longrightarrow \begin{array}{r} 0.375 \\ 8\overline{)3.000} \\ \underline{2\,4}\phantom{00} \\ 60 \\ \underline{56} \\ 40 \\ \underline{40} \\ 0 \end{array}$$

$0.375 > 0.25$, so $\frac{3}{8} > \frac{1}{4}$.

$\frac{3}{8}$ cup is greater.

**Example 2:** Compare $1\frac{4}{5}$ and $1\frac{1}{2}$.

$$1\frac{4}{5} \qquad \frac{4}{5} \longrightarrow \begin{array}{r} 0.8 \\ 5\overline{)4.0} \\ \underline{4\,0} \\ 0 \end{array} \qquad 1\frac{1}{2} \qquad \frac{1}{2} \longrightarrow \begin{array}{r} 0.5 \\ 2\overline{)1.0} \\ \underline{1\,0} \\ 0 \end{array}$$

So $1\frac{4}{5} = 1.8$.  So $1\frac{1}{2} = 1.5$.

$1.8 > 1.5$, so $1\frac{4}{5} > 1\frac{1}{2}$.

**Example 3:** Compare $\frac{3}{8}$ and $\frac{1}{3}$.

$$\frac{3}{8} = 0.375$$
$$\frac{1}{3} = 0.333 \cdots$$
**same**

$7 > 3$, so $\frac{3}{8} > \frac{1}{3}$.

## EXERCISES

Determine if each statement is true or false by changing each fraction or mixed number to its decimal equivalent.

1. $\frac{1}{2} < \frac{3}{4}$

2. $\frac{3}{6} = \frac{4}{8}$

3. $\frac{4}{5} > \frac{7}{8}$

4. $\frac{7}{10} = \frac{3}{5}$

5. $\frac{1}{4} > \frac{5}{8}$

6. $\frac{5}{8} < \frac{3}{4}$

7. $\frac{7}{20} < \frac{3}{5}$

8. $\frac{9}{25} > \frac{3}{10}$

9. $\frac{5}{12} > \frac{1}{2}$

10. $\frac{1}{2} > \frac{1}{3}$

11. $\frac{8}{10} = \frac{3}{5}$

12. $\frac{2}{5} < \frac{3}{8}$

13. $3\frac{1}{4} < 3\frac{2}{5}$

14. $11\frac{3}{4} > 11\frac{9}{16}$

15. $1\frac{9}{10} < 1\frac{4}{5}$

16. $3\frac{1}{4} > 3\frac{1}{3}$

17. $4\frac{1}{2} < 4\frac{1}{4}$

18. $7\frac{1}{5} < 7\frac{3}{10}$

19. $1\frac{1}{6} > 1\frac{1}{8}$

20. $1\frac{2}{3} = 1\frac{4}{6}$

21. $1\frac{5}{6} < 1\frac{2}{3}$

22. $3\frac{1}{2} < 3\frac{3}{6}$

23. $4\frac{1}{4} > 4\frac{1}{6}$

24. $3\frac{7}{10} > 3\frac{2}{3}$

EXTRA PRACTICE page 485, set 39

---

## CALCULATOR NOTE

You can compare fractions by using a calculator.

**Example:** Compare $\frac{1}{5}$ and $\frac{1}{4}$. Use a calculator to change the fractions to decimals.

| Fraction | ENTER | DISPLAY |
|---|---|---|
| $\frac{1}{5}$ | 1 ÷ 5 = | $0.2$ |
| $\frac{1}{4}$ | 1 ÷ 4 = | $0.25$ |

$0.2 < 0.25$, so $\frac{1}{5} < \frac{1}{4}$.

Check your answers to exercises 1–12 above by using a calculator.

133

**Two wrestlers were weighed before the first meet of the season. Mike gained $6\frac{1}{2}$ pounds during the summer, and Joe gained $6\frac{3}{4}$ pounds. Who gained more weight?**

**Read:**   *Given:*   Mike gained $6\frac{1}{2}$ pounds.

Joe gained $6\frac{3}{4}$ pounds.

*To find:*   who gained more weight

**Plan:**   Compare $6\frac{1}{2}$ and $6\frac{3}{4}$.

**Compute:**   $6\frac{1}{2}=6\frac{2}{4}, \ 6\frac{3}{4}$

$3>2$, so $6\frac{3}{4}>6\frac{2}{4}$.
Then $6\frac{3}{4}>6\frac{1}{2}$.

**Answer:**   Joe gained more weight.

**Check:**   $6\frac{3}{4}=6.75, \ 6\frac{1}{2}=6.5$

$6.75>6.5$ ✔

## EXERCISES

**1.** A share of Bertron, Inc., stock costs $8\frac{7}{8}$ dollars. A share of Wentfield Manufacturing stock costs $8\frac{3}{8}$ dollars. Which stock costs less?

**2.** On Monday, $\frac{1}{2}$ inch of rain fell. On Tuesday, it rained a total of $\frac{1}{4}$ inch. Which day had the greater rainfall?

**3.** The City National Bank offers an interest rate of $5\frac{1}{2}$ percent on its savings accounts. The First National Bank offers $5\frac{1}{4}$ percent on its savings accounts. Which interest rate is higher?

**4.** A diet sheet indicates that Naomi can drink $\frac{1}{2}$ cup of orange juice or $\frac{1}{3}$ cup of grapefruit juice for breakfast. Which amount of juice is smaller?

**5.** A man has a large amount of money and land that he wants to leave to different relatives. His will states that his nephew is to inherit $\frac{1}{3}$ of the estate and his cousin is to inherit $\frac{2}{5}$ of it. Which person will receive the smaller portion of the estate?

**6.** Bill is buying a cabinet for his stereo. His turntable needs a shelf space $20\frac{7}{8}$ inches wide. A cabinet on sale has a turntable shelf that is $20\frac{1}{8}$ inches wide. Is that wide enough?

**7.** Is a $\frac{7}{16}$-inch wrench too big or too small to turn a $\frac{1}{2}$-inch bolt?

**8.** You try a $\frac{7}{16}$-inch socket wrench and find that it is too small. Should you try the $\frac{3}{8}$-inch or the $\frac{1}{2}$-inch socket next?

**9.** Would a dishwasher $24\frac{7}{8}$ inches wide fit into a space $24\frac{15}{16}$ inches wide?

**10.** A bench vise can open up to a width of $5\frac{1}{4}$ inches. Is this wide enough for a piece of wood $5\frac{5}{16}$ inches wide?

*SKILLS REVIEW*

Subtract.

**11.**  $\begin{array}{r} 87 \\ -53 \\ \hline \end{array}$

**12.**  $\begin{array}{r} 50 \\ -32 \\ \hline \end{array}$

**13.**  $\begin{array}{r} 406 \\ -189 \\ \hline \end{array}$

**14.**  $\begin{array}{r} 753 \\ -289 \\ \hline \end{array}$

**15.**  $\begin{array}{r} 3471 \\ -1084 \\ \hline \end{array}$

**16.**  $\begin{array}{r} 1296 \\ -879 \\ \hline \end{array}$

**17.**  $\begin{array}{r} 15,400 \\ -13,398 \\ \hline \end{array}$

**18.**  $\begin{array}{r} 14,803 \\ -12,677 \\ \hline \end{array}$

## 5.4 SUBTRACTING LIKE FRACTIONS

Ed Hoppe Photography

One ring Nancy is looking at has a band $\frac{5}{16}$ inch wide. Another band is $\frac{3}{16}$ inch wide. How much wider is the $\frac{5}{16}$-inch band?

**Example 1:** Find $\frac{5}{16} - \frac{3}{16}$.

$$
\begin{array}{r}
\frac{5}{16} \\
-\frac{3}{16} \\
\hline
\frac{2}{16} = \frac{1}{8}
\end{array}
$$

The denominators are the same.
Subtract the numerators.

Reduce the fraction to lowest terms.

The band on the first ring is $\frac{1}{8}$ inch wider.

**Example 2:**
$$
\begin{array}{r}
\frac{4}{5} \\
-\frac{3}{5} \\
\hline
\frac{1}{5}
\end{array}
$$

You can check your answer by adding.
$$
\begin{array}{r}
\frac{3}{5} \\
+\frac{1}{5} \\
\hline
\frac{4}{5}
\end{array} \text{✔}
$$

## EXERCISES

Subtract. Reduce to lowest terms. Check each answer by adding.

1.
$$
\begin{array}{r}
\frac{2}{3} \\
-\frac{1}{3} \\
\hline
\end{array}
$$

2.
$$
\begin{array}{r}
\frac{4}{5} \\
-\frac{1}{5} \\
\hline
\end{array}
$$

3.
$$
\begin{array}{r}
\frac{3}{4} \\
-\frac{1}{4} \\
\hline
\end{array}
$$

4.
$$
\begin{array}{r}
\frac{3}{5} \\
-\frac{2}{5} \\
\hline
\end{array}
$$

5.
$$
\begin{array}{r}
\frac{4}{5} \\
-\frac{3}{5} \\
\hline
\end{array}
$$

6.
$$
\begin{array}{r}
\frac{3}{5} \\
-\frac{1}{5} \\
\hline
\end{array}
$$

7.
$$
\begin{array}{r}
\frac{7}{8} \\
-\frac{5}{8} \\
\hline
\end{array}
$$

8.
$$
\begin{array}{r}
\frac{9}{10} \\
-\frac{7}{10} \\
\hline
\end{array}
$$

**9.** $\dfrac{3}{8}$ $-\dfrac{1}{8}$

**10.** $\dfrac{3}{10}$ $-\dfrac{1}{10}$

**11.** $\dfrac{14}{25}$ $-\dfrac{8}{25}$

**12.** $\dfrac{2}{5}$ $-\dfrac{1}{5}$

**13.** $\dfrac{11}{12}$ $-\dfrac{7}{12}$

**14.** $\dfrac{17}{25}$ $-\dfrac{4}{25}$

**15.** $\dfrac{5}{8}$ $-\dfrac{3}{8}$

**16.** $\dfrac{9}{10}$ $-\dfrac{1}{10}$

**17.** $\dfrac{5}{8}$ $-\dfrac{1}{8}$

**18.** $\dfrac{21}{25}$ $-\dfrac{4}{25}$

**19.** $\dfrac{7}{12}$ $-\dfrac{5}{12}$

**20.** $\dfrac{7}{8}$ $-\dfrac{1}{8}$

**21.** $\dfrac{7}{12}$ $-\dfrac{1}{12}$

**22.** $\dfrac{7}{8}$ $-\dfrac{3}{8}$

**23.** $\dfrac{7}{10}$ $-\dfrac{3}{10}$

**24.** $\dfrac{11}{20}$ $-\dfrac{9}{20}$

**25.** $\dfrac{9}{10}$ $-\dfrac{3}{10}$

**26.** $\dfrac{11}{12}$ $-\dfrac{5}{12}$

**27.** $\dfrac{5}{6}$ $-\dfrac{1}{6}$

**28.** $\dfrac{11}{12}$ $-\dfrac{1}{12}$

**29.** $\dfrac{9}{20}$ $-\dfrac{3}{20}$

**30.** $\dfrac{17}{20}$ $-\dfrac{1}{20}$

**31.** $\dfrac{7}{10}$ $-\dfrac{1}{10}$

**32.** $\dfrac{5}{12}$ $-\dfrac{1}{12}$

*EXTRA PRACTICE page 486, set 40*

## SKILLS REVIEW

Subtract.

**33.** $\begin{array}{r} 1.35 \\ -0.024 \\ \hline \end{array}$

**34.** $\begin{array}{r} 4.3 \\ -0.275 \\ \hline \end{array}$

**35.** $\begin{array}{r} 6.408 \\ -1.2 \\ \hline \end{array}$

**36.** $\begin{array}{r} 15.03 \\ -2.473 \\ \hline \end{array}$

**37.** $\begin{array}{r} 3.05 \\ -0.4 \\ \hline \end{array}$

**38.** $\begin{array}{r} 15.3 \\ -12.67 \\ \hline \end{array}$

**39.** $\begin{array}{r} 3.09 \\ -1.106 \\ \hline \end{array}$

**40.** $\begin{array}{r} 8.6 \\ -0.39 \\ \hline \end{array}$

# SUBTRACTING UNLIKE FRACTIONS

Artstreet

**Barry is cutting glass to make a stained-glass window. He has a piece $\frac{3}{4}$ inch wide that he needs to cut down to $\frac{1}{2}$ inch. How much should he cut off?**

You can subtract $\frac{1}{2}$ from $\frac{3}{4}$ to find how much should be cut off. But first you must change the fractions so that they have a common denominator.

**Example 1:** Subtract $\frac{1}{2}$ from $\frac{3}{4}$.

$$\frac{3}{4} = \frac{3}{4}$$
$$-\frac{1}{2} = \frac{2}{4}$$
$$\frac{1}{4}$$

Change the fractions to equivalent fractions with a common denominator. Subtract the numerators.

Barry should cut off $\frac{1}{4}$ inch.

**Example 2:**
$$\frac{5}{6} = \frac{5}{6}$$
$$-\frac{1}{3} = \frac{2}{6}$$
$$\frac{3}{6} = \frac{1}{2}$$

Reduce the fraction to lowest terms.

Check:
$$\frac{1}{3} = \frac{2}{6}$$
$$+\frac{1}{2} = \frac{3}{6}$$
$$\frac{5}{6} \quad ✔$$

## EXERCISES

Subtract. Reduce to lowest terms. Check each answer by adding.

1. $\frac{7}{8}$
   $-\frac{1}{4}$

2. $\frac{5}{8}$
   $-\frac{1}{2}$

3. $\frac{7}{10}$
   $-\frac{2}{5}$

4. $\frac{3}{4}$
   $-\frac{1}{2}$

5. $\frac{7}{8}$
   $-\frac{3}{4}$

6. $\frac{11}{12}$
   $-\frac{1}{2}$

7. $\frac{11}{16}$
   $-\frac{1}{4}$

8. $\frac{9}{10}$
   $-\frac{3}{5}$

9. $\frac{7}{20}$
   $-\frac{1}{5}$

10. $\frac{5}{16}$
    $-\frac{1}{8}$

11. $\frac{13}{16}$
    $-\frac{1}{4}$

12. $\frac{3}{10}$
    $-\frac{1}{5}$

13. $\frac{9}{16}$
    $-\frac{1}{8}$

14. $\frac{21}{32}$
    $-\frac{1}{2}$

15. $\frac{3}{20}$
    $-\frac{1}{10}$

**16.**  $\dfrac{5}{16}$
$-\dfrac{1}{8}$

**17.**  $\dfrac{1}{4}$
$-\dfrac{1}{8}$

**18.**  $\dfrac{7}{32}$
$-\dfrac{1}{8}$

**19.**  $\dfrac{2}{5}$
$-\dfrac{1}{3}$

**20.**  $\dfrac{3}{8}$
$-\dfrac{1}{3}$

**21.**  $\dfrac{5}{8}$
$-\dfrac{1}{6}$

**22.**  $\dfrac{4}{5}$
$-\dfrac{2}{3}$

**23.**  $\dfrac{1}{2}$
$-\dfrac{2}{5}$

**24.**  $\dfrac{3}{5}$
$-\dfrac{1}{3}$

**25.**  $\dfrac{3}{5}$
$-\dfrac{1}{2}$

**26.**  $\dfrac{14}{25}$
$-\dfrac{1}{10}$

**27.**  $\dfrac{7}{10}$
$-\dfrac{1}{4}$

**28.**  $\dfrac{4}{5}$
$-\dfrac{1}{2}$

**29.**  $\dfrac{7}{10}$
$-\dfrac{1}{3}$

**30.**  $\dfrac{3}{10}$
$-\dfrac{1}{4}$

**31.**  $\dfrac{4}{5}$
$-\dfrac{3}{10}$

**32.**  $\dfrac{7}{8}$
$-\dfrac{1}{3}$

**33.**  $\dfrac{5}{6}$
$-\dfrac{1}{2}$

**34.**  $\dfrac{7}{10}$
$-\dfrac{1}{2}$

**35.**  $\dfrac{19}{20}$
$-\dfrac{3}{4}$

EXTRA PRACTICE page 486, set 41

## CHECKPOINT

Which symbol, $>$ or $<$, should replace each ●?

**1.** $\dfrac{7}{10}$ ● $\dfrac{3}{10}$

**2.** $\dfrac{5}{8}$ ● $\dfrac{3}{8}$

**3.** $\dfrac{2}{5}$ ● $\dfrac{3}{10}$

Determine if each statement is true or false by changing each fraction or mixed number to its decimal equivalent.

**4.** $\dfrac{2}{3} > \dfrac{5}{8}$

**5.** $1\dfrac{3}{4} < 1\dfrac{1}{4}$

**6.** $5\dfrac{7}{8} < 5\dfrac{9}{10}$

Subtract. Reduce to lowest terms.

**7.**  $\dfrac{5}{8}$
$-\dfrac{1}{8}$

**8.**  $\dfrac{4}{5}$
$-\dfrac{1}{2}$

**9.**  $\dfrac{7}{8}$
$-\dfrac{1}{3}$

Solve.

**10.** Which has a larger opening, a $\dfrac{7}{8}$-inch wrench or a $\dfrac{15}{16}$-inch wrench?

**139**

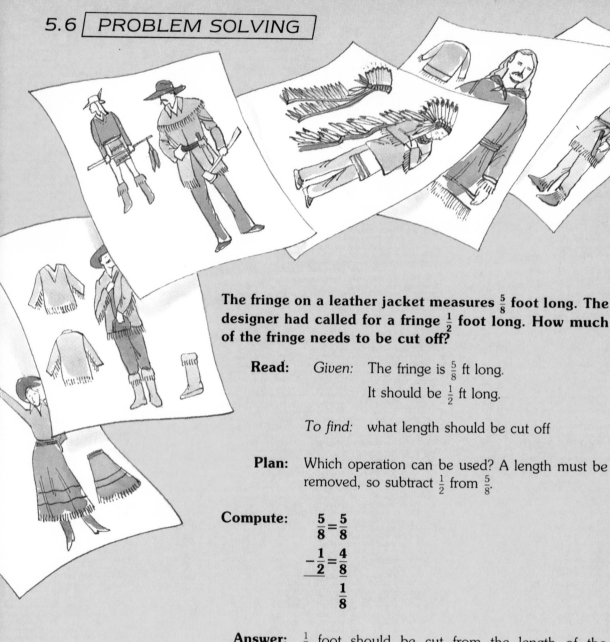

**The fringe on a leather jacket measures $\frac{5}{8}$ foot long. The designer had called for a fringe $\frac{1}{2}$ foot long. How much of the fringe needs to be cut off?**

**Read:**   *Given:*   The fringe is $\frac{5}{8}$ ft long.

It should be $\frac{1}{2}$ ft long.

*To find:*   what length should be cut off

**Plan:**   Which operation can be used? A length must be removed, so subtract $\frac{1}{2}$ from $\frac{5}{8}$.

**Compute:**

$$\frac{5}{8} = \frac{5}{8}$$
$$-\frac{1}{2} = \frac{4}{8}$$
$$\frac{1}{8}$$

**Answer:**   $\frac{1}{8}$ foot should be cut from the length of the fringe.

**Check:**

$$\frac{1}{2} = \frac{4}{8}$$
$$+\frac{1}{8} = \frac{1}{8}$$
$$\frac{5}{8} \quad \checkmark$$

# EXERCISES

**1.**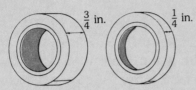

$\frac{3}{4}$ in.     $\frac{1}{4}$ in.

How much wider is the $\frac{3}{4}$-inch tape?

**2.**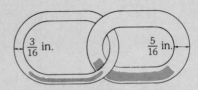

$\frac{3}{16}$ in.     $\frac{5}{16}$ in.

How much thicker is the $\frac{5}{16}$-inch chain link?

**3.** Seams in a homemade garment are usually either $\frac{5}{8}$ inch or $\frac{3}{8}$ inch wide. How much wider is a $\frac{5}{8}$-inch seam?

**4.** After it was cooked, $\frac{3}{4}$ pound of bacon weighed only $\frac{1}{2}$ pound. How much more did it weigh before cooking?

**5.** A metal plate measuring $\frac{15}{16}$ inch long and $\frac{7}{8}$ inch wide is being shaved down to make a $\frac{3}{4}$-inch square. How much metal must be shaved off the length? The width?

**6.** Which is wider, an elastic band $\frac{1}{4}$ inch wide or one $\frac{3}{8}$ inch wide?

**7.** Four months ago, Bob was $\frac{3}{4}$ inch shorter than his father. Since then, Bob has grown $\frac{1}{8}$ inch. How much shorter than his father is Bob now?

**8.** Brand X cereal provides $\frac{1}{4}$ of the daily requirement of iron, and Brand Y provides $\frac{1}{10}$ of the requirement. Which brand provides more iron? How much more?

**9.** One perfume bottle contains $\frac{1}{4}$ ounce. Another contains $\frac{5}{16}$ ounce. How much more than $\frac{1}{4}$ ounce is $\frac{5}{16}$ ounce?

**10.** A party-mix recipe calls for $\frac{2}{3}$ cup of peanuts and $\frac{1}{4}$ cup of cashews. The amount of peanuts used is how much more than the amount of cashews?

EXTRA PRACTICE page 486, set 42

## MATH NOTE

When you work with an electrical circuit, you find the total resistance by adding all of the resistances in the circuit.

The total resistance of a circuit having two resistances is $\frac{7}{8}$ ohm. If one resistance is $\frac{1}{2}$ ohm, what is the other resistance?

# SUBTRACTING MIXED NUMBERS

H. Armstrong Roberts

David has a board $5\frac{3}{4}$ feet long. He needs a piece $3\frac{1}{4}$ feet long for a stereo stand he is building. What is the length of the board that will be left after he cuts off $3\frac{1}{4}$ feet?

**Example 1:** Find $5\frac{3}{4} - 3\frac{1}{4}$.

$$
\begin{array}{r}
5\frac{3}{4} \\
-3\frac{1}{4} \\
\hline
2\frac{2}{4} = 2\frac{1}{2}
\end{array}
$$

The fractions have a common denominator. Subtract the fractions, and subtract the whole numbers. Simplify if necessary.

$2\frac{1}{2}$ feet of board will remain.

**Example 2:**

$$
\begin{array}{r}
4\frac{7}{8} = 4\frac{21}{24} \\
-2\frac{1}{3} = 2\frac{8}{24} \\
\hline
2\frac{13}{24}
\end{array}
$$

Change the fractions to equivalent fractions with a common denominator.

**Example 3:**

$$
\begin{array}{r}
9\frac{1}{4} = 9\frac{3}{12} = 8\frac{15}{12} \\
-3\frac{2}{3} = 3\frac{8}{12} = 3\frac{8}{12} \\
\hline
5\frac{7}{12}
\end{array}
$$

Think: $9\frac{3}{12} = 8 + 1\frac{3}{12} = 8\frac{15}{12}$

**Example 4:**

$$
\begin{array}{r}
10 = 9\frac{8}{8} \\
-4\frac{1}{8} = 4\frac{1}{8} \\
\hline
5\frac{7}{8}
\end{array}
$$

## EXERCISES

Subtract. Simplify each answer. Check by adding.

**1.** $\begin{array}{r} 9\frac{3}{8} \\ -4\frac{1}{8} \\ \hline \end{array}$

**2.** $\begin{array}{r} 15\frac{3}{5} \\ -10\frac{1}{5} \\ \hline \end{array}$

**3.** $\begin{array}{r} 10\frac{7}{8} \\ -4\frac{3}{8} \\ \hline \end{array}$

**4.** $\begin{array}{r} 7\frac{5}{8} \\ -3\frac{3}{8} \\ \hline \end{array}$

**5.** $\begin{array}{r} 4\frac{9}{10} \\ -3\frac{1}{10} \\ \hline \end{array}$

**6.** $2\frac{7}{12}$
$-1\frac{5}{12}$

**7.** $4\frac{5}{12}$
$-1\frac{1}{12}$

**8.** $8\frac{8}{15}$
$-2\frac{7}{15}$

**9.** $14\frac{3}{20}$
$-11\frac{1}{20}$

**10.** $18\frac{11}{12}$
$-7\frac{5}{12}$

**11.** $15\frac{17}{20}$
$-14\frac{3}{20}$

**12.** $3\frac{4}{25}$
$-2\frac{1}{25}$

**13.** $51\frac{17}{25}$
$-29\frac{14}{25}$

**14.** $2\frac{5}{9}$
$-1\frac{2}{9}$

**15.** $5\frac{5}{6}$
$-1\frac{1}{6}$

**16.** $5\frac{9}{10}$
$-3\frac{1}{2}$

**17.** $14\frac{4}{5}$
$-2\frac{1}{3}$

**18.** $8$
$-3\frac{2}{15}$

**19.** $7\frac{5}{8}$
$-2\frac{1}{3}$

**20.** $10$
$-3\frac{1}{4}$

**21.** $7$
$-4\frac{3}{4}$

**22.** $8\frac{7}{20}$
$-3\frac{1}{4}$

**23.** $4$
$-3\frac{14}{15}$

**24.** $8\frac{7}{8}$
$-3\frac{1}{4}$

**25.** $15$
$-3\frac{2}{25}$

**26.** $7\frac{4}{5}$
$-2\frac{1}{10}$

**27.** $13\frac{7}{12}$
$-4\frac{1}{3}$

**28.** $8\frac{9}{10}$
$-4\frac{3}{4}$

**29.** $5\frac{3}{4}$
$-2\frac{1}{16}$

**30.** $3\frac{5}{9}$
$-1\frac{1}{18}$

**31.** $7\frac{1}{4}$
$-3\frac{5}{8}$

**32.** $6\frac{1}{3}$
$-4\frac{2}{3}$

**33.** $10\frac{2}{9}$
$-6\frac{2}{3}$

**34.** $4\frac{1}{2}$
$-3\frac{5}{8}$

**35.** $15\frac{5}{8}$
$-3\frac{7}{8}$

**36.** $6\frac{3}{4}$
$-4\frac{15}{16}$

**37.** $3\frac{1}{8}$
$-2\frac{3}{4}$

**38.** $5\frac{1}{3}$
$-2\frac{5}{6}$

**39.** $3\frac{5}{12}$
$-1\frac{3}{4}$

**40.** $13\frac{1}{5}$
$-2\frac{3}{8}$

**41.** $7\frac{3}{4}$
$-4\frac{19}{20}$

**42.** $1\frac{1}{5}$
$-\frac{17}{25}$

**43.** $9\frac{1}{6}$
$-3\frac{3}{8}$

**44.** $12\frac{7}{8}$
$-4\frac{9}{16}$

**45.** $25\frac{1}{10}$
$-14\frac{2}{5}$

Solve.

**46.** Darlene wants to swim 30 laps every day. She swam $12\frac{1}{2}$ laps this morning. How many more laps must she swim today to meet her goal?

**47.** Eric needs a piece of trim $3\frac{1}{4}$ feet long to put over a doorway. He has a piece $3\frac{1}{3}$ feet long. How much should he cut from this length?

*EXTRA PRACTICE page 487, set 43*

# 5.8 PRACTICE ADDING AND SUBTRACTING

Addition and subtraction of fractions can be written in a horizontal form.

**Example 1:** $\dfrac{3}{8}-\dfrac{1}{4}$  Change $\frac{1}{4}$ to $\frac{2}{8}$.

$\dfrac{3}{8}-\dfrac{2}{8}$  Subtract.

$\dfrac{1}{8}$

**Example 2:** $1\dfrac{1}{2}+2\dfrac{5}{6}$  Change $1\frac{1}{2}$ to $1\frac{3}{6}$.

$1\dfrac{3}{6}+2\dfrac{5}{6}$  Add.

$3\dfrac{8}{6}$  Think: $3\frac{8}{6}=3+1\frac{2}{6}$

$4\dfrac{2}{6}$  Simplify.

$4\dfrac{1}{3}$

**Example 3:** $4\dfrac{1}{2}+3\dfrac{3}{8}+6\dfrac{5}{16}$  Change the fractions so that they have a common denominator.

$4\dfrac{8}{16}+3\dfrac{6}{16}+6\dfrac{5}{16}$  Add.

$13\dfrac{19}{16}$  Think: $13\frac{19}{16}=13+1\frac{3}{16}$

$14\dfrac{3}{16}$

# EXERCISES

Add or subtract. Simplify each answer.

**1.** $\dfrac{5}{8}-\dfrac{1}{8}$

**2.** $\dfrac{1}{4}+\dfrac{3}{4}+\dfrac{3}{4}$

**3.** $\dfrac{7}{10}-\dfrac{3}{10}$

**4.** $2\dfrac{1}{3}+3\dfrac{1}{3}+6\dfrac{2}{3}$

**5.** $5\dfrac{3}{4}+14\dfrac{3}{4}$

**6.** $\dfrac{9}{10}+\dfrac{7}{10}$

144

**7.** $8\frac{1}{4} + 2\frac{7}{8}$

**8.** $\frac{1}{3} + \frac{1}{6}$

**9.** $\frac{3}{4} + \frac{5}{16}$

**10.** $3\frac{5}{8} - 2\frac{1}{2}$

**11.** $\frac{7}{16} + \frac{3}{8}$

**12.** $7\frac{1}{10} - 5\frac{2}{5}$

**13.** $\frac{1}{5} + \frac{3}{10} + \frac{2}{5}$

**14.** $5\frac{1}{2} + 3\frac{3}{4} + 10\frac{1}{4}$

**15.** $31\frac{1}{2} + 2\frac{1}{10}$

**16.** $3\frac{1}{8} + 2\frac{5}{8} + 3\frac{1}{2}$

**17.** $\frac{7}{12} - \frac{1}{4}$

**18.** $19\frac{1}{3} + 21\frac{5}{6}$

**19.** $\frac{1}{3} + \frac{1}{2} + \frac{1}{6}$

**20.** $\frac{3}{10} - \frac{1}{5}$

**21.** $21\frac{1}{2} - 13\frac{3}{4}$

**22.** $84\frac{1}{4} + 27\frac{1}{2}$

**23.** $\frac{3}{8} + \frac{1}{2}$

**24.** $\frac{2}{5} - \frac{1}{10}$

**25.** $9\frac{7}{8} - 4\frac{1}{4}$

**26.** $\frac{9}{16} + \frac{3}{4} + \frac{1}{2}$

**27.** $8\frac{1}{4} - 3\frac{5}{6}$

**28.** $4\frac{1}{2} + 5\frac{1}{3} + 6\frac{5}{6}$

**29.** $2\frac{1}{4} + 3\frac{1}{2} + 16\frac{1}{8}$

**30.** $\frac{7}{8} + \frac{1}{2} + \frac{3}{4}$

**31.** $4\frac{3}{4} - 1\frac{5}{6}$

**32.** $6\frac{1}{3} + 2\frac{1}{4} + 5\frac{5}{12}$

**33.** $\frac{1}{6} + 3\frac{7}{12}$

**34.** $1\frac{1}{8} + 3\frac{1}{6} + 7\frac{1}{12}$

**35.** $8\frac{2}{3} - 6\frac{1}{5}$

**36.** $2\frac{7}{8} + 5\frac{1}{10}$

**37.** $14\frac{3}{4} + 21\frac{2}{3}$

**38.** $8\frac{1}{4} - 2\frac{4}{5}$

**39.** $3\frac{7}{8} + 1\frac{2}{3} + 2\frac{1}{2}$

**40.** $6 - 3\frac{5}{8}$

**41.** $2\frac{5}{8} + \frac{2}{3} + 1\frac{3}{4}$

**42.** $16\frac{3}{4} + 5$

**43.** $4\frac{3}{8} + 7\frac{1}{10}$

**44.** $12 - 3\frac{4}{5}$

**45.** $1\frac{1}{2} + 3\frac{5}{6} + 4\frac{3}{4}$

Solve.

**46.** Jo worked $1\frac{1}{2}$ hours on Monday, $2\frac{1}{4}$ hours on Wednesday, and $1\frac{3}{4}$ hours on Thursday. How many hours did she work in all?

**47.** Craig worked $4\frac{3}{4}$ hours on Saturday and $2\frac{1}{3}$ hours on Monday. How much longer did he work on Saturday?

**You are knitting a scarf. The pattern says to knit until the scarf is 60 inches long. It is now $37\frac{1}{4}$ inches long. How many more inches must you knit?**

**Read:**   *Given:*   Scarf should be 60 in. It is now $37\frac{1}{4}$ in.

                *To find:*   how many more inches are to be knitted

**Plan:**   Which operation can be used? Since you must find out how much more, subtract $37\frac{1}{4}$ from 60.

**Compute:**

$$
\begin{array}{r}
60 = 59\frac{4}{4} \\
-\,37\frac{1}{4} = 37\frac{1}{4} \\
\hline
22\frac{3}{4}
\end{array}
$$

**Answer:**   You must knit $22\frac{3}{4}$ more inches.

**Check:**   $37\frac{1}{4} + 22\frac{3}{4}$

               $59\frac{4}{4}$

               $60$ ✔

# EXERCISES

**1.**

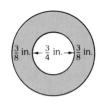

What is the outside diameter of the tube?

**2.**

How much material is needed to make all 3 pieces?

**3.** A bolt of fabric contains $21\frac{5}{8}$ yards. The clerk cuts off $3\frac{1}{4}$ yards. How many yards of material are left on the bolt?

**4.** The inseam on a pair of slacks measures 32 inches. The length must be shortened to $29\frac{3}{4}$ inches. By how much must the slacks be shortened?

**5.** Kim's goal is to run 15 laps around the track every day. She ran $11\frac{1}{2}$ laps in the morning. How many more laps must she run to meet her goal?

**6.** Mrs. Hirota roasted $3\frac{1}{4}$ pounds of sunflower seeds in one batch and $5\frac{1}{2}$ pounds in a second batch. How many pounds of sunflower seeds did she roast in all?

**7.** Margo is 75 inches tall. Juli is $60\frac{1}{2}$ inches tall. How much taller than Juli is Margo?

**8.** Alex weighed $8\frac{1}{2}$ pounds at birth. A month later, he weighed $9\frac{1}{4}$ pounds. How much weight did he gain?

**9.** In Frank's aquarium, the longest fish measures $1\frac{5}{16}$ inches long. The shortest fish measures $\frac{7}{8}$ inch. By how much do the longest and the shortest fish differ in length?

**10.** A stock that was worth $42\frac{1}{2}$ dollars dropped $3\frac{5}{8}$ dollars in value. How much was it worth then?

**11.** A gas tank can hold $11\frac{1}{10}$ gallons of gas. How many gallons were in the tank if it took $8\frac{3}{10}$ gallons to fill it?

**12.** You have driven $3\frac{7}{10}$ miles of the $5\frac{3}{4}$ miles from the airport to the hotel. How much farther is the hotel?

**13.** A piece of metal measures $3\frac{5}{64}$ inches long. It should have been $3\frac{1}{16}$ inches. How much should be shaved off?

**14.** A piece of metal $\frac{7}{32}$ inch thick was glued to another piece $\frac{9}{16}$ inch thick. What was the total thickness?

*EXTRA PRACTICE page 487, set 44*

Kenji Kerins

Feet, pounds, and gallons are three of the nonmetric units for measuring length, weight, and capacity. Other units and equivalent measurements are listed in the table below.

| Measure | Units | Equivalents |
|---|---|---|
| Length | inches (in.), feet (ft), yards (yd), miles (mi) | 1 ft = 12 in.<br>1 yd = 3 ft<br>1 mi = 5280 ft |
| Weight | ounces (oz), pounds (lb), tons | 1 lb = 16 oz<br>1 ton = 2000 lb |
| Capacity (liquid) | cups (c), pints (pt), quarts (qt), gallons (gal) | 1 pt = 2 c<br>1 qt = 2 pt<br>1 gal = 4 qt |

**To convert from a larger unit to a smaller unit, multiply.**

**Example 1:**  4 qt = ? pt
1 qt = 2 pt, so multiply 4 by 2.
4 qt = 8 pt

**To convert from a smaller unit to a larger unit, divide.**

**Example 2:**  14 ft = ? yd
3 ft = 1 yd, so divide 14 by 3.
14 ft = $4\frac{2}{3}$ yd

## EXERCISES

Complete each statement, using *in., ft, yd,* or *mi.*

**1.** The distance between New York City and Chicago is about 810 ___.

**2.** The height of an adult male giraffe is about 6 ___.

**3.** The height of a room is about 8 _____.

**4.** The width of a notebook is about $8\frac{1}{2}$ _____.

Complete each statement, using *oz, lb,* or *tons.*

**5.** A package of lunch meat weighs about 12 _____.

**6.** A bag of carrots weighs about 2 _____.

**7.** An elephant weighs about 6 _____.

Complete each statement, using *c, pt, qt,* or *gal.*

**8.** A can of motor oil contains 1 _____.

**9.** A serving of soup is about 1 _____.

**10.** The amount of paint needed to cover 4 walls of a room is about 1 _____.

Complete.

**11.** 1 mile = _____ feet

**12.** 1 quart = _____ pints

**13.** 1 ton = _____ pounds

**14.** 1 pound = _____ ounces

**15.** 1 gallon = _____ quarts

**16.** 1 pint = _____ cups

**17.** 1 yard = _____ feet

**18.** 1 foot = _____ inches

**19.** 3 ft = _____ in.

**20.** 16 in. = _____ ft

**21.** 32 oz = _____ lb

**22.** 6 c = _____ pt

**23.** 2 yd = _____ ft

**24.** 10 ft = _____ yd

**25.** 2 tons = _____ lb

**26.** 5000 lb = _____ tons

**27.** 10 lb = _____ oz

**28.** 7 pt = _____ qt

**29.** 3 pt = _____ c

**30.** 3 mi = _____ ft

**31.** 10 gal = _____ qt

**32.** 18 ft = _____ yd

**33.** 2640 ft = _____ mi

**34.** 5 qt = _____ pt

**35.** 36 in. = _____ ft

**36.** 4 gal = _____ qt

Solve.

**37.** A loaf of bread weighs 20 ounces. How much does it weigh in pounds?

**38.** A room measures 12 feet wide. How many yards wide is it?

EXTRA PRACTICE page 487, set 45

**149**

**1.** Melissa sold 8 tickets to a band concert on Friday, 15 on Saturday, and 12 on Sunday. How many did she sell in all?

**2.** A farmer harvested 2448 pumpkins. An equal number of pumpkins is to be sent to each of 6 stands, where they will be sold. How many should be sent to each stand?

**3.** If one ticket to a concert costs $15, how much will 6 tickets cost?

**4.** Lawrence earned $624 for working 52 hours. How much does he make per hour?

**5.** Fritz drove 274.5 miles and his car used 18.3 gallons of gasoline. How many miles per gallon did the car average?

**6.** A pattern calls for $1\frac{1}{4}$ yards of fabric for a vest and $1\frac{3}{4}$ yards for slacks. What is the total length of fabric needed?

**7.** Elizabeth made deposits to her checking account in the amounts of $50.00, $25.34, and $10.95. Find the total deposits to her account.

**8.** Frank bought 12 tomato plants, 6 pepper plants, and 48 onion sets. What is the total number of plants he bought?

**9.** A class project requires two thicknesses of balsa wood. One is $\frac{3}{32}$ inch thick; the other, $\frac{1}{8}$ inch. Which is thicker? By how much?

**10.** To frame a picture, Faye needs 2 pieces of wood 20 inches long and 2 pieces 16 inches long. What is the total number of inches of wood she needs?

**11.** A fireplace is sold in a small size and a standard size. The small size costs $459.89; the standard size costs $529.99. How much more does the standard size cost?

**12.** A team played 12 games and won 7 of them. What part of the games played did the team win?

**13.** Anthony was assigned 35 pages of reading. He has finished 24 pages. How many more pages must he read?

**14.** Darlene must repay a loan of $281.88 in 12 equal payments. How much will each payment be?

**15.** Hamburger is $1.19 per pound. What will 2.09 pounds cost (to the nearest cent)?

**16.** One book costs $2.95. How much will 8 copies of the book cost?

**17.** Felicia worked $2\frac{1}{2}$ hours on Monday, $3\frac{1}{4}$ hours on Tuesday, and $1\frac{1}{2}$ hours on Thursday. How many hours did she work?

**18.** One roll of wallpaper contains 71 square feet. Sheila needs 7 rolls to cover a room. How many square feet of wallpaper is this?

**19.** A rectangular rug has a total length of 36 inches. This includes $3\frac{3}{4}$ inches of fringe at each end. What is the length of the rug, not including the fringe?

**20.** A folding door can fit an opening that measures up to 32 inches. How many feet is this?

A machinist's work includes drilling, boring, planing, grinding, and sawing metal to specified sizes and shapes. A machinist must be able to make very accurate measurements to meet the specifications on a blueprint.

One blueprint is shown below.

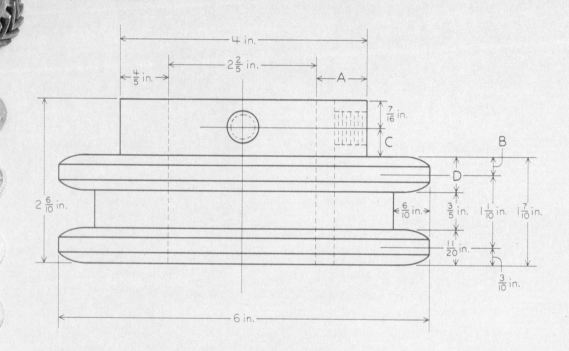

Find each of the lengths.

**1.** $A$

**2.** $B$

**3.** $C$

**4.** $D$

Brent Jones

Mrs. Harper wants to order items from a catalog. Some questions she must consider are below.

### Chairs

| Style of chair | Back size Height | Width |
|---|---|---|
| High Back | $17\frac{3}{4}$ in. | 15 in. (at bottom) 13 in. (at top) |
| Standard | $10\frac{1}{2}$ in. | $16\frac{1}{2}$ in. |

1. How much taller is the back of the high-back chair than that of the standard chair?

2. How much wider is the back of the standard than the widest part of the high back?

### Indoor/Outdoor Carpets

| Type | Height of pile |
|---|---|
| "Green grass" | $\frac{5}{16}$ inch |
| "Natural look" | $\frac{1}{4}$ inch |

3. Which carpet has the higher pile?

### Lawn Mowers

| Type | Cutting range (height to which grass can be cut) |
|---|---|
| Push-type, rear-bagger | $\frac{1}{2}$ to $2\frac{1}{2}$ in. |
| Push-type, electric, rear-bagger | $\frac{7}{8}$ to $2\frac{5}{8}$ in. |
| Push-type, cordless electric | $1\frac{1}{2}$ to $3\frac{5}{8}$ in. |
| Push-type, 2-speed engine | $\frac{7}{8}$ to $3\frac{1}{8}$ in. |

4. Find the difference between the highest and the lowest cutting height for each. Which mower has the greatest range of cutting heights?

# CHAPTER REVIEW

Complete each sentence. Choose from these words.
*multiply, numerator, divide, less than, denominator, capacity, weight*

**1.** $\frac{3}{8} < \frac{5}{8}$, since 3 is _____ 5.      5.1

**2.** To subtract two fractions, you may have to change them so that they have a common _____.      5.5

**3.** To convert from a larger unit of measurement to a smaller one, _____.      5.10

**4.** To convert from a smaller unit of measurement to a larger one, _____.

**5.** The gallon is a unit of _____.

Which symbol, $>$ or $<$, should replace each ●?      5.1

**6.** $\frac{3}{4}$ ● $\frac{1}{4}$          **7.** $\frac{2}{5}$ ● $\frac{4}{5}$          **8.** $1\frac{3}{10}$ ● $1\frac{4}{5}$

Determine if each statement is true or false by changing each fraction or mixed number to its decimal equivalent.      5.2

**9.** $\frac{1}{2} < \frac{5}{8}$          **10.** $\frac{5}{8} < \frac{2}{3}$          **11.** $3\frac{7}{10} > 3\frac{5}{6}$

Subtract. Simplify each answer.

**12.** $\begin{array}{r} \frac{5}{8} \\ -\frac{3}{8} \\ \hline \end{array}$    **13.** $\begin{array}{r} \frac{9}{10} \\ -\frac{3}{10} \\ \hline \end{array}$    **14.** $\begin{array}{r} \frac{5}{7} \\ -\frac{2}{7} \\ \hline \end{array}$    **15.** $\begin{array}{r} \frac{4}{9} \\ -\frac{2}{9} \\ \hline \end{array}$    5.4

**16.** $\begin{array}{r} \frac{3}{5} \\ -\frac{1}{3} \\ \hline \end{array}$    **17.** $\begin{array}{r} \frac{7}{8} \\ -\frac{1}{2} \\ \hline \end{array}$    **18.** $\begin{array}{r} \frac{5}{6} \\ -\frac{1}{4} \\ \hline \end{array}$    **19.** $\begin{array}{r} \frac{2}{3} \\ -\frac{1}{4} \\ \hline \end{array}$    5.5

**20.** $\begin{array}{r} \frac{5}{8} \\ -\frac{1}{4} \\ \hline \end{array}$    **21.** $\begin{array}{r} \frac{2}{3} \\ -\frac{5}{12} \\ \hline \end{array}$    **22.** $\begin{array}{r} \frac{7}{8} \\ -\frac{1}{6} \\ \hline \end{array}$    **23.** $\begin{array}{r} \frac{7}{8} \\ -\frac{1}{5} \\ \hline \end{array}$

**24.** $\begin{array}{r} 10\frac{5}{8} \\ -8\frac{1}{8} \\ \hline \end{array}$    **25.** $\begin{array}{r} 3\frac{7}{10} \\ -2\frac{9}{10} \\ \hline \end{array}$    **26.** $\begin{array}{r} 14\frac{3}{4} \\ -9\frac{1}{4} \\ \hline \end{array}$    **27.** $\begin{array}{r} 15\frac{1}{2} \\ -10\frac{11}{12} \\ \hline \end{array}$    5.7

**28.** $6\frac{1}{4}$
$-2\frac{1}{10}$

**29.** $3\frac{7}{8}$
$-1\frac{1}{4}$

**30.** $12\frac{5}{6}$
$-9\frac{1}{3}$

**31.** $4\frac{7}{10}$
$-1\frac{1}{2}$

**32.** $14\frac{1}{4}$
$-7\frac{3}{8}$

**33.** $23\frac{1}{6}$
$-14\frac{9}{10}$

**34.** $4\frac{2}{5}$
$-1\frac{9}{10}$

**35.** $6\frac{7}{8}$
$-3\frac{11}{12}$

**36.** $6$
$-4\frac{1}{3}$

**37.** $12$
$-3\frac{4}{5}$

**38.** $7$
$-3\frac{5}{12}$

**39.** $13$
$-4\frac{5}{6}$

Find each answer.

5.8

**40.** $\frac{15}{16}-\frac{3}{4}$

**41.** $1\frac{4}{5}-\frac{3}{4}$

**42.** $2\frac{1}{6}+1\frac{1}{2}$

**43.** $\frac{3}{4}+1\frac{1}{2}+2\frac{1}{4}$

**44.** $3\frac{1}{5}+2\frac{3}{4}$

**45.** $1\frac{3}{8}+2\frac{1}{5}+6\frac{2}{5}$

**46.** $5\frac{3}{4}-2\frac{5}{16}$

**47.** $3\frac{9}{10}-1\frac{1}{5}$

Complete.

5.10

**48.** 6 c = ___ pt

**49.** 3 tons = ___ lb

**50.** 72 in. = ___ ft

**51.** 4 yd = ___ ft

**52.** 48 oz = ___ lb

**53.** 3 gal = ___ qt

Solve.

**54.** One calculator is $\frac{3}{8}$ in. thick, and another is $\frac{9}{32}$ in. thick. Is the first or the second calculator thinner?

5.3

**55.** How much more perfume is in a bottle holding $\frac{1}{3}$ ounce than is in a bottle holding $\frac{1}{4}$ ounce?

5.6

**56.** One set of car ramps is 12 inches high. Another set is $10\frac{1}{4}$ inches high. How much higher is the first set?

5.9

**57.** Erica bought 2 gallons of motor oil. How many quarts is that?

5.10

CHAPTER REVIEW

Which symbol, $>$ or $<$, should replace each ●?

**1.** $\frac{4}{5}$ ● $\frac{3}{5}$

**2.** $\frac{3}{8}$ ● $\frac{1}{2}$

Determine if each statement is true or false by changing each fraction or mixed number to its decimal equivalent.

**3.** $3\frac{2}{5} > 3\frac{1}{4}$

**4.** $\frac{3}{8} > \frac{1}{2}$

Subtract. Simplify each answer.

**5.** $\begin{array}{r} \frac{6}{7} \\ -\frac{3}{7} \\ \hline \end{array}$

**6.** $\begin{array}{r} \frac{7}{9} \\ -\frac{5}{9} \\ \hline \end{array}$

**7.** $\begin{array}{r} \frac{5}{8} \\ -\frac{1}{8} \\ \hline \end{array}$

**8.** $\begin{array}{r} \frac{11}{12} \\ -\frac{7}{12} \\ \hline \end{array}$

**9.** $\begin{array}{r} \frac{4}{5} \\ -\frac{1}{10} \\ \hline \end{array}$

**10.** $\begin{array}{r} \frac{7}{8} \\ -\frac{1}{3} \\ \hline \end{array}$

**11.** $\begin{array}{r} 5\frac{7}{10} \\ -2\frac{3}{10} \\ \hline \end{array}$

**12.** $\begin{array}{r} 8\frac{2}{3} \\ -5\frac{1}{6} \\ \hline \end{array}$

**13.** $\begin{array}{r} 8 \\ -3\frac{4}{5} \\ \hline \end{array}$

**14.** $\begin{array}{r} 4 \\ -2\frac{3}{8} \\ \hline \end{array}$

**15.** $\begin{array}{r} 7\frac{3}{5} \\ -2\frac{3}{10} \\ \hline \end{array}$

**16.** $\begin{array}{r} 6\frac{2}{3} \\ -3\frac{1}{9} \\ \hline \end{array}$

**17.** $\begin{array}{r} 9\frac{4}{5} \\ -2\frac{1}{3} \\ \hline \end{array}$

**18.** $\begin{array}{r} 4\frac{7}{8} \\ -2\frac{2}{5} \\ \hline \end{array}$

**19.** $\begin{array}{r} 6\frac{1}{2} \\ -2\frac{5}{8} \\ \hline \end{array}$

Find each answer.

**20.** $\frac{9}{10} - \frac{3}{4}$

**21.** $11\frac{4}{5} + 2\frac{3}{4}$

**22.** $1\frac{4}{5} + 2\frac{1}{2} + 4\frac{1}{3}$

Complete.

**23.** 1 yd = ____ ft

**24.** 2000 lb = ____ ton

**25.** 3 qt = ____ gal

Solve.

**26.** A major-league baseball bat cannot have a diameter of more than $2\frac{3}{4}$ inches at its widest part. Is $2\frac{11}{16}$ inches acceptable as the widest diameter?

**27.** A carpenter has a board $5\frac{1}{2}$ feet long. If $3\frac{1}{4}$ feet is cut off, what is the length of the piece that is left?

## PREVIEW TEST

Use the diagrams to answer the multiplication exercise.

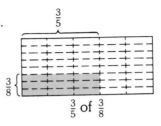

**1.** $\frac{3}{5} \times \frac{3}{8} =$ ____

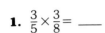 

Multiply. Simplify each answer.

**2.** $\frac{3}{7} \times \frac{3}{5}$

**3.** $\frac{1}{3} \times \frac{5}{8}$

**4.** $\frac{3}{4} \times \frac{4}{5}$

**5.** $\frac{5}{10} \times \frac{3}{10}$

**6.** $1\frac{3}{4} \times 3\frac{2}{5}$

**7.** $6\frac{2}{3} \times 1\frac{1}{2}$

Find the reciprocal of each number.

**8.** $\frac{3}{4}$

**9.** $1\frac{4}{5}$

Rewrite the division exercise as a multiplication exercise.

**10.** $\frac{3}{4} \div \frac{4}{5}$

**11.** $1\frac{1}{2} \div 2\frac{3}{4}$

Divide. Simplify each answer.

**12.** $\frac{1}{2} \div \frac{1}{3}$

**13.** $\frac{3}{4} \div \frac{2}{3}$

**14.** $\frac{3}{4} \div \frac{9}{16}$

**15.** $3\frac{3}{8} \div 4$

**16.** $18 \div 1\frac{1}{2}$

**17.** $2\frac{3}{5} \div 1\frac{1}{4}$

Complete.

**18.** 3 gal = ____ pt

**19.** 1600 oz = ____ ton

**20.** 80 in. = ____ yd

**21.** 32 c = ____ qt

**22.** $3\frac{1}{2}$ yd = ____ in.

**23.** 5 yd 2 ft = ____ ft

Solve.

**24.** $3\frac{1}{2}$ million dollars is to be shared equally by 2 charities. How much money will each receive?

**25.** If it takes $1\frac{1}{4}$ yards of material to make one vest, how much material will it take to make 5 vests?

157

## SHOWING MULTIPLICATION OF FRACTIONS

$\frac{1}{4}$ **cup of rug cleaner should be mixed with a gallon of water. Julio wants to make** $\frac{1}{2}$ **of this amount. How much rug cleaner should he use?**

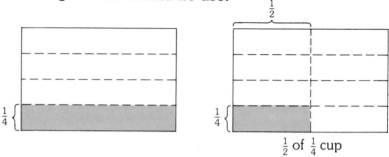

$\frac{1}{2}$ of $\frac{1}{4}$ cup

There are 8 small rectangles of equal size in the second diagram. One of them is colored red. $\frac{1}{8}$ of the diagram is colored red.

$\frac{1}{2}$ of $\frac{1}{4}$ means $\frac{1}{2} \times \frac{1}{4}$.

From the second diagram,

$$\frac{1}{2} \times \frac{1}{4} = \frac{1}{8}. \quad \longleftarrow \text{ red rectangles} \atop \longleftarrow \text{ total rectangles}$$

Julio should use $\frac{1}{8}$ cup of rug cleaner.

**Example:** Use diagrams to find $\frac{5}{6} \times \frac{7}{8}$.

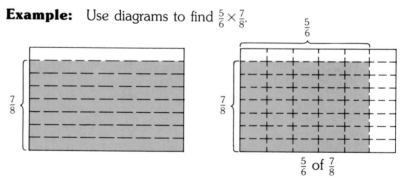

$\frac{5}{6}$ of $\frac{7}{8}$

From the second diagram, $\frac{5}{6}$ of $\frac{7}{8}$ is $\frac{35}{48}$. So

$$\frac{5}{6} \times \frac{7}{8} = \frac{35}{48}. \quad \longleftarrow \text{ red rectangles} \atop \longleftarrow \text{ total rectangles}$$

# EXERCISES

Use the diagrams to complete the exercises.

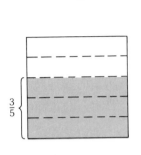 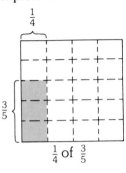 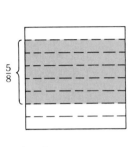 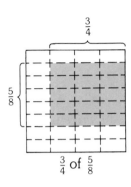

**1.** $\frac{1}{4} \times \frac{3}{5} =$ \_\_\_\_

**2.** $\frac{3}{4} \times \frac{5}{8} =$ \_\_\_\_

Copy and shade to show each multiplication exercise.

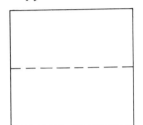 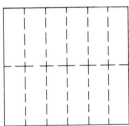 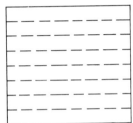 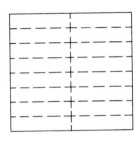

**3.** $\frac{5}{6} \times \frac{1}{2} =$ \_\_\_\_

**4.** $\frac{1}{2} \times \frac{7}{8} =$ \_\_\_\_

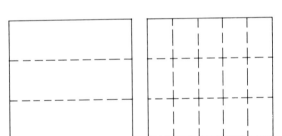 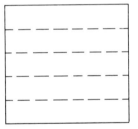 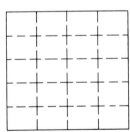

**5.** $\frac{2}{5} \times \frac{2}{3} =$ \_\_\_\_

**6.** $\frac{3}{4} \times \frac{1}{5} =$ \_\_\_\_

Solve.

**7.** A recipe calls for $\frac{3}{4}$ pound of hamburger. If Steve is making $\frac{1}{2}$ of the recipe amount, how much hamburger does he need?

**8.** Mary found $\frac{1}{3}$ of a pizza in the refrigerator. She took half of it to warm for lunch. What part of the original pizza did she warm?

Artstreet

**Carol bought some liquid vitamin for her dog. The directions on the bottle say to add $\frac{1}{2}$ ounce to the food of a puppy or an active dog. For an inactive dog, you add only $\frac{1}{2}$ as much vitamin. If Carol's dog is inactive, how much vitamin should she add to its food?**

The diagram method gives us the answer.

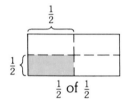

$\frac{1}{2}$ of $\frac{1}{2}$

1 of the 4 rectangles is red.

So $\frac{1}{2}$ of $\frac{1}{2} = \frac{1}{2} \times \frac{1}{2} = \frac{1}{4}$.

She should add $\frac{1}{4}$ ounce of the vitamin.

Another way to find the answer is to multiply $\frac{1}{2}$ by $\frac{1}{2}$.

Multiply the numerators: $\frac{1}{2} \times \frac{1}{2} = \frac{1 \times 1}{} = \frac{1}{}$

Multiply the denominators: $\frac{1}{2} \times \frac{1}{2} = \frac{1 \times 1}{2 \times 2} = \frac{1}{4}$

**Example 1:** $\dfrac{2}{3} \times \dfrac{4}{5} = \dfrac{2 \times 4}{3 \times 5}$

$= \dfrac{8}{15}$

**Example 2:** $\dfrac{3}{5} \times \dfrac{9}{10} = \dfrac{27}{50}$

# EXERCISES

Replace each ☐ with the correct number.

1. $\frac{3}{4} \times \frac{9}{10} = \frac{☐ \times 9}{4 \times 10}$    2. $\frac{5}{8} \times \frac{1}{3} = \frac{5 \times ☐}{8 \times 3}$    3. $\frac{3}{5} \times \frac{7}{8} = \frac{3 \times 7}{☐ \times 8}$

4. $\frac{5}{8} \times \frac{3}{4} = \frac{☐ \times 3}{8 \times 4}$    5. $\frac{5}{7} \times \frac{2}{3} = \frac{5 \times 2}{7 \times ☐}$    6. $\frac{3}{7} \times \frac{5}{8} = \frac{3 \times ☐}{7 \times 8}$

Multiply.

7. $\frac{1}{3} \times \frac{4}{5}$    8. $\frac{3}{10} \times \frac{1}{5}$    9. $\frac{9}{10} \times \frac{3}{4}$

10. $\frac{3}{8} \times \frac{1}{2}$    11. $\frac{2}{3} \times \frac{1}{5}$    12. $\frac{3}{10} \times \frac{3}{5}$

13. $\frac{1}{10} \times \frac{1}{3}$    14. $\frac{2}{3} \times \frac{4}{5}$    15. $\frac{7}{12} \times \frac{1}{2}$

16. $\frac{4}{5} \times \frac{3}{5}$    17. $\frac{3}{7} \times \frac{3}{8}$    18. $\frac{7}{9} \times \frac{2}{5}$

19. $\frac{4}{7} \times \frac{2}{5}$    20. $\frac{13}{20} \times \frac{3}{4}$    21. $\frac{6}{7} \times \frac{3}{5}$

22. $\frac{7}{12} \times \frac{1}{3}$    23. $\frac{3}{5} \times \frac{7}{8}$    24. $\frac{3}{5} \times \frac{4}{7}$

25. $\frac{5}{8} \times \frac{7}{12}$    26. $\frac{1}{6} \times \frac{7}{8}$    27. $\frac{2}{3} \times \frac{5}{9}$

28. $\frac{4}{15} \times \frac{2}{3}$    29. $\frac{5}{9} \times \frac{4}{7}$    30. $\frac{5}{7} \times \frac{5}{12}$

31. $\frac{11}{12} \times \frac{5}{6}$    32. $\frac{8}{9} \times \frac{2}{5}$    33. $\frac{14}{15} \times \frac{1}{3}$

34. $\frac{23}{50} \times \frac{1}{4}$    35. $\frac{7}{10} \times \frac{1}{3}$    36. $\frac{19}{20} \times \frac{3}{4}$

EXTRA PRACTICE page 488, set 46

## SKILLS REVIEW

Multiply.

37. $\begin{array}{r} 34 \\ \times 8 \\ \hline \end{array}$    38. $\begin{array}{r} 506 \\ \times 7 \\ \hline \end{array}$    39. $\begin{array}{r} 231 \\ \times 14 \\ \hline \end{array}$    40. $\begin{array}{r} 57 \\ \times 89 \\ \hline \end{array}$

41. $\begin{array}{r} 2.31 \\ \times 5.4 \\ \hline \end{array}$    42. $\begin{array}{r} 3.09 \\ \times 1.37 \\ \hline \end{array}$    43. $\begin{array}{r} 14.2 \\ \times 0.3 \\ \hline \end{array}$    44. $\begin{array}{r} 10.02 \\ \times 0.04 \\ \hline \end{array}$

## 6.3 CHANGING PRODUCTS TO LOWEST TERMS

**Bob is repainting his car. The instructions say that he should add $\frac{1}{2}$ quart of thinner to each gallon of paint. Bob has only $\frac{2}{3}$ gallon of paint. How much thinner should he mix with it?**

**Example 1:** Find $\frac{2}{3} \times \frac{1}{2}$.

$$\frac{2}{3} \times \frac{1}{2} = \frac{2}{6}$$

2 divides both 2 and 6.

So, $\frac{2}{6} = \frac{2 \div 2}{6 \div 2}$

$$= \frac{1}{3}.$$

Bob should use $\frac{1}{3}$ quart of thinner.

Answers can be reduced to lowest terms *after* you multiply. However, it may save you time to simplify *first*.

**Example 2:** $\frac{1}{\underset{1}{\cancel{2}}} \times \frac{\overset{2}{\cancel{4}}}{5} = \frac{2}{5}$

**Example 3:** $\frac{\overset{1}{\cancel{3}}}{\underset{1}{\cancel{4}}} \times \frac{\overset{2}{\cancel{8}}}{\underset{3}{\cancel{9}}} = \frac{2}{3}$

Remember: You must be able to divide a *numerator* and a *denominator* by the same number.

## EXERCISES

Multiply. Reduce to lowest terms.

**1.** $\frac{7}{8} \times \frac{4}{5}$      **2.** $\frac{1}{2} \times \frac{4}{5}$      **3.** $\frac{4}{5} \times \frac{7}{10}$      **4.** $\frac{1}{4} \times \frac{8}{9}$

**5.** $\frac{1}{3} \times \frac{3}{4}$    **6.** $\frac{1}{5} \times \frac{5}{8}$    **7.** $\frac{3}{4} \times \frac{4}{5}$    **8.** $\frac{7}{12} \times \frac{4}{5}$

**9.** $\frac{1}{4} \times \frac{2}{5}$    **10.** $\frac{1}{6} \times \frac{3}{10}$    **11.** $\frac{3}{5} \times \frac{1}{3}$    **12.** $\frac{7}{8} \times \frac{4}{5}$

**13.** $\frac{5}{8} \times \frac{4}{15}$    **14.** $\frac{15}{32} \times \frac{4}{5}$    **15.** $\frac{8}{9} \times \frac{3}{4}$    **16.** $\frac{3}{4} \times \frac{2}{3}$

**17.** $\frac{3}{5} \times \frac{5}{12}$    **18.** $\frac{3}{8} \times \frac{2}{15}$    **19.** $\frac{3}{8} \times \frac{5}{24}$    **20.** $\frac{5}{6} \times \frac{3}{20}$

**21.** $\frac{4}{5} \times \frac{15}{16}$    **22.** $\frac{3}{16} \times \frac{4}{9}$    **23.** $\frac{5}{12} \times \frac{3}{10}$    **24.** $\frac{3}{5} \times \frac{5}{9}$

**25.** $\frac{3}{7} \times \frac{14}{15}$    **26.** $\frac{3}{7} \times \frac{14}{33}$    **27.** $\frac{7}{10} \times \frac{5}{14}$    **28.** $\frac{7}{10} \times \frac{14}{15}$

*EXTRA PRACTICE page 488, set 47*

---

## CALCULATOR NOTE

When multiplying fractions, you can check your answer by using a calculator.

$$\frac{3}{8} \times \frac{2}{5} = \frac{\overset{3}{\cancel{6}}}{\underset{20}{\cancel{40}}} = \frac{3}{20}$$

On the calculator, do the following:

**Multiply the denominators.**    **Multiply the numerators.**    **Divide the numerator by the denominator.**

ENTER                                                                    DISPLAY

8 $\boxed{\times}$ 5 $\boxed{=}$ $\boxed{\text{M+}}$    3 $\boxed{\times}$ 2 $\boxed{=}$    $\boxed{\div}$ $\boxed{\text{RM}}$ $\boxed{=}$

      ↑

**Store the result in the calculator's memory**

**Pressing** $\boxed{\text{RM}}$ **recalls 40 from the calculator's memory**

**Check your answer:** ENTER          DISPLAY

    3 $\boxed{\div}$ 20 $\boxed{=}$     ✔

Dr. E.R. Degginger

**Diane has $\frac{1}{4}$ acre to use for a garden plot. She wants to plant corn in $\frac{1}{3}$ of the garden. What part of an acre will she plant in corn?**

**Read:**  *Given:*  $\frac{1}{4}$ acre for a garden;

$\frac{1}{3}$ of the garden to be planted in corn

*To find:*  what part of an acre will be in corn

**Plan:**  Which operation can be used? Since you are to find $\frac{1}{3}$ of $\frac{1}{4}$, multiply $\frac{1}{3} \times \frac{1}{4}$.

**Compute:**  $\dfrac{1}{3} \times \dfrac{1}{4} = \dfrac{1}{12}$

**Answer:**  $\frac{1}{12}$ acre will be planted in corn.

**Check:**  You can check by drawing diagrams.

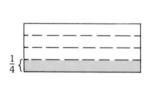
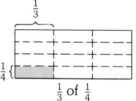

The diagrams show that $\frac{1}{3} \times \frac{1}{4} = \frac{1}{12}$. ✔

## EXERCISES

**1.** A board was $\frac{2}{3}$ yard long. Doug cut it in half. How long is each piece?

**2.** A recipe calls for $\frac{3}{4}$ pound of sausage. If you wanted to make $\frac{1}{3}$ as much as the recipe would make, how much sausage should you use?

**3.** A glass bottle holds $\frac{1}{2}$ gallon when completely full. What part of a gallon does the bottle hold when it is $\frac{2}{3}$ full?

**4.** A truck delivered $\frac{3}{4}$ ton of bricks to a building site. One project required $\frac{2}{3}$ of these bricks. What was the weight of the bricks used for the project?

**5.** A wooden rod weighs $\frac{7}{8}$ pound. What does $\frac{2}{3}$ of the rod weigh?

**6.** Sioux Falls received $\frac{1}{2}$ inch of rain one day. Detroit received $\frac{1}{2}$ as much rain. How much rain did Detroit receive that day?

**7.** The smallest toad measures about $\frac{9}{10}$ inch high. The smallest tree frog is about $\frac{2}{3}$ of this height. About how high is the smallest tree frog?

**8.** The lettering for a newspaper advertisement is $\frac{3}{8}$ inch high. A copying machine can reduce the print to $\frac{1}{2}$ of that size. What would be the height of a letter from the ad if it is run through the copier?

**9.** A nurse must keep a record of how much food some patients eat. If Mr. Williams is served $\frac{3}{4}$ cup of spinach and eats $\frac{1}{3}$ of the serving, what amount should the nurse indicate he had eaten?

**10.** What should the nurse record if Ms. Koncar is served $\frac{2}{3}$ cup of milk and drinks $\frac{1}{2}$ of it?

**11.** In the United States, the smallest baby born alive weighed $\frac{3}{4}$ pound. A baby born in England weighed $\frac{5}{8}$ pound at birth. How much more did the baby from the United States weigh?

**12.** The average human hair measures about $\frac{1}{500}$ inch in diameter. The diameter of the smallest tubing made in the world is $\frac{1}{4}$ of this measurement. What is the diameter of this tubing?

*EXTRA PRACTICE* page 488, set 48

---

## CHECKPOINT

Multiply. Reduce to lowest terms.

**1.** $\frac{1}{6} \times \frac{1}{6}$

**2.** $\frac{3}{5} \times \frac{1}{2}$

**3.** $\frac{2}{3} \times \frac{3}{8}$

**4.** $\frac{4}{5} \times \frac{5}{6}$

Copy and shade the diagrams to show the multiplication $\frac{3}{4} \times \frac{3}{5}$.

**5.** $\frac{3}{4} \times \frac{3}{5} =$ _____

 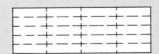

**6.** A recipe calls for $\frac{1}{2}$ teaspoon of salt. How much salt should you use to make $\frac{1}{2}$ of that amount?

165

Ann has a dowel $\frac{3}{4}$ yard long. She wants to cut it into pieces $\frac{1}{8}$ yard long for a coat rack she is making. How many pieces can she get from the $\frac{3}{4}$-yard length?

**Example 1:** How many $\frac{1}{8}$'s are in $\frac{3}{4}$?

The diagram shows that

$$\frac{3}{4} \div \frac{1}{8} = 6.$$

This gives the same answer as

$$\overset{2}{\underset{1}{\cancel{\frac{3}{4}}}} \times \frac{\cancel{8}}{1} = \frac{6}{1} = 6.$$

Ann can get 6 pieces from the dowel.

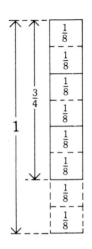

**Example 2:** Use a diagram to find $\frac{4}{5} \div \frac{2}{5}$.

$$\frac{4}{5} \div \frac{2}{5} = 2$$

This gives the same answer as

$$\overset{2}{\underset{1}{\cancel{\frac{4}{5}}}} \times \overset{1}{\underset{1}{\cancel{\frac{5}{2}}}} = \frac{2}{1} = 2.$$

Do you notice a pattern?

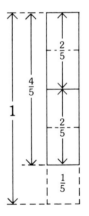

**Example 3:** Find $\frac{5}{6} \div \frac{1}{12}$.

$$\frac{5}{6} \div \frac{1}{12} = \frac{5}{\cancel{6}_{1}} \times \frac{\overset{2}{\cancel{12}}}{1}$$

$$= \frac{10}{1}$$

$$= 10$$

## EXERCISES

Which division is illustrated by the diagram?

**1.**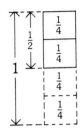

a. $\frac{1}{2} \div \frac{1}{4} = 2$    b. $\frac{1}{4} \div \frac{1}{2} = 2$

c. $\frac{1}{4} \div 2 = 2$    d. $4 \div 2 = 2$

**2.**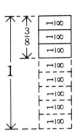

a. $\frac{1}{8} \div \frac{3}{8} = 3$    b. $\frac{3}{8} \div \frac{1}{8} = 3$

c. $1 \div \frac{3}{8} = 3$    d. $\frac{3}{8} \div 1 = 3$

**3.**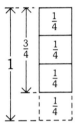

a. $\frac{1}{4} \div \frac{3}{4} = 3$    b. $1 \div \frac{3}{4} = 3$

c. $\frac{3}{4} \div 4 = 3$    d. $\frac{3}{4} \div \frac{1}{4} = 3$

**4.**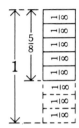

a. $\frac{5}{8} \div 1 = 5$    b. $1 \div \frac{5}{8} = 5$

c. $\frac{1}{8} \div \frac{5}{8} = 5$    d. $\frac{5}{8} \div \frac{1}{8} = 5$

What number should replace each ⬚?

**5.** $\frac{3}{4} \div \frac{1}{4} = \frac{3}{4} \times \frac{4}{⬚}$

**6.** $\frac{1}{2} \div \frac{3}{4} = \frac{1}{2} \times \frac{⬚}{3}$

**7.** $\frac{3}{10} \div \frac{1}{10} = \frac{3}{10} \times \frac{10}{⬚}$

**8.** $\frac{1}{3} \div \frac{1}{6} = \frac{1}{3} \times \frac{⬚}{1}$

**9.** $\frac{3}{4} \div \frac{3}{16} = \frac{3}{4} \times \frac{⬚}{3}$

**10.** $\frac{3}{4} \div \frac{9}{16} = \frac{3}{4} \times \frac{16}{⬚}$

**11.** $\frac{5}{6} \div \frac{1}{12} = \frac{5}{6} \times \frac{12}{⬚}$

**12.** $\frac{5}{6} \div \frac{5}{12} = \frac{5}{6} \times \frac{⬚}{5}$

**13.** $\frac{1}{3} \div \frac{2}{3} = \frac{1}{3} \times \frac{3}{⬚}$

**14.** $\frac{1}{4} \div \frac{1}{16} = \frac{1}{4} \times ⬚$

**15.** $\frac{3}{4} \div \frac{5}{16} = \frac{3}{4} \times ⬚$

**16.** $\frac{5}{8} \div \frac{1}{16} = \frac{5}{8} \times ⬚$

**17.** $\frac{2}{3} \div \frac{1}{6} = \frac{2}{3} \times ⬚$

**18.** $\frac{3}{5} \div \frac{3}{10} = \frac{3}{5} \times ⬚$

**19.** $\frac{4}{5} \div \frac{1}{10} = \frac{4}{5} \times ⬚$

## 6.6 RECIPROCALS

**How many tiles $\frac{1}{6}$ foot long can be placed end-to-end to fill in a space 1 foot long?**

$$\frac{1}{6} \quad \frac{2}{6} \quad \frac{3}{6} \quad \frac{4}{6} \quad \frac{5}{6} \quad \frac{6}{6}=1$$

6 tiles are needed.

$$6 \times \frac{1}{6} = \frac{\overset{1}{\cancel{6}}}{1} \times \frac{1}{\underset{1}{\cancel{6}}}$$

$$= \frac{1}{1}$$

$$= 1$$

If the product of two numbers is 1, the numbers are called **reciprocals**.

**Example 1:** Are $\frac{7}{10}$ and $\frac{10}{7}$ reciprocals?

$$\frac{\overset{1}{\cancel{7}}}{\underset{1}{\cancel{10}}} \times \frac{\overset{1}{\cancel{10}}}{\underset{1}{\cancel{7}}} = \frac{1}{1} = 1$$

Yes, $\frac{7}{10}$ and $\frac{10}{7}$ are reciprocals, since their product is 1.

Notice that the numerator of $\frac{7}{10}$ is the denominator of $\frac{10}{7}$, and vice versa. The first fraction can be inverted to obtain the second fraction.

**Example 2:** Find the reciprocal of $2\frac{3}{4}$.

First write $2\frac{3}{4}$ as an improper fraction.

$$2\frac{3}{4} = \frac{11}{4}$$

The reciprocal is $\frac{4}{11}$.

**168**

## EXERCISES

Are these two numbers reciprocals? Write *yes* or *no*.

**1.** $\frac{2}{3}, \frac{3}{2}$

**2.** $\frac{1}{4}, 4$

**3.** $\frac{1}{3}, \frac{3}{2}$

**4.** $\frac{2}{9}, \frac{9}{3}$

**5.** $\frac{3}{10}, \frac{10}{3}$

**6.** $\frac{1}{2}, 2$

**7.** $\frac{5}{12}, \frac{5}{12}$

**8.** $\frac{5}{12}, \frac{12}{7}$

**9.** $1\frac{1}{4}, \frac{4}{5}$

**10.** $\frac{2}{3}, 1\frac{1}{3}$

**11.** $2\frac{4}{5}, \frac{5}{12}$

**12.** $3\frac{1}{2}, \frac{2}{7}$

Find the reciprocal of each fraction.

**13.** $\frac{2}{3}$

**14.** $\frac{1}{2}$

**15.** $\frac{3}{8}$

**16.** $\frac{9}{10}$

**17.** $\frac{5}{8}$

**18.** $\frac{3}{4}$

**19.** $\frac{4}{5}$

**20.** $\frac{5}{12}$

**21.** $\frac{7}{12}$

**22.** $\frac{7}{8}$

**23.** $\frac{11}{12}$

**24.** $\frac{4}{9}$

Find the reciprocal of each mixed number.

**25.** $1\frac{1}{2}$

**26.** $2\frac{1}{4}$

**27.** $5\frac{1}{3}$

**28.** $3\frac{1}{5}$

**29.** $1\frac{1}{6}$

**30.** $8\frac{1}{8}$

**31.** $1\frac{2}{3}$

**32.** $4\frac{2}{5}$

**33.** $2\frac{5}{6}$

**34.** $2\frac{3}{8}$

**35.** $10\frac{5}{8}$

**36.** $1\frac{7}{8}$

## SKILLS REVIEW

Divide.

**37.** $7\overline{)42}$

**38.** $5\overline{)1520}$

**39.** $4\overline{)348}$

**40.** $36\overline{)432}$

**41.** $83\overline{)16932}$

**42.** $67\overline{)2814}$

**43.** $203\overline{)3045}$

**44.** $135\overline{)8505}$

**45.** $472\overline{)13688}$

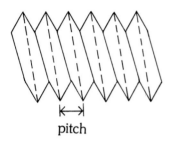

pitch

A machinist is to put threads on $\frac{3}{4}$ inch of a bolt. To find out how many threads will have to be cut, the machinist divides the length by the pitch. How many threads are needed for the $\frac{3}{4}$-inch length if the pitch is $\frac{1}{20}$ inch?

**Example 1:** Find $\frac{3}{4} \div \frac{1}{20}$.

$$\frac{3}{4} \div \frac{1}{20} = \frac{3}{\cancel{4}_1} \times \frac{\cancel{20}^5}{1} \longleftarrow \text{ the reciprocal of } \frac{1}{20}$$

$$= \frac{15}{1}$$

$$= 15$$

The machinist will need 15 threads.

**To divide with fractions, multiply the dividend by the reciprocal of the divisor.**

For example,

dividend   divisor

$$\overset{\downarrow}{\phantom{x}}\quad\overset{\downarrow}{\phantom{x}}$$

$$\underset{\uparrow}{\frac{3}{5}} \div \underset{\uparrow}{\frac{1}{2}} = \frac{3}{5} \times \underset{\uparrow}{\frac{2}{1}} \longleftarrow \text{ reciprocal of divisor}$$

division   multiplication

**Example 2:**   $\frac{2}{3} \div \frac{5}{12} = \frac{2}{\cancel{3}_1} \times \frac{\cancel{12}^4}{5}$

$$= \frac{8}{5}$$

$$= 1\frac{3}{5}$$

**Example 3:**   $\frac{1}{3} \div \frac{4}{5} = \frac{1}{3} \times \frac{5}{4}$

$$= \frac{5}{12}$$

# EXERCISES

Divide. Simplify.

1. $\frac{1}{2} \div \frac{3}{4}$

2. $\frac{1}{2} \div \frac{1}{4}$

3. $\frac{1}{4} \div \frac{1}{2}$

4. $\frac{1}{2} \div \frac{3}{5}$

5. $\frac{2}{3} \div \frac{1}{3}$

6. $\frac{1}{3} \div \frac{2}{3}$

7. $\frac{5}{8} \div \frac{3}{4}$

8. $\frac{1}{8} \div \frac{1}{2}$

9. $\frac{1}{2} \div \frac{1}{6}$

10. $\frac{1}{2} \div \frac{5}{6}$

11. $\frac{5}{12} \div \frac{3}{4}$

12. $\frac{3}{8} \div \frac{2}{3}$

13. $\frac{3}{4} \div \frac{1}{2}$

14. $\frac{4}{5} \div \frac{1}{3}$

15. $\frac{4}{5} \div \frac{1}{2}$

16. $\frac{1}{2} \div \frac{1}{5}$

17. $\frac{5}{8} \div \frac{1}{4}$

18. $\frac{3}{10} \div \frac{1}{5}$

19. $\frac{2}{3} \div \frac{3}{5}$

20. $\frac{5}{6} \div \frac{1}{2}$

21. $\frac{3}{4} \div \frac{5}{6}$

22. $\frac{7}{12} \div \frac{1}{4}$

23. $\frac{11}{12} \div \frac{2}{3}$

24. $\frac{5}{12} \div \frac{5}{8}$

In the next exercises, remember to do the operation indicated in the parentheses *first*.

**Example:** $\left(\frac{1}{3} \div \frac{1}{4}\right) \div \frac{5}{6} = \left(\frac{1}{3} \times \frac{4}{1}\right) \div \frac{5}{6}$

$$= \frac{4}{3} \div \frac{5}{6}$$

$$= \frac{4}{3} \times \frac{\overset{2}{\cancel{6}}}{5}$$

$$= \frac{8}{5} = 1\frac{3}{5}$$

25. $\left(\frac{1}{2} \div \frac{1}{4}\right) \div \frac{1}{8}$

26. $\left(\frac{3}{4} \div \frac{1}{2}\right) \div \frac{5}{8}$

27. $\left(\frac{1}{3} \div \frac{1}{6}\right) \div \frac{1}{2}$

EXTRA PRACTICE page 489, set 49

## SKILLS REVIEW

Divide.

28. $0.2\overline{)1.66}$

29. $2.4\overline{)4.08}$

30. $3.6\overline{)3.24}$

31. $5.2\overline{)0.364}$

32. $0.3\overline{)0.0126}$

33. $8.9\overline{)0.534}$

34. $3.3\overline{)13.53}$

35. $0.007\overline{)0.357}$

Mary Elenz Tranter

**Marge has a ribbon $\frac{3}{4}$ foot long. A "bow tie" for a doll's shirt requires $\frac{1}{12}$ foot of ribbon. How many "bow ties" can she make?**

**Read:**    *Given:*   has $\frac{3}{4}$ ft of ribbon;
                   each "bow tie" requires $\frac{1}{12}$ ft

          *To find:*   how many "bow ties"

**Plan:**   What operation can be used? You want to know how many equal lengths can be cut from the given length.

          So divide $\frac{3}{4}$ by $\frac{1}{12}$.

**Compute:**   $\dfrac{3}{4} \div \dfrac{1}{12} = \dfrac{3}{\overset{}{\underset{1}{4}}} \times \dfrac{\overset{3}{\cancel{12}}}{1}$

                 $= \dfrac{9}{1}$

                 $= 9$

**Answer:**   Marge can make 9 "bow ties."

**Check:** You can check by drawing a diagram.

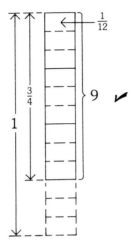

## EXERCISES

**1.** Weights for an ankle spat are $\frac{1}{4}$ pound each. Joyce is told to use $\frac{3}{4}$ pound on each ankle while exercising so that she can begin toning up her leg muscles. How many weights should she put on each ankle spat?

**2.** Weights for a wrist belt are $\frac{1}{5}$ pound each. How many weights should be added to the belt to increase the weight by $\frac{4}{5}$ pound?

**3.** How many strips of silver, each weighing $\frac{1}{16}$ pound, can be formed from a bar of silver weighing $\frac{3}{4}$ pound?

**4.** A stack of pennies measures $\frac{7}{16}$ inch high. If each penny is $\frac{1}{16}$ inch high, how many pennies are in the stack?

**5.** Before cooking, a hamburger weighs $\frac{1}{4}$ pound. How many hamburgers can be made from $\frac{3}{4}$ pound of meat?

**6.** A picture of an insect is $\frac{3}{4}$ inch long. The insect is really $\frac{1}{3}$ as long as that. How long is the insect?

**7.** Mark brought $\frac{3}{4}$ gallon of apple cider to work. How many people can share the cider if each receives $\frac{1}{16}$ gallon?

**8.** A farmer has $\frac{7}{8}$ acre he wants to turn into pens. If each pen is to be $\frac{1}{16}$ acre, how many pens can he make?

**9.** A recipe for 6 servings calls for $\frac{3}{4}$ cup of blueberries. How much should you use if you want to make $\frac{2}{3}$ of the recipe amount?

**10.** Lynn had $\frac{3}{8}$ yard of material. She used $\frac{2}{3}$ of it in making a pillow kit. What length did she use?

The fastest growth rate ever recorded for a tree was recorded in Malaysia. The tree grew about $2\frac{1}{8}$ feet per month. How much did it grow in the first 5 months?

**Example 1:** Multiply $2\frac{1}{8} \times 5$.

$$2\frac{1}{8} \times 5 = \frac{17}{8} \times \frac{5}{1}$$ Change each number to an improper fraction.

$$= \frac{85}{8}$$ Change the fraction to a mixed number.

$$= 10\frac{5}{8}$$

The tree grew about $10\frac{5}{8}$ feet in the first 5 months.

**Example 2:** $2\frac{1}{4} \times 1\frac{1}{2} = \frac{9}{4} \times \frac{3}{2}$

$$= \frac{27}{8}$$

$$= 3\frac{3}{8}$$

**Example 3:** $6\frac{3}{4} \times 2\frac{2}{3} = \frac{\overset{9}{\cancel{27}}}{\underset{1}{\cancel{4}}} \times \frac{\overset{2}{\cancel{8}}}{\underset{1}{\cancel{3}}}$

$$= \frac{18}{1}$$

$$= 18$$

## EXERCISES

What number should replace each ⸮?

**1.** $1\frac{2}{5} \times 3\frac{7}{8} = \frac{⸮}{5} \times \frac{31}{8}$

**2.** $2\frac{1}{2} \times 5\frac{1}{4} = \frac{5}{⸮} \times \frac{21}{4}$

**3.** $6\frac{1}{3} \times 1\frac{1}{4} = \frac{19}{3} \times \frac{⸮}{4}$

**4.** $2\frac{1}{4} \times 3\frac{1}{6} = \frac{9}{4} \times \frac{19}{⸮}$

**5.** $4\frac{1}{6} \times 3\frac{1}{10} = \frac{⸮}{6} \times \frac{31}{10}$

**6.** $2\frac{5}{12} \times 1\frac{1}{2} = \frac{29}{12} \times \frac{⸮}{2}$

Multiply. Simplify each answer.

**7.** $4\frac{1}{2} \times 6$

**8.** $8\frac{1}{3} \times 2\frac{2}{5}$

**9.** $3\frac{1}{4} \times 2$

**10.** $6\frac{2}{3} \times \frac{1}{2}$

**11.** $3\frac{1}{5} \times 1\frac{1}{2}$

**12.** $4 \times 3\frac{1}{8}$

**13.** $1\frac{3}{10} \times 2\frac{1}{2}$

**14.** $\frac{3}{4} \times 8$

**15.** $5\frac{3}{4} \times 1\frac{1}{3}$

**16.** $3\frac{3}{8} \times 2\frac{2}{3}$

**17.** $4\frac{1}{2} \times 3\frac{1}{3}$

**18.** $1\frac{4}{5} \times 5$

**19.** $2\frac{2}{3} \times 1\frac{7}{8}$

**20.** $5\frac{5}{8} \times 2\frac{2}{3}$

**21.** $1\frac{1}{4} \times 2\frac{2}{3}$

**22.** $7\frac{1}{2} \times \frac{3}{5}$

**23.** $2 \times 7\frac{1}{4}$

**24.** $1\frac{1}{3} \times 3\frac{1}{6}$

**25.** $3\frac{1}{2} \times \frac{3}{8}$

**26.** $3\frac{5}{6} \times 1\frac{1}{8}$

**27.** $4\frac{3}{4} \times 1\frac{1}{2}$

**28.** $6\frac{7}{8} \times 2\frac{1}{5}$

**29.** $2\frac{7}{8} \times 1\frac{1}{3}$

**30.** $3\frac{5}{6} \times 2\frac{1}{4}$

**31.** $1\frac{3}{4} \times 2\frac{1}{2}$

**32.** $3\frac{5}{12} \times 1\frac{1}{5}$

**33.** $2 \times 3\frac{11}{12}$

**34.** $2\frac{7}{10} \times 4\frac{2}{3}$

**35.** $3\frac{1}{6} \times 4$

**36.** $\frac{2}{3} \times 4\frac{1}{6}$

**37.** $3\frac{5}{12} \times 2\frac{2}{5}$

**38.** $3\frac{3}{4} \times 2\frac{4}{5}$

**39.** $5\frac{7}{10} \times 1\frac{2}{3}$

**40.** $5 \times 6\frac{9}{10}$

**41.** $2\frac{1}{5} \times 1\frac{1}{5}$

**42.** $\frac{4}{5} \times 5\frac{2}{3}$

**43.** $3\frac{5}{6} \times 2\frac{2}{3}$

**44.** $8\frac{1}{2} \times 1\frac{3}{5}$

**45.** $2\frac{1}{5} \times 3\frac{1}{8}$

**46.** $1\frac{5}{16} \times 2\frac{2}{3}$

**47.** $2\frac{3}{16} \times 1\frac{3}{5}$

**48.** $6\frac{2}{5} \times 1\frac{9}{16}$

*EXTRA PRACTICE page 489, set 50*

---

## MATH NOTE

A piano piece ("Vexations") was once written that would take $1\frac{1}{3}$ minutes to play through once. But the composer wanted the piece played 841 times! How many minutes would be required to play this piano piece that many times? About how many hours is this?

William Rivelli/Photo Trends

**How many drapery panels can be cut from 36 yards of material if each panel is to be $2\frac{1}{4}$ yards long?**

**Example 1:**  Divide 36 by $2\frac{1}{4}$.

$$36 \div 2\frac{1}{4} = \frac{36}{1} \div \frac{9}{4}$$ Change each number to an improper fraction.

$$= \frac{\overset{4}{\cancel{36}}}{1} \times \frac{4}{\cancel{9}_{1}}$$

$$= \frac{16}{1}$$

$$= 16$$

16 panels can be cut from the material.

**Example 2:**  $$1\frac{1}{5} \div \frac{9}{10} = \frac{6}{5} \div \frac{9}{10}$$

$$= \frac{\overset{2}{\cancel{6}}}{\underset{1}{5}} \times \frac{\overset{2}{\cancel{10}}}{\underset{3}{\cancel{9}}}$$

$$= \frac{4}{3} = 1\frac{1}{3}$$

**Example 3:**  $$6\frac{4}{5} \div 7\frac{1}{5} = \frac{34}{5} \div \frac{36}{5}$$

$$= \frac{\overset{17}{\cancel{34}}}{5} \times \frac{\overset{1}{\cancel{5}}}{\underset{18}{\cancel{36}}}$$

$$= \frac{17}{18}$$

# EXERCISES

What number should replace each ?

**1.** $5\frac{1}{4} \div 6 = \frac{21}{4} \div \frac{6}{1} = \frac{21}{4} \times \boxed{?}$

**2.** $1\frac{1}{2} \div 2\frac{1}{4} = \frac{3}{2} \div \frac{9}{4} = \frac{3}{2} \times \boxed{?}$

**3.** $3\frac{3}{4} \div 1\frac{2}{3} = \frac{15}{4} \div \frac{5}{3} = \boxed{?} \times \frac{3}{5}$

**4.** $2\frac{1}{4} \div 1\frac{1}{2} = \frac{9}{4} \div \frac{3}{2} = \boxed{?} \times \frac{2}{3}$

Divide. Simplify each answer.

**5.** $1\frac{1}{2} \div 1\frac{1}{4}$

**6.** $3\frac{3}{8} \div 1\frac{1}{2}$

**7.** $1\frac{1}{3} \div 2\frac{2}{3}$

**8.** $6 \div \frac{3}{8}$

**9.** $4\frac{1}{2} \div 2$

**10.** $3\frac{3}{10} \div 1\frac{1}{2}$

**11.** $8\frac{1}{3} \div \frac{5}{12}$

**12.** $2\frac{1}{6} \div 3\frac{5}{6}$

**13.** $4\frac{1}{2} \div 1\frac{1}{2}$

**14.** $3\frac{4}{5} \div 5$

**15.** $1\frac{7}{8} \div 1\frac{7}{8}$

**16.** $4\frac{2}{3} \div 3\frac{1}{2}$

**17.** $6 \div 1\frac{1}{2}$

**18.** $2\frac{1}{4} \div 5$

**19.** $2\frac{2}{5} \div 2\frac{1}{4}$

**20.** $4\frac{1}{8} \div \frac{3}{4}$

**21.** $1\frac{1}{2} \div 3\frac{1}{10}$

**22.** $1\frac{7}{8} \div 1\frac{2}{3}$

**23.** $6\frac{1}{2} \div 8$

**24.** $10 \div 2\frac{1}{2}$

**25.** $1\frac{1}{6} \div 2$

**26.** $2\frac{1}{3} \div \frac{5}{12}$

**27.** $1\frac{1}{2} \div 3\frac{3}{8}$

**28.** $2\frac{3}{8} \div 5\frac{1}{4}$

**29.** $2\frac{5}{12} \div 3\frac{1}{2}$

**30.** $3\frac{5}{12} \div 1\frac{2}{3}$

**31.** $5\frac{7}{8} \div 1\frac{1}{2}$

**32.** $2\frac{1}{5} \div 1\frac{3}{4}$

**33.** $3\frac{7}{8} \div 2$

**34.** $1\frac{1}{2} \div 3\frac{1}{5}$

**35.** $14\frac{1}{3} \div 3$

**36.** $5\frac{3}{4} \div 2\frac{1}{2}$

**37.** $6\frac{2}{3} \div 3\frac{1}{8}$

**38.** $2\frac{1}{2} \div 3\frac{1}{4}$

**39.** $6\frac{3}{8} \div 2\frac{1}{4}$

**40.** $3\frac{1}{6} \div 2$

**41.** $2\frac{1}{3} \div 1\frac{11}{12}$

**42.** $3\frac{4}{5} \div 5\frac{1}{10}$

**43.** $2\frac{3}{10} \div 1\frac{1}{2}$

**44.** $3\frac{1}{8} \div 2\frac{5}{8}$

**45.** $7\frac{2}{5} \div 4$

**46.** $3\frac{3}{10} \div 4\frac{5}{8}$

**47.** $6\frac{1}{12} \div 2\frac{1}{4}$

**48.** $3\frac{5}{6} \div 2\frac{1}{12}$

**49.** $10\frac{1}{4} \div 1\frac{7}{8}$

Solve.

**50.** Wood strips are $3\frac{3}{8}$ inches wide. How many would you need to fill in a wall space $175\frac{1}{2}$ inches wide?

EXTRA PRACTICE page 489, set 51

Stephen Feld

**Luke wants to line his cabinet shelves with shelf paper. He has a total length of $23\frac{1}{3}$ feet of shelf space, 24 inches deep. A role of shelf paper is 24 inches wide and 6 feet long. How many rolls should he buy?**

**Read:**   *Given:*  $23\frac{1}{3}$ ft to line;

                     6 ft per roll

          *To find:*  how many rolls are needed

**Plan:**  What operation can be used? You need to know how many equal amounts are in a given amount, so divide $23\frac{1}{3}$ by 6.

**Compute:**  $23\dfrac{1}{3} \div 6 = \dfrac{70}{3} \div \dfrac{6}{1}$

$$= \dfrac{\overset{35}{\cancel{70}}}{3} \times \dfrac{1}{\underset{3}{\cancel{6}}}$$

$$= \dfrac{35}{9}$$

$$= 3\dfrac{8}{9}$$

**Answer:**  Since Luke can't buy $3\frac{8}{9}$ rolls, he must buy 4 rolls of shelf paper.

**Check:** $4 \times 6 = 24$

$24 > 23\frac{1}{3}$

He will have enough. ✔

Sometimes the answer you want will be the number resulting from the computation. Sometimes it will be the next smaller or the next larger whole number.

## EXERCISES

1. A vest requires $7\frac{1}{2}$ yards of trim. How many packages of trim are needed if each package contains 3 yards?

2. A recipe calls for $2\frac{1}{2}$ cups of grated zucchini. Jan finds she has enough eggs to make $\frac{3}{4}$ of the recipe amount. How much zucchini should she use?

3. Julie works $3\frac{1}{2}$ hours after school 3 nights a week. How many hours does she work during one week?

4. A board is 18 feet long and 4 inches wide. How many boards 4 inches wide and $2\frac{1}{2}$ feet long can be cut from it?

5. How many cans of soup must you open to serve 6 people if each can makes $2\frac{1}{2}$ servings?

6. A quilt pattern calls for 5 different prints of material. If $1\frac{3}{4}$ yards of each print are needed, what is the total yardage needed for the quilt?

7. A coal distributor purchased 20 tons of coal. How many trips must he make to transfer the coal to his storage site if his truck can carry $1\frac{1}{4}$ tons each trip?

8. A recipe calls for $2\frac{1}{3}$ cups of flour. How much flour should Melissa use if she wants to make $2\frac{1}{2}$ times as much?

9. A perfume bottle holds $3\frac{1}{2}$ fluid ounces. How many bottles can be filled from a batch containing 100 fluid ounces?

10. A bread recipe calls for $5\frac{1}{2}$ cups of flour. Later you must use another $\frac{1}{3}$ cup of flour. How much flour do you use in all?

11. Kevin is buying a stock costing $18\frac{1}{8}$ dollars per share. What will 20 shares of the stock cost him?

12. How many strips of material $4\frac{1}{2}$ inches long can be cut from a length of material measuring 96 inches?

*EXTRA PRACTICE page 490, set 52*

**EQUIVALENT NONMETRIC MEASUREMENTS**

Debbie Dean

Recall the table of nonmetric equivalents from Chapter 5.

| Measure | Equivalents |
|---|---|
| Length | 1 ft = 12 in. |
| | 1 yd = 3 ft |
| | 1 mi = 5280 ft |
| Weight | 1 lb = 16 oz |
| | 1 ton = 2000 lb |
| Capacity (liquid) | 1 pt = 2 c |
| | 1 qt = 2 pt |
| | 1 gal = 4 qt |

A thermos bottle holds 4 pints of liquid. How many quarts does it hold?

**Example 1:**   4 pt = ? qt
1 qt = 2 pt, so divide 4 by 2.
4 pt = 2 qt

The thermos holds 2 quarts.

**Example 2:**   2 gal = ? pt
Convert to quarts.
1 gal = 4 qt, so multiply 2 by 4.
2 gal = 8 qt
Convert to pints.
1 qt = 2 pt, so multiply 8 by 2.
8 qt = 16 pt

Debra is 5 feet 3 inches tall. A question on the form at the doctor's office asks for her height in inches.

**Example 3:**   5 ft 3 in. = ? in.
1 ft = 12 in., so multiply 5 by 12.
5 ft = 60 in.

$$\begin{array}{r} 60 \\ +\ 3 \\ \hline 63 \end{array}$$

Debra is 63 inches tall.

**180**

## EXERCISES

Complete.

1. 36 in. = ___ ft

2. $\frac{1}{4}$ lb = ___ oz

3. 5 pt = ___ qt

4. 80 oz = ___ lb

5. 6 qt = ___ pt

6. 9 ft = ___ yd

7. 5 qt = ___ gal

8. 2 lb = ___ oz

9. 4 yd = ___ ft

10. 3 mi = ___ ft

11. 14 c = ___ pt

12. 1000 lb = ___ ton

13. 21 ft = ___ yd

14. 8 oz = ___ lb

15. 4000 lb = ___ tons

16. 3 ft = ___ in.

17. 6 yd = ___ ft

18. 72 in. = ___ yd

19. 22.4 oz = ___ lb

20. 10 pt = ___ gal

21. 10 in. = ___ ft

22. $3\frac{1}{2}$ lb = ___ oz

23. $2\frac{1}{2}$ pt = ___ c

24. 50 qt = ___ gal

25. 24 in. = ___ yd

26. $2\frac{1}{2}$ yd = ___ in.

27. 48 oz = ___ lb

28. 3 qt = ___ c

29. 2.5 tons = ___ lb

30. 6 in. = ___ ft

31. $\frac{1}{4}$ qt = ___ c

32. 3 c = ___ qt

33. 5 ft = ___ yd

34. 5 c = ___ gal

35. 32 qt = ___ c

36. 2640 ft = ___ mi

37. $\frac{1}{2}$ ton = ___ oz

38. 1.5 mi = ___ ft

39. 8000 oz = ___ ton

40. 4 yd 1 ft = ___ ft

41. 3 gal 3 qt = ___ qt

Solve.

42. A roast weighs 4 pounds 3 ounces. How many ounces is this?

EXTRA PRACTICE page 490, set 53

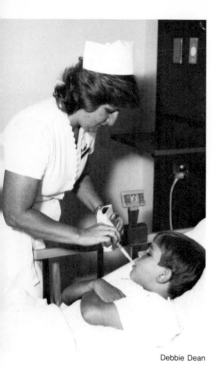

Debbie Dean

A registered nurse performs many services for people who are ill. A nurse's duties include routine care of patients, supervising meals and exercise, and observing the general condition of each patient.

One important duty a nurse must perform is to give just the right amount of medicine to a patient.

For an infant under 1 year old, a nurse uses this formula:

Infant's dose = (Age of infant in months ÷ 150) × Adult dose, where the 150 stands for 150 months, or $12\frac{1}{2}$ years.

**1.** If an adult's dose is $\frac{1}{20}$ grain (a grain is the weight of one drop of water), what is the dose for a 10-month-old child?

Another formula a nurse often uses is

| Number of tablets | × | Medication per tablet | = | Total medication. |

**2.** A nurse gives Mr. Keller $\frac{1}{3}$ of a $\frac{1}{4}$-grain tablet. How much of the drug did he receive?

**3.** A tablet contains $7\frac{1}{2}$ grains of medicine. Mrs. Richards is to receive $\frac{3}{4}$ of the tablet. How much medicine will she receive?

To figure out how many tablets are needed for dosage, a nurse uses the formula

| Total medication | ÷ | Medication per tablet | = | Number of tablets. |

**4.** A nurse is to give a patient $\frac{1}{10}$ grain of medicine from $\frac{1}{30}$-grain tablets. How many tablets should the nurse use?

**5.** Billy is to receive $\frac{3}{4}$ grain of medicine from a tablet of $1\frac{1}{2}$ grains. What part of a tablet should the nurse give him?

Choose the best answer.

Words to choose from: *fraction, reciprocal, numerators, multiply, denominators, divide*

**1.** To find $\frac{3}{8}$ of $\frac{4}{5}$ means to _____ $\frac{3}{8}$ and $\frac{4}{5}$.                    6.1

**2.** In the multiplication $\frac{3}{5} \times \frac{3}{4} = \frac{9}{20}$, the 9 is found by multiplying the _____;    6.2
the 20 is found by multiplying the _____.

**3.** To find $\frac{1}{2} \div \frac{3}{8}$, you would multiply $\frac{1}{2}$ by the _____ of $\frac{3}{8}$.    6.7

**4.** To multiply or divide by a mixed number, you can first write it as a _____.    6.9,
6.10

Use the diagrams to answer the multiplication exercises.                    6.1

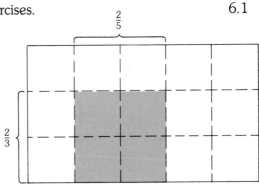

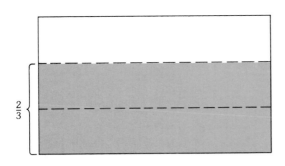

**5.** $\frac{2}{5} \times \frac{2}{3} =$ ___

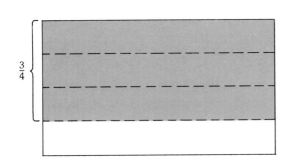

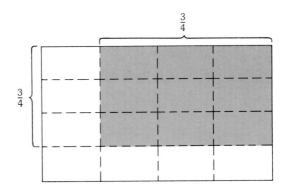

**6.** $\frac{3}{4} \times \frac{3}{4} =$ ___

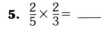

**183**

Copy and shade the diagrams to show the multiplication exercises.

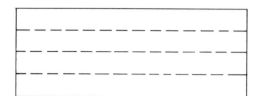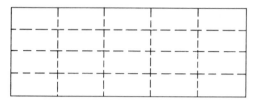

**7.** $\frac{3}{5} \times \frac{3}{4} =$ _____

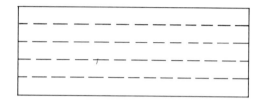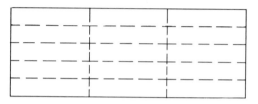

**8.** $\frac{2}{3} \times \frac{4}{5} =$ _____

Multiply. Simplify each answer.

**9.** $\frac{3}{8} \times \frac{1}{2}$     **10.** $\frac{3}{4} \times \frac{1}{4}$     **11.** $\frac{3}{5} \times \frac{1}{4}$     **12.** $\frac{1}{2} \times \frac{3}{5}$     6.2

**13.** $\frac{5}{12} \times \frac{3}{4}$     **14.** $\frac{3}{8} \times \frac{2}{3}$     **15.** $\frac{5}{8} \times \frac{3}{10}$     **16.** $\frac{2}{3} \times \frac{1}{2}$     6.3

**17.** $3\frac{3}{4} \times 2\frac{4}{5}$     **18.** $6\frac{7}{8} \times \frac{1}{2}$     **19.** $3 \times 4\frac{3}{5}$     **20.** $4 \times 2\frac{1}{3}$     6.9

**21.** $5\frac{1}{2} \times 1\frac{2}{3}$     **22.** $\frac{3}{4} \times 4\frac{1}{2}$     **23.** $2 \times 6\frac{1}{3}$     **24.** $3 \times \frac{4}{5}$

What division exercise is illustrated by each diagram?     6.5

**25.** 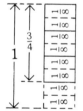       **26.**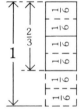

a. $\frac{1}{8} \div \frac{3}{4} = 6$    b. $\frac{3}{4} \div \frac{1}{8} = 6$      a. $\frac{2}{3} \div 1 = 4$    b. $\frac{1}{6} \div 1 = 4$

c. $1 \div \frac{3}{4} = 6$    d. $1 \div \frac{1}{8} = 6$      c. $\frac{1}{6} \div \frac{2}{3} = 4$    d. $\frac{2}{3} \div \frac{1}{6} = 4$

**184**

Find the reciprocal of each number.

6.6

**27.** $\frac{3}{8}$

**28.** $\frac{4}{5}$

**29.** $3\frac{5}{8}$

**30.** $1\frac{2}{3}$

Rewrite the division exercise as a multiplication exercise.

6.5

**31.** $\frac{3}{5} \div \frac{3}{8}$

**32.** $\frac{5}{8} \div \frac{1}{16}$

**33.** $\frac{3}{5} \div 1\frac{1}{2}$

Divide. Simplify each answer.

**34.** $\frac{3}{4} \div \frac{1}{2}$

**35.** $\frac{1}{6} \div \frac{1}{3}$

**36.** $\frac{2}{5} \div \frac{1}{4}$

**37.** $\frac{3}{4} \div \frac{5}{8}$

6.7

**38.** $3\frac{3}{16} \div \frac{1}{4}$

**39.** $1\frac{3}{4} \div 2\frac{1}{2}$

**40.** $3\frac{1}{4} \div 2\frac{1}{8}$

**41.** $1\frac{3}{8} \div 1\frac{5}{8}$

6.10

**42.** $4\frac{1}{5} \div 1\frac{2}{3}$

**43.** $3\frac{5}{8} \div 1\frac{1}{2}$

**44.** $2\frac{1}{4} \div 1\frac{1}{2}$

**45.** $4\frac{1}{3} \div 5\frac{2}{3}$

Complete.

6.12

**46.** 4 yd = ___ in.

**47.** $\frac{3}{4}$ gal = ___ pt

**48.** 63 c = ___ qt

**49.** 5 tons = ___ lb

**50.** $3\frac{1}{2}$ qt = ___ c

**51.** 66 in. = ___ yd

**52.** $5\frac{1}{2}$ yd = ___ ft

**53.** 85 oz = ___ lb

**54.** 48 in. = ___ yd

**55.** 8 lb 3 oz = ___ oz

**56.** 3 qt 1 c = ___ c

Solve.

**57.** A recipe calls for $\frac{2}{3}$ cup of chopped nuts. How much would you need for $\frac{1}{2}$ of the recipe amount?

6.4

**58.** How many threads will be needed for a $\frac{1}{2}$-inch length of a bolt if the pitch is $\frac{1}{20}$ inch? (Divide the length by the pitch.)

6.8

**59.** Spinach plants must grow 6 weeks before they can be harvested. Onion sets must grow $2\frac{1}{3}$ times as long. After how many weeks can onions be harvested?

6.11

**60.** A recipe for eggnog yields 6 cups. How many quarts is this?

6.12

Copy and shade the diagrams to show the multiplication exercise $\frac{3}{5} \times \frac{3}{4}$.

**1.** $\frac{3}{5} \times \frac{3}{4} =$ ___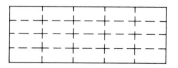

Multiply. Simplify each answer.

**2.** $\frac{7}{8} \times \frac{3}{4}$  **3.** $\frac{3}{8} \times \frac{4}{5}$  **4.** $\frac{2}{5} \times \frac{1}{2}$  **5.** $\frac{3}{4} \times \frac{5}{6}$  **6.** $1\frac{2}{3} \times 3\frac{5}{8}$

Find the reciprocal of each number.

**7.** $\frac{7}{8}$  **8.** $3\frac{1}{2}$

Rewrite the division exercise as a multiplication exercise.

**9.** $\frac{3}{8} \div \frac{4}{5}$  **10.** $6\frac{1}{4} \div 8\frac{2}{5}$

Divide. Simplify each answer.

**11.** $\frac{3}{4} \div \frac{4}{5}$  **12.** $\frac{1}{6} \div \frac{2}{5}$  **13.** $\frac{5}{8} \div \frac{15}{16}$  **14.** $6\frac{1}{3} \div 2$  **15.** $4 \div 1\frac{1}{4}$

Complete.

**16.** 16 pt = ___ gal  **17.** $\frac{1}{10}$ ton = ___ oz

**18.** $\frac{3}{4}$ yd = ___ in.  **19.** 3 c = ___ qt

**20.** 108 in. = ___ yd  **21.** 2 ft 9 in. = ___ in.

Solve.

**22.** A recipe for rice pudding calls for $\frac{1}{2}$ cup of raisins. How much would $2\frac{1}{2}$ times the recipe amount be?

**23.** A pitcher holds 8 cups of juice. How many servings of $\frac{3}{4}$ cup is this?

Write a symbol for each figure.

**1.** • A

**2.**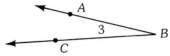

**3.** N    M

**4.** G    F

**5.**

Write four names for the angle shown above.

**6.**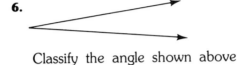

Classify the angle shown above as acute, right, or obtuse.

**7.**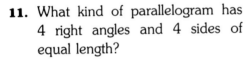

Are the lines shown above parallel, perpendicular, or neither?

**8.**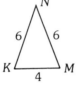

Classify the polygon shown above according to the number of sides.

Choose the correct answer.

**9.** △KMN is (right, acute, obtuse).

**10.** △KMN is (equilateral, isosceles, scalene).

**11.** What kind of parallelogram has 4 right angles and 4 sides of equal length?

Use the circle to name the following:

**12.** a diameter    **13.** a radius

**14.** a chord that is not a diameter

Complete. △ABC ≅ △DEF.

**15.** $\overline{BA} \cong$ ____    **16.** $\overline{CB} \cong$ ____

**17.** $\overline{AC} \cong$ ____

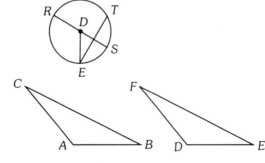

**18.**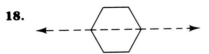

Is the dashed line a line of symmetry?

**19.**

5 ft

Joe built a garden shaped like a regular pentagon. If one side was 5 feet long, what was the distance around the garden?

| *POINTS, LINES, AND PLANES*

William L. Widmayer

From the size, the shape, the position, and other features of the objects around us, we have developed ideas called **geometric figures.** The period at the end of this sentence is a model of a **point.** The painted stripe down the middle of a straight road is a model of a **line.** The flat roof of a building is a model of a **plane.**

| Name | Description | We draw: | We say: | We write: |
|---|---|---|---|---|
| **point** | has no size, is only a position | •P | point P | P |
| **line** | has no width or thickness and extends without end in opposite directions | A  B | line AB or line BA | $\overleftrightarrow{AB}$ or $\overleftrightarrow{BA}$ |
| **plane** | is a flat surface that has no thickness and extends without end on all sides | n | plane n | plane n |
| **ray** | has one endpoint, extends without end in one direction | C  D | ray CD (name endpoint first) | $\overrightarrow{CD}$ |
| **segment** | has two endpoints | E  F | segment EF or segment FE | $\overline{EF}$ or $\overline{FE}$ |

If two lines meet at a point, they are called **intersecting lines.** $\overleftrightarrow{AB}$ intersects $\overleftrightarrow{CD}$ at point E.

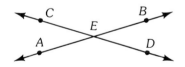

## EXERCISES

Match the following:

1. point          a. extends without end in one direction

2. line           b. has two endpoints

3. plane          c. has no width or thickness and extends without end in opposite directions

4. ray            d. only shows a position

5. segment        e. is a flat surface that has no thickness and extends without end on all sides

Using the diagram, name an example of each figure.

6. a point

7. a segment

8. a plane

9. a ray

10. a line

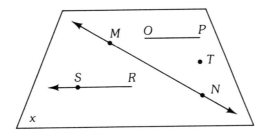

Draw and label each figure.

11. $\overrightarrow{MN}$        12. point $D$          13. plane $y$

14. $\overleftrightarrow{ST}$        15. $\overline{CD}$          16. $\overrightarrow{AB}$

17. plane $z$          18. $\overline{EF}$          19. $\overline{PQ}$

20. $\overrightarrow{GH}$        21. plane $e$          22. $\overleftrightarrow{XY}$

Draw an example of the following:

23. a line with 3 points on the line labeled

24. a plane with 4 points in the plane labeled

25. 3 lines intersecting at the same point

26. a plane with a line drawn in the plane

27. a ray with 2 points on the ray labeled

28. a plane with a line segment drawn in the plane

# ANGLES AND DEGREE MEASURE

Frank Siteman/Taurus

When a spider spins its web, many different angles are formed.

An **angle** is formed by two rays with a common endpoint. The common endpoint is called the **vertex** of the angle. The rays are called the **sides** of the angle.

| We say: | We write: |
|---------|-----------|
| angle $CBA$ | $\angle CBA$ |
| angle $ABC$ | $\angle ABC$ |
| angle 1 | $\angle 1$ |
| angle $B$ | $\angle B$ |

Notice that the angle above is named in four ways. An angle can be named by a number or, if there is no chance of confusion, by the vertex letter. Otherwise, three points are used to name the angle, with the vertex letter as the middle letter.

A **protractor** is used to measure an angle in **degrees.**

**Example:** Use a protractor to find the measure of $\angle RST$.

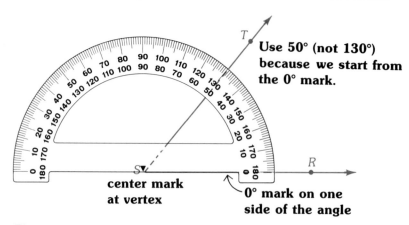

Use 50° (not 130°) because we start from the 0° mark.

center mark
at vertex

0° mark on one
side of the angle

The measure of $\angle RST$ is 50 degrees. This can be written $m\angle RST = 50°$.

# EXERCISES

Give four names for each angle. Use the symbol ∠ in each name.

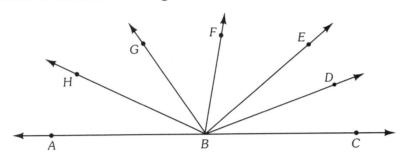

**1.** A, B, 3, C

**2.** X, 5, Y, Z

**3.** D, 7, E, F

**4.** M, 2, N, O

Use a protractor to measure each angle named below.

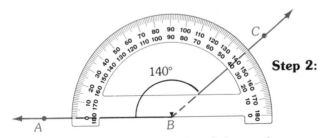

F, G, E, H, D, A, B, C

**5.** ∠CBD     **6.** ∠FBC     **7.** ∠HBC     **8.** ∠ABG     **9.** ∠CBE

**10.** ∠GBF     **11.** ∠DBE     **12.** ∠CBA     **13.** ∠GBC     **14.** ∠ABH

**15.** ∠ABF     **16.** ∠GBE     **17.** ∠ABC     **18.** ∠EBC     **19.** ∠FBE

You can use a protractor to *draw* angles with given measures.

**Example:** Draw ∠ABC with a measure of 140°. (m∠ABC = 140°)

140°

**Step 2:** Use this 140° mark because we start from the 0° mark. Draw the other side.

**Step 1:** Draw one side of the angle. Put the center mark at the vertex.

Using a protractor, draw each angle. Then label the angle with three letters and its measure, as above.

**20.** m∠RST = 75°     **21.** m∠DEF = 35°     **22.** m∠KLM = 90°

**23.** m∠UVW = 125°     **24.** m∠NOP = 140°     **25.** m∠XYZ = 46°

EXTRA PRACTICE page 490, set 54

Joseph A. Di Chello, Jr.

Angles are classified according to their degree measure.

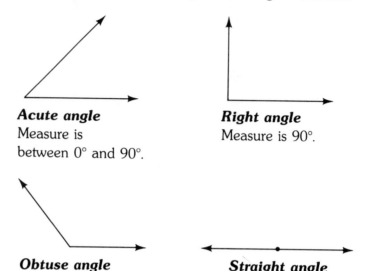

**Acute angle**
Measure is
between 0° and 90°.

**Right angle**
Measure is 90°.

**Obtuse angle**
Measure is
between 90° and 180°.

**Straight angle**
Measure is 180°.

**Example:** Copy and complete each statement. Then classify the angle as acute, right, obtuse, or straight.

**1.** $m\angle RNP = $ ____

**2.** $m\angle RNW = $ ____

**3.** $m\angle RNT = $ ____

**4.** $m\angle RNM = $ ____

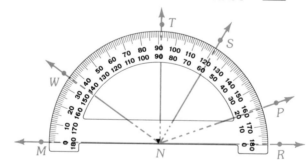

*Solutions:*

**1.** $m\angle RNP = 20°$, acute

**2.** $m\angle RNW = 145°$, obtuse

**3.** $m\angle RNT = 90°$, right

**4.** $m\angle RNM = 180°$, straight

# EXERCISES

Copy and complete each statement. Then classify the angle as acute, obtuse, right, or straight.

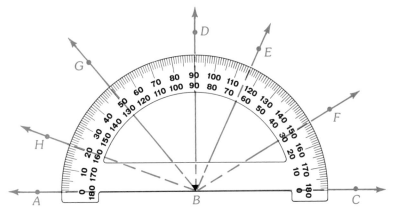

**1.** m∠ABD = ____  **2.** m∠CBF = ____  **3.** m∠GBC = ____  **4.** m∠ABC = ____

**5.** m∠CBD = ____  **6.** m∠EBC = ____  **7.** m∠HBC = ____  **8.** m∠ABH = ____

**9.** m∠ABG = ____  **10.** m∠EBA = ____  **11.** m∠ABF = ____  **12.** m∠CBA = ____

Using a protractor, measure each angle. Then classify the angle as acute, right, obtuse, or straight.

**13.**

**14.**

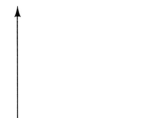

**15.**

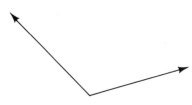

**16.**

**17.**

**18.**

*EXTRA PRACTICE page 491, set 55*

# PARALLEL AND PERPENDICULAR LINES

Mary Elenz Tranter

The directions for hanging a suspended ceiling state that the intersecting supports must be perpendicular to each other. So Cecilia made the intersecting supports form a 90° angle.

**Perpendicular** lines intersect to form right angles.

**Example 1:**

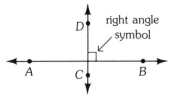

Line *AB* is perpendicular to line *CD* because the two lines form 90° angles. We write: $\overleftrightarrow{AB} \perp \overleftrightarrow{CD}$.

Jack Corn/Corn's Photo Service

In the picture, the railroad tracks seem to meet in the distance. But you know that the tracks actually never meet. Railroad tracks are really an example of parallel lines. **Parallel** lines are lines in the same plane that do not intersect.

**Example 2:**

Line *AB* is parallel to line *CD* because they never meet even if extended without end. We write: $\overleftrightarrow{AB} \parallel \overleftrightarrow{CD}$.

## EXERCISES

Complete the following:

**1.** The symbol for "is perpendicular to" is _____.

**2.** The symbol for "is parallel to" is _____.

**3.** Perpendicular lines intersect to form _____ angles.

**4.** Lines in the same plane that do not intersect are called _____ lines.

**5.** Which of the following are perpendicular?

a.
b.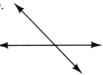
c.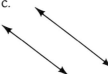
d.

**6.** Which of the following are parallel?

a.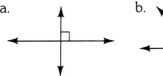
b.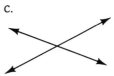
c.
d.

Use the diagram.

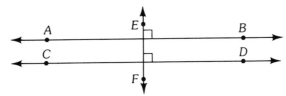

**7.** Name a line perpendicular to $\overleftrightarrow{AB}$.

**8.** Name a line parallel to $\overleftrightarrow{AB}$.

**9.** $\overleftrightarrow{CD} \perp$ _____

**10.** $\overleftrightarrow{CD} \parallel$ _____

EXTRA PRACTICE page 491, set 56

*SKILLS REVIEW*

Change to fractions.

**11.** $3 \div 5$

**12.** $9\overline{)4}$

**13.** 8

**14.** 12

**15.** 0.9

**16.** 0.25

**17.** $3\frac{1}{2}$

**18.** $4\frac{2}{3}$

Reduce to lowest terms.

**19.** $\frac{4}{8}$

**20.** $\frac{6}{9}$

**21.** $\frac{10}{15}$

**22.** $\frac{24}{36}$

Express as a mixed number. Simplify.

**23.** $\frac{16}{9}$

**24.** $\frac{18}{5}$

**25.** $\frac{14}{6}$

**26.** $\frac{20}{8}$

Camerique

In order to pass her driver's license examination, Lisa had to identify road signs by their shape. The shape of each sign below is roughly a **polygon.**

A polygon is formed by three or more line segments joined at their endpoints. The segments are called the **sides** of the polygon. Polygons are classified according to the number of sides.

**Triangle**    **Quadrilateral**    **Pentagon**    **Hexagon**    **Octagon**
3 sides      4 sides       5 sides      6 sides      8 sides

**Example 1:**   Which figure is a polygon?

Figure B is a polygon. Figure A is not a polygon because not all the segments are joined at their endpoints.

Each pair of sides that meet forms an angle of a polygon. Notice that each polygon above has the same number of angles as sides.

A **regular polygon** has all sides of equal length and all angles of equal measure.

Marks like these show that angles are equal in measure.

Marks like these show that sides are equal in length.

**Example 2:**   Which figure is a regular polygon?

Figure A is a regular polygon. Figure B is not a regular polygon because the angles do not have the same measure.

## EXERCISES

Is each figure a polygon?

**1.**   **2.**   **3.**   **4.**

Classify each polygon and tell if it is regular or not.

**5.**   **6.** 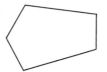  **7.**   **8.**

**9.**   **10.**   **11.**   **12.**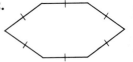

Parts of an automobile are pictured below. Classify each polygon.

**13.**   **14.**   **15.**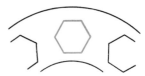

Draw an example of each of the following:

**16.** quadrilateral  **17.** hexagon  **18.** regular triangle

**19.** pentagon  **20.** regular quadrilateral  **21.** octagon

EXTRA PRACTICE page 492, set 57

---

## MATH NOTE

A man fenced his yard so that the fence formed a square. There were 12 fence posts on each side. How many posts did he use?

Triangular shapes are used very often in buildings and designs. Triangles can be classified according to the lengths of their *sides*.

**Equilateral triangle**
3 sides of equal length

**Isosceles triangle**
2 sides of equal length

**Scalene triangle**
no sides of equal length

Triangles can also be classified according to their angle measures.

**Right triangle**
1 right angle

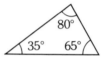

**Acute triangle**
3 acute angles

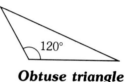

**Obtuse triangle**
1 obtuse angle

In each of the six triangles above, the sum of the angle measures is 180°.

On a piece of paper, draw a triangle. Cut it out and label the three angles $\angle 1$, $\angle 2$, and $\angle 3$. Tear off the angles, and place the vertices (plural of vertex) together. At least one side of each angle must touch a side of another.

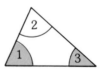 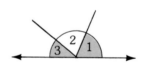

The angles of any triangle form a straight angle. A straight angle has a measure of 180°. So the sum of the angle measures of any triangle is 180°.

**Example:** Find the measure of $\angle D$.

$$\begin{array}{r} 50° \\ +60° \\ \hline 110° \end{array} \qquad \begin{array}{r} 180° \\ -110° \\ \hline 70° \end{array}$$

$m\angle D = 70°$

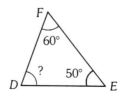

# EXERCISES

Without using a protractor, find each angle measure that is not given.

**1.**

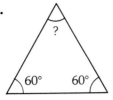

**2.**

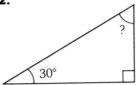

**3.**

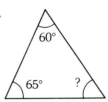

**4.**

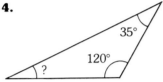

**5.**

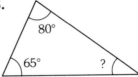

**6.**

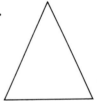

Measure the lengths of the sides of each triangle. Then classify the triangle according to the lengths of its sides.

**7.**

**8.**

**9.**

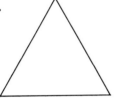

Measure the angles in each triangle. Then classify the triangle according to its angle measures.

**10.**

**11.**

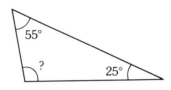

**12.**

**13.**

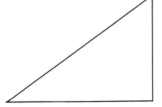

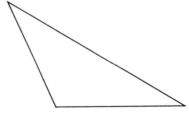

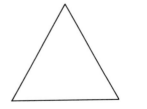

EXTRA PRACTICE page 492, set 58

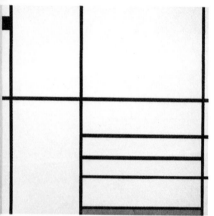

Some kinds of quadrilaterals have special names. A quadrilateral in which opposite sides are parallel and equal in length is called a **parallelogram.**

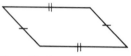

**Parallelogram**

A **rectangle,** a **rhombus,** and a **square** are each a special kind of parallelogram.

**Rectangle**          **Rhombus**          **Square**
four right angles    four sides of       four right angles
                     equal length        and four sides of
                                          equal length

There is another kind of quadrilateral, which is not a parallelogram. A **trapezoid** has only one pair of opposite sides that are parallel.

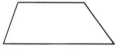

**Trapezoid**

## EXERCISES

Write the most specific name for each kind of quadrilateral.

**1.** 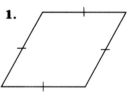   **2.**    **3.**    **4.**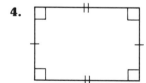

Draw the following:

**5.** a rhombus          **6.** a square          **7.** a rectangle          **8.** a trapezoid

Write the most specific name for each quadrilateral pictured below.

**9.**

baseball diamond

**10.**

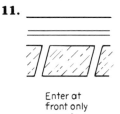

football field

**11.** _____

bus window

**12.**

blade for
carpenter's knife

Match the figures with the descriptions. More than one figure may fit a description.

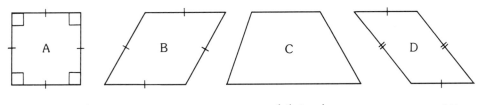

**13.** a rectangle

**16.** a rhombus

**14.** a quadrilateral

**17.** a trapezoid

**15.** a parallelogram

**18.** a square

---

## CHECKPOINT

Choose the best answer.

**1.** A (line, ray) extends without end in only one direction.

**2.** Angles are measured in (degrees, inches).

**3.** The measure of an acute angle is (more, less) than 90°.

**4.** (Perpendicular, Parallel) lines never meet.

**5.** A four-sided figure is called a (pentagon, quadrilateral).

**6.** A triangle with two sides of the same length is called a(n) (scalene, isosceles) triangle.

**7.** A quadrilateral with only one pair of opposite sides parallel is called a (rhombus, trapezoid).

# 7.8 | PROBLEM SOLVING

A contractor is working on some new roads. River Road will intersect First Avenue, forming two angles. If the measure of angle 1 is 25°, what is the measure of angle 2?

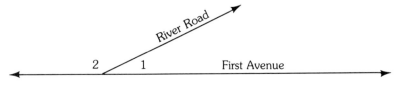

**Read:**   *Given:*   The measure of ∠1 is 25°.

*To find:*   the measure of ∠2

**Plan:**   Which operation can be used?

Because there are 180° in a straight angle (First Avenue), subtract 25° from 180°.

**Compute:**
$$\begin{array}{r} 180° \\ -\ \ 25° \\ \hline 155° \end{array}$$

**Answer:**   The measure of ∠2 is 155°.

**Check:**
$$\begin{array}{r} 155° \\ +\ \ 25° \\ \hline 180° \end{array} \ \ \ \text{✔}$$

# EXERCISES

**1.**

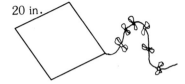

20 in.

A kite is shaped like a rhombus. If the length of one side is 20 inches, how long must a string that goes around the outside of the kite be?

**2.**

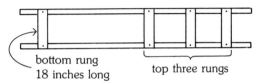

bottom rung
18 inches long    top three rungs

The sides of a ladder are parallel. The bottom rung is 18 inches long. Can the top three rungs be cut from a 60-inch board?

**3.**

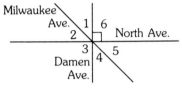

Milwaukee Ave.    1  6
                  2     North Ave.
                  3   5
               Damen  4
               Ave.

Three streets intersect, forming six angles, as shown above. If the measure of ∠1 is 45°, what is the measure of each of the other angles? (Hint: m∠1=m∠4, m∠2=m∠5, and m∠3=m∠6)

**4.**

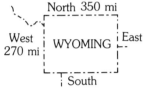

North 350 mi
West          East
270 mi   WYOMING
         South

The state of Wyoming is roughly rectangular. The north boundary line is about 350 miles long, and the west boundary line is about 270 miles long. How long are the east and south boundary lines together?

**5.**

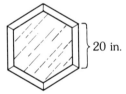

20 in.

Edna wants to put a wooden frame around a window that is shaped like a regular hexagon. If one side of the window is 20 inches long, how many inches of lumber will she need?

**6.**

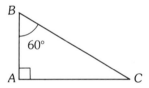

B
60°
A          C

An architect has to design one part of a bridge, using a right triangle. If the measure of ∠B is 60°, what is the measure of ∠C?

**7.**

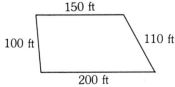

150 ft
100 ft        110 ft
     200 ft

A farmer has a field shaped like a trapezoid. How many feet of fencing are needed to enclose the field?

Dave works in a pizza parlor. In cutting one pizza, he made two cuts as shown below.

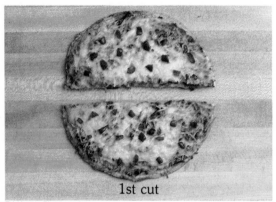
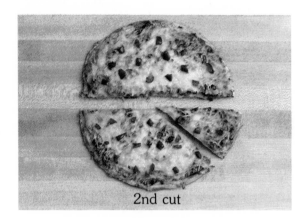

1st cut          2nd cut

Ed Hoppe Photography

The first cut is an example of a **_diameter_** of a circle.

The second cut is an example of a **_radius_** of a circle.

The figure above illustrates the following terms:

**_Circle_**—the set of all points in a plane that are the same distance from a fixed point, called the **_center._** A circle is named by its center. So the circle above is circle A. Points B, D, and C are the same distance from A.

**_Diameter_**—a segment through the center with its endpoints on the circle. $\overline{BC}$ is a diameter.

**_Radius_**—a segment with the center and any point on the circle as its endpoints. $\overline{AD}$ is a radius. $\overline{AB}$ and $\overline{AC}$ are radii also. (NOTE: A radius is half as long as the diameter. A diameter is twice as long as the radius.)

**_Chord_**—a segment with both of its endpoints on the circle. $\overline{BD}$ is a chord, as is $\overline{BC}$. ($\overline{BC}$ is also a diameter.)

**_Arc_**—a part of the circle consisting of two points on the circle and all the points between. Any two points of a circle are the endpoints of two arcs. Arc DC ($\overset{\frown}{DC}$) is the shorter arc. Arc DBC ($\overset{\frown}{DBC}$) is the longer arc.

# EXERCISES

Use the figure at the right.

**1.** Name the circle.

**2.** Name a diameter of the circle.

**3.** Name three radii of the circle.

**4.** Name two chords of the circle.

**5.** Name the longer arc with endpoints $W$ and $Z$.

**6.** Name the shorter arc with endpoints $W$ and $Z$.

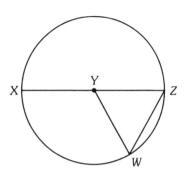

Use the figure at the right to match the following. You may use an answer more than once.

**7.** $\overline{AE}$

**8.** $\overline{BC}$

**9.** $\overset{\frown}{ED}$

**10.** $B$

**11.** $\overset{\frown}{AG}$

**12.** $\overline{BE}$

**13.** $\overline{GD}$

**14.** $\overline{BA}$

    a. radius

    b. center

    c. chord

    d. arc

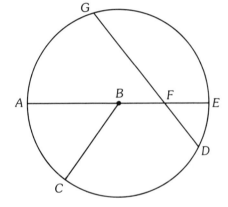

EXTRA PRACTICE page 493, set 59

## SKILLS REVIEW

Add. Simplify.

**15.** $\frac{1}{5}$
$+\frac{3}{5}$

**16.** $2\frac{4}{9}$
$+3\frac{1}{9}$

**17.** $\frac{1}{8}$
$+\frac{1}{4}$

**18.** $4\frac{1}{3}$
$+1\frac{2}{9}$

**19.** $\frac{1}{2}$
$+\frac{1}{6}$

**20.** $6\frac{1}{12}$
$+8\frac{3}{4}$

**21.** $\frac{3}{4}$
$+\frac{2}{3}$

**22.** $5\frac{5}{6}$
$+2\frac{1}{3}$

Two classes entered floats in the homecoming parade. The frames had to be the same shape and size.

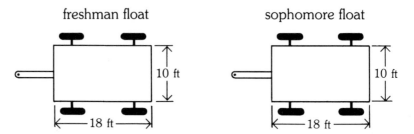

freshman float                sophomore float

Figures that have the same shape and size are called **congruent figures.** If two figures are congruent, then there would be a perfect match if one were placed on top of the other.

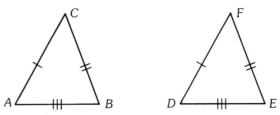

Triangle *ABC* is congruent to triangle *DEF* because they have the same size and shape.

We say:   Triangle *ABC* is congruent to triangle *DEF*.

We write:   △*ABC*≅△*DEF*.

Congruent figures have matching vertices.

$A \longleftrightarrow D$          $B \longleftrightarrow E$          $C \longleftrightarrow F$

△*ABC* and △*DEF* have corresponding (matching) sides and corresponding angles. Corresponding parts of congruent figures are also congruent.

| Corresponding sides | Corresponding angles |
|---|---|
| $\overline{AC} \cong \overline{DF}$ | $\angle A \cong \angle D$ |
| $\overline{CB} \cong \overline{FE}$ | $\angle B \cong \angle E$ |
| $\overline{AB} \cong \overline{DE}$ | $\angle C \cong \angle F$ |

# EXERCISES

Copy and complete. Quadrilateral $ABCD\cong$ quadrilateral $EFGH$.

**1.** $\angle A\cong$ ___

**2.** $\overline{EF}\cong$ ___

**3.** $\overline{AD}\cong$ ___

**4.** $\angle H\cong$ ___

**5.** $\angle F\cong$ ___

**6.** $\overline{CD}\cong$ ___

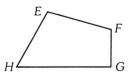

Copy and complete. $\triangle MNP\cong\triangle QRS$.

**7.** $m\angle Q=$ ___°

**8.** The length of $\overline{MN}$ is ___.

**9.** $m\angle P=$ ___°

**10.** The length of $\overline{QS}$ is ___.

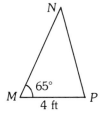
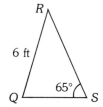

Copy and complete. $\triangle XYZ\cong\triangle MNO$.

**11.** $\angle M$ is a(n) ___ angle.

**12.** The longest side of $\triangle MNO$ is ___.

**13.** The length of $\overline{YZ}$ is ___.

**14.** The shortest side of $\triangle MNO$ is ___.

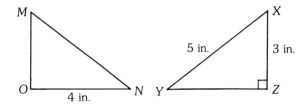

EXTRA PRACTICE page 493, set 60

## SKILLS REVIEW

Subtract. Simplify.

**15.** $\dfrac{7}{9}$
$-\dfrac{5}{9}$

**16.** $3\dfrac{4}{5}$
$-2\dfrac{1}{5}$

**17.** $\dfrac{3}{4}$
$-\dfrac{2}{3}$

**18.** $6\dfrac{5}{8}$
$-4\dfrac{1}{4}$

**19.** $\dfrac{5}{6}$
$-\dfrac{1}{3}$

**20.** $7\dfrac{9}{10}$
$-3\dfrac{2}{5}$

**21.** $5$
$-1\dfrac{2}{3}$

**22.** $9\dfrac{3}{8}$
$-6\dfrac{2}{3}$

Laura cut out hearts for a Valentine's Day dance by first folding a sheet of paper in half. See Figure A below. Then she cut out half a heart, as shown in Figure B. When the paper was opened, the figure was a complete heart, as in Figure C.

A          B          C

The heart has **line symmetry** because it can be folded to form two congruent parts that fit one on top of the other. The fold line is the **line of symmetry.**

**Example 1:** These figures have only *one* line of symmetry each.

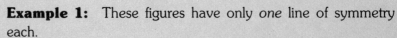

**Example 2:** These figures have more than one line of symmetry.

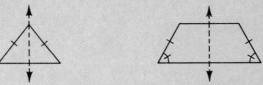

# EXERCISES

Is the dashed line a line of symmetry? Yes or no?

**1.**

**2.**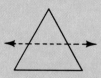

**3.**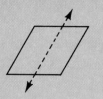

**4.**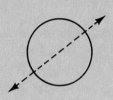

**5.**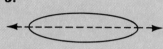

**6.**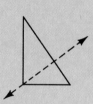

**7.**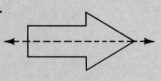

**8.**

**9.**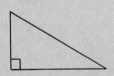

How many lines of symmetry, if any, does each of the following figures have?

**10.**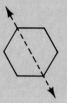

**11.**

**12.**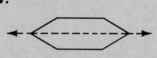

**13.**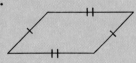

**14.**

**15.**

How many lines of symmetry does each letter have? Trace each letter and draw any lines of symmetry.

**16.** A   **17.** D   **18.** H   **19.** J   **20.** M

**21.**  O   **22.** R   **23.** T   **24.** V   **25.** X

EXTRA PRACTICE page 494, set 61

Brent Jones

**Josef works on the park district maintenance crew. One of his jobs is to put chalk lines around two soccer fields that are congruent. He knows the width of Field A is 46 meters and the length of Field B is 91 meters. What is the distance around each field?**

46 m | Field A |        | Field B |
                                  91 m

**Read:**  *Given:*  Field A is 46 meters wide.

Field B is 91 meters long.

Field A and Field B are congruent.

*To find:*  the distance around each field

**Plan:**  Which operation can be used?

You know that corresponding sides of congruent figures are congruent. Add the measures of the four sides to find the distance around.

**Compute:**
| 46 | 91 | 182 |
|---|---|---|
| +46 | +91 | + 92 |
| 92 | 182 | 274 |

**Answer:**  The distance around Field A is 274 meters. Because Field A and Field B are congruent, the distance around Field B is also 274 meters.

**Check:**  Does it seem reasonable that the distance around each field is 274 meters?  ✔

# EXERCISES

**1.**

A radius of a clock face is 8 inches long. What is the length of a diameter?

**2.**

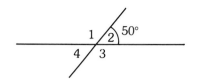

Two streets intersect, forming 4 angles. Angle 2 has a measure of 50°. How many degrees are in angle 3?

**3.**

overhead view

Rosa divided a large room into two rooms with the same size and shape. If she put ceiling molding around the walls of Room B, how much molding did she need?

**4.**

The Leaning Tower of Pisa in Italy forms about an 83° angle with the ground. How many degrees would the tower have to be straightened to be perpendicular to the ground?

**5.**

Mike put two triangle-shaped gardens in his backyard. One garden was for corn, and the other was for tomatoes. The two gardens have the same size and shape. How long will a fence around the tomato garden have to be?

**6.**

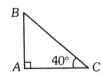

The headquarters of the Department of Defense in Washington, D.C., is called the Pentagon because it is a regular pentagon in shape. If one side of the Pentagon is 281 meters long, what is the distance around the entire building?

**7.**

One face of the Great Pyramid in Egypt is shaped like an equilateral triangle. The base is 755 feet long. What is the sum of the lengths of the other two sides?

**8.**

A roof truss is shaped like a right triangle. If the measure of the angle at the base (∠C) is 40°, what is the measure of the angle at the top (∠B)?

EXTRA PRACTICE page 494, set 62

Most wallpaper patterns are based on a repeating design. Some patterns have a larger "repeat" than others. When the design is simple, the repeat might be small, such as a 2-inch repeat. However, a large, complicated pattern might have a repeat such as 18 inches. The larger the repeat, the more likely it is that you will have to waste some of the paper to make all the pieces match correctly.

Which of the following wallpaper designs do you think has the largest repeat? The smallest repeat?

Ed Hoppe Photography

A carpenter often deals with different geometric figures during a workday. Because different parts of a building contain many angles and shapes, a carpenter must have a working knowledge of geometry. Here are some typical problems a carpenter might have to solve.

Billy E. Barnes

Use with exercise 1.

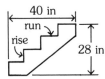

Use with exercises 2–5.

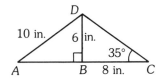

Use with exercise 6.

Use with exercise 7.

1. A carpenter must cut a set of stairs. If the runs are congruent to one another and the rises are congruent to one another, what is the length of each run and each rise in the figure at the left?

2. The bookends in the figure at the left form two congruent triangles ($\triangle ABD \cong \triangle CBD$). What is the length of $\overline{AB}$?

3. What is the measure of $\angle DBC$?

4. What is the length of $\overline{DC}$?

5. What is the measure of $\angle ADB$?

6. A patio is shaped like a regular pentagon. A fence must be built around all but one of the sides. How long must the fence be if one side is 9 feet?

7. Two rectangular flower gardens are congruent. The width of one is 6 feet, and the length of the other is 10 feet. A fence is to be put around each garden. How much fencing is needed?

**213**

Choose the correct answer. 7.1

**1.** A (line, ray) has one endpoint and extends without end in one direction.

**2.** A (point, plane) has no size and shows only a position.

**3.** A (line segment, plane) has two endpoints.

Draw and label each figure.

**4.** $\overleftrightarrow{AB}$          **5.** $\overline{GH}$          **6.** $\overrightarrow{RS}$          **7.** point $F$

Give four names for each angle. Use the symbol $\angle$ in each name. 7.2

**8.** 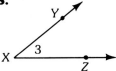          **9.**           **10.**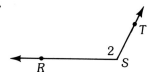

Using a protractor, draw each angle. Then label the angle with three letters and its measure. 7.3

**11.** $m\angle XYZ = 30°$          **12.** $m\angle ABC = 90°$

**13.** $m\angle MNO = 135°$          **14.** $m\angle DEF = 180°$

Choose the correct answer.

**15.** $\angle ABC$ is (acute, right, obtuse).

**16.** $\angle BAC$ is (acute, right, obtuse).

**17.** $\angle ACB$ is (acute, right, obtuse).

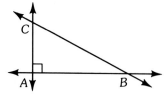

Are the following lines perpendicular? 7.4

**18.** 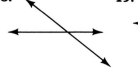          **19.**           **20.** 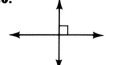          **21.**

Are the following lines parallel?

**22.**     **23.**     **24.**     **25.**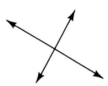

Classify each polygon and tell if it is regular or not.                    7.5

**26.**     **27.**     **28.**     **29.**

Without using a protractor, find each angle measure that is not given.                    7.6

**30.** 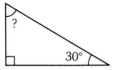    **31.**     **32.**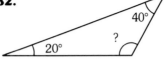

Classify each triangle according to the lengths of the sides.

**33.** 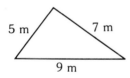    **34.**     **35.**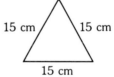

Classify each triangle according to the angle measures.

**36.** 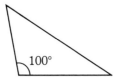    **37.**     **38.**

Match the figures with the descriptions. More than one figure may fit a                    7.7
description.

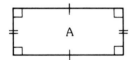        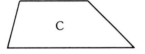

**39.** a trapezoid          **40.** a rhombus          **41.** a rectangle

**42.** a square          **43.** a quadrilateral

Use the figure at the right to classify the following: 7.9

**44.** $F$ **45.** $\overline{AB}$
**46.** $\overline{FC}$ **47.** $\overline{ED}$
**48.** $\widehat{AD}$ **49.** $\widehat{ABD}$

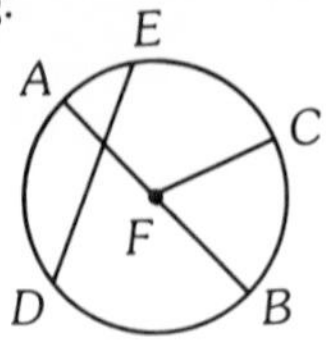


Copy and complete. Quadrilateral $WXYZ \cong$ quadrilateral $RSTU$. 7.10

**50.** $\angle W \cong$ ___ **51.** $\overline{YZ} \cong$ ___
**52.** $\overline{RS} \cong$ ___ **53.** $\angle Z \cong$ ___
**54.** $\angle X \cong$ ___ **55.** $\overline{WX} \cong$ ___
**56.** $\overline{ST} \cong$ ___ **57.** $\angle T \cong$ ___

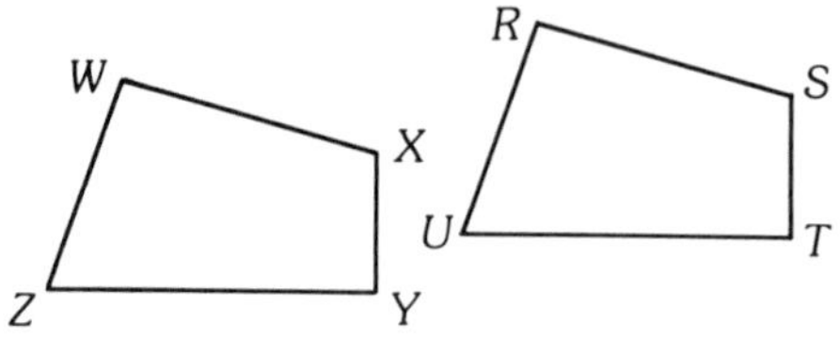


Copy and complete. $\triangle DEF \cong \triangle MNO$.

**58.** The length of $\overline{DF}$ is ___.
**59.** $\angle M$ is a(n) ___ angle.
**60.** The length of $\overline{ON}$ is ___.
**61.** The length of $\overline{NM}$ is ___.

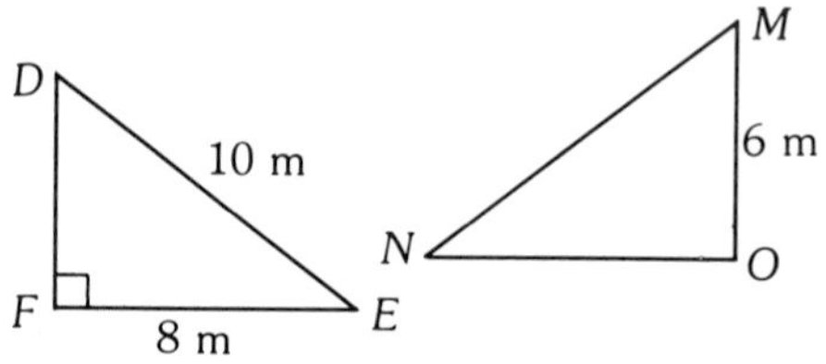


Is the dashed line a line of symmetry? 7.11

**62.**

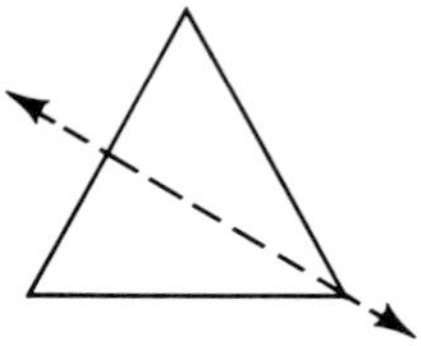

**63.**

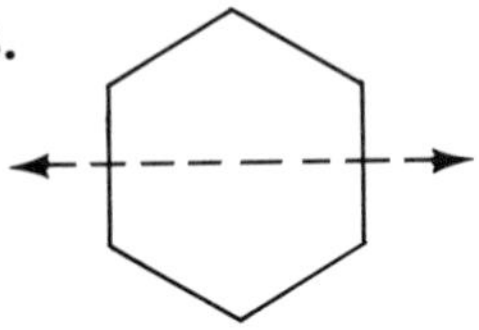

**64.**

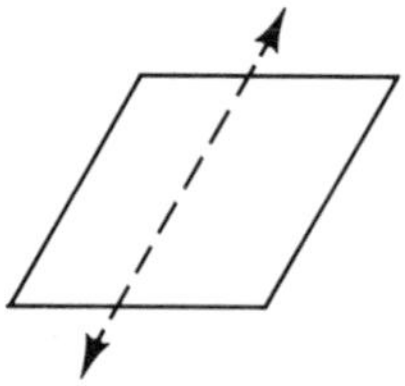

How many lines of symmetry does each of the following figures have?

**65.**

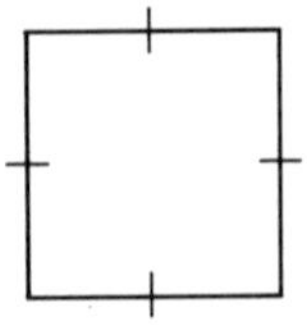

**66.**

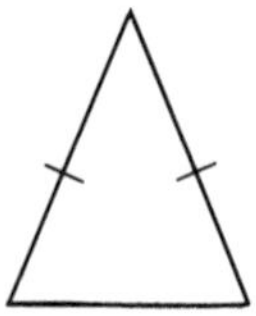

**67.**

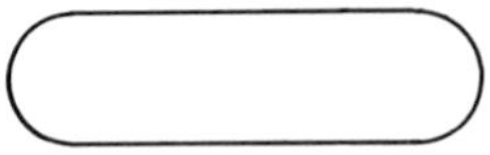

Solve. 7.8, 7.12

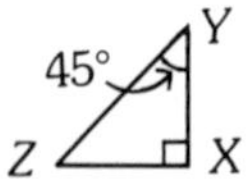


**68.** A bridge support is shaped like a right triangle. If the measure of $\angle Y$ is 45°, what is the measure of $\angle Z$?

Classify each figure.

1.   2.  3. •  4.

5.

Write four names for the angle above.

6.

Classify the angle above as acute, right, or obtuse.

7.

Are the lines above parallel, perpendicular, or neither?

8.

Classify the polygon above according to the number of sides.

Choose the correct answer.

9. △XWY is (equilateral, isosceles, scalene).

10. △XWY is (right, acute, obtuse).

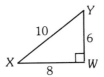

11. What kind of quadrilateral has 2 sides that are parallel and 2 sides that are not parallel?

Use the circle to name the following:

12. a diameter        13. a radius

14. a chord that is not a diameter

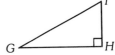

Complete.  △MNO≅△GHI.

15. $\overline{MN}$≅ ___        16. $\overline{HI}$≅ ___

17. $\overline{IG}$≅ ___

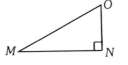

18.

Is the dashed line a line of symmetry?

19.

A sign is shaped like a right triangle. If ∠Y has a measure of 45°, what is the measure of ∠Z?

Write in place-value form.

**1.** thirty-six thousand, twenty-seven

**2.** four billion, fifty million, eighty-nine thousand

**3.** one and fifteen thousandths

Name the place value of each underlined digit.

**4.** 2̲37,896          **5.** 24,7̲42          **6.** 15.86̲3

Compare. Write $<$, $=$, or $>$ for each ●.

**7.** 83 ● 87          **8.** 590 ● 509          **9.** 2.10 ● 2.1

Arrange in order from least to greatest.

**10.** 328, 382, 238, 283          **11.** 4, 0.04, 0.40, 4.04

Add.

**12.**  502
       $+897$

**13.**  16.3
       $+\ 4.8$

**14.**  20.3
       $+18.89$

**15.** $2.61 + 3.507$

Subtract.

**16.**  342
       $-156$

**17.**  37.8
       $-19.6$

**18.**  8.7
       $-3.904$

**19.** $5.6 - 3.45$

Round to the largest place value.

**20.** 874          **21.** 14.6          **22.** 3.704

Estimate each sum or difference.

**23.**  831
       $+\ 15.6$

**24.**  12.74
       $+\ 5.01$

**25.**  18.94
       $-\ 6.01$

**26.**  89.8
       $-72.3$

Solve.

**27.** Joshua bought a book for $12.95. The sales tax was $0.78. What was the total bill?

**28.** Beth wants to save $150. She now has $72.35. How much more does she need to save?

Copy and complete by placing the decimal point in the product.

**29.**
$$4.87 \\ \underline{\times 0.4} \\ 1948$$

**30.**
$$0.85 \\ \underline{\times 0.07} \\ 595$$

Multiply.

**31.** $7 \times 8$

**32.**
$$18 \\ \underline{\times 4}$$

**33.**
$$73 \\ \underline{\times 54}$$

**34.**
$$209 \\ \underline{\times 81}$$

**35.** $19 \times 10$

**36.** $85 \times 100$

**37.** $260 \times 40$

**38.**
$$27 \\ \underline{\times 0.4}$$

**39.**
$$3.8 \\ \underline{\times 0.5}$$

**40.**
$$38.6 \\ \underline{\times 2.3}$$

**41.**
$$15.7 \\ \underline{\times 5.6}$$

**42.** $0.02 \times 10$

**43.** $0.0043 \times 100$

**44.** $83.6 \times 0.01$

Estimate.

**45.**
$$829 \\ \underline{\times 57}$$

**46.**
$$234 \\ \underline{\times 806}$$

Solve.

**47.** Carl bought 4 notebooks at $1.19 each. How much did the notebooks cost?

**48.** A parking lot has 8 rows, with 20 meters in each row. How many meters are in the parking lot?

Divide and check. Write any remainder as a whole number.

**49.** $7\overline{)1498}$

**50.** $23\overline{)1039}$

**51.** $584\overline{)35049}$

Divide until the remainder is 0. Check.

**52.** $6\overline{)25.62}$

**53.** $14\overline{)1.26}$

**54.** $231\overline{)1160.544}$

**55.** $0.8\overline{)256}$

**56.** $9.2\overline{)312.8}$

**57.** $0.31\overline{)217}$

**58.** $84.3 \div 10$

**59.** $247 \div 1000$

**60.** $83.6 \div 100$

Divide. Round the quotient to the nearest whole number.

**61.** $19\overline{)83}$

**62.** $3.1\overline{)12.47}$

Solve.

**63.** 2500 eggs were put into cartons of 12 each. How many eggs were left over?

**64.** Paula worked 3.75 hours and made $19.50. How much did she earn per hour?

Reduce to lowest terms.

**65.** $\frac{8}{12}$

**66.** $\frac{5}{10}$

**67.** $\frac{6}{24}$

Express as a decimal.

**68.** $\frac{3}{100}$

**69.** $\frac{7}{10}$

**70.** $\frac{3}{5}$

Express as a fraction. Reduce to lowest terms.

**71.** 0.8

**72.** 0.25

**73.** 0.04

Change each pair of fractions to equivalent fractions with a common denominator.

**74.** $\frac{3}{4}, \frac{5}{12}$

**75.** $\frac{5}{6}, \frac{3}{8}$

Add. Simplify.

**76.** $\frac{2}{7} + \frac{3}{7}$

**77.** $\frac{7}{12} + \frac{3}{12}$

**78.** $\frac{1}{4} + \frac{2}{3}$

**79.** $2\frac{7}{8} + 1\frac{5}{6}$

**80.** Express $\frac{49}{5}$ as a mixed number.

**81.** Express $2\frac{3}{4}$ as a fraction.

Solve.

**82.** A sheet of veneer $\frac{3}{64}$ inch thick is glued to a piece of wood $\frac{3}{8}$ inch thick. What is the total thickness?

**83.** Carol worked $2\frac{1}{2}$ hours on Friday and $3\frac{3}{4}$ hours on Saturday. How long did she work in all?

Which symbol, > or <, should replace each ●?

**84.** $\frac{7}{8}$ ● $\frac{5}{8}$

**85.** $\frac{3}{4}$ ● $\frac{4}{5}$

**86.** $1\frac{9}{10}$ ● $1\frac{7}{12}$

Determine if each statement is true or false by changing each fraction or mixed number to its decimal equivalent.

**87.** $\frac{3}{8} < \frac{4}{5}$

**88.** $\frac{2}{3} > \frac{1}{2}$

**89.** $1\frac{3}{4} < 1\frac{2}{5}$

**220**

Subtract. Simplify each answer.

**90.**  $\dfrac{7}{8}$
      $-\dfrac{3}{8}$

**91.**  $\dfrac{4}{5}$
      $-\dfrac{1}{4}$

**92.**  $3\dfrac{7}{12}$
      $-2\dfrac{1}{3}$

**93.**  $8\dfrac{1}{4}$
      $-3\dfrac{5}{6}$

Find each answer.

**94.** $\dfrac{4}{5}-\dfrac{3}{8}$

**95.** $\dfrac{1}{2}+\dfrac{3}{5}$

**96.** $1\dfrac{1}{4}+2\dfrac{1}{3}+1\dfrac{5}{6}$

Complete.

**97.** 2 qt = ___ pt

**98.** 12 in. = ___ ft

**99.** 2 lb = ___ oz

Solve.

**100.** One compact refrigerator measures $22\dfrac{1}{8}$ inches wide. Another is $21\dfrac{7}{8}$ inches wide. How much wider is the first one?

**101.** Which has a smaller opening, a $\dfrac{1}{4}$-inch wrench or a $\dfrac{3}{16}$-inch wrench?

Multiply. Simplify each answer.

**102.** $\dfrac{4}{5}\times\dfrac{2}{3}$

**103.** $\dfrac{3}{4}\times\dfrac{4}{9}$

**104.** $1\dfrac{1}{6}\times1\dfrac{1}{3}$

**105.** $3\dfrac{1}{3}\times4\dfrac{2}{5}$

Find the reciprocal of each number.

**106.** $\dfrac{3}{5}$

**107.** $2\dfrac{3}{4}$

Rewrite each division exercise as a multiplication exercise.

**108.** $\dfrac{3}{4}\div\dfrac{2}{5}$

**109.** $1\dfrac{2}{3}\div3\dfrac{4}{5}$

Divide. Simplify each answer.

**110.** $\dfrac{1}{2}\div\dfrac{2}{3}$

**111.** $\dfrac{2}{5}\div\dfrac{3}{10}$

**112.** $1\dfrac{1}{2}\div\dfrac{3}{4}$

**113.** $2\dfrac{7}{8}\div3\dfrac{3}{4}$

Complete.

**114.** 14 c = ___ qt

**115.** $\dfrac{1}{10}$ ton = ___ lb

**116.** 3 yd 1 ft = ___ ft

Solve.

**117.** A recipe calls for $\frac{3}{4}$ cup of mashed banana. How much banana would twice the recipe amount require?

**118.** Donna is filling a 40-quart aquarium, using a $2\frac{1}{2}$-qt saucepan to carry the water. How many trips will she make before the aquarium is full?

Write a symbol for each figure.

**119.**

**120.**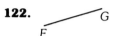

**121.** • E

**122.**

**123.**

Write four names for the angle.

**124.**

Classify the angle.

**125.**

Are the lines parallel, perpendicular, or neither?

**126.**

Classify the polygon according to the number of sides.

Choose the correct answer.

**127.** △MNO is (right, acute, obtuse).

**128.** △MNO is (equilateral, isosceles, scalene).

**129.** What kind of parallelogram has four right angles and adjacent sides of different lengths?

Use the circle to name the following:

**130.** a diameter

**131.** a radius

Complete. △ABC≅△DEF.

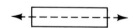

**132.** $\overline{AB}$≅ ____

**133.** $\overline{EF}$≅ ____

**134.** $\overline{CA}$≅ ____

**135.** Is the dashed line a line of symmetry?

Solve.

**136.** Margaret is putting a fence around her square yard. How many feet of fencing will she need if each side is 60 feet?

**1.** □ □ □ □ □ □ △ △ △

Write the ratio of the number of squares to the number of triangles.

**2.** First express both amounts in the same unit, and then simplify the following ratio: 6 feet to 3 yards

**3.** Express the following ratio as a rate: 86 words in 2 minutes

**4.** Is each proportion true?

   a. $\dfrac{4}{3} = \dfrac{8}{5}$

   b. $\dfrac{10}{12} = \dfrac{15}{18}$

**5.** Solve the proportion by copying and completing the table. $\dfrac{2}{3} = \dfrac{6}{?}$

Solve the proportions by using equivalent fractions.

**6.** $\dfrac{4}{5} = \dfrac{?}{25}$

**7.** $\dfrac{2}{?} = \dfrac{6}{21}$

**8.** $\dfrac{?}{10} = \dfrac{6}{15}$

Solve the proportions by using cross products.

**9.** $\dfrac{8}{3} = \dfrac{?}{9}$

**10.** $\dfrac{2}{?} = \dfrac{12}{30}$

**11.** $\dfrac{12}{16} = \dfrac{9}{?}$

**12.**

Draw a 1:3 reduction.

**13.**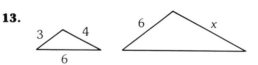

Use the similar figures to find x.

**14.** ← $1\frac{1}{4}$ in. →

Amtown         Beaton

Scale:   1 in. to 16 mi

How far apart are the two towns?

Use proportions to solve.

**15.** Shoes are on sale at 2 pairs for $40. What will 5 pairs cost?

**16.** 3 ounces of perfume sell for $3.36. What would 5 ounces sell for?

**Darrell is displaying the 10 tools shown. How many out of the 10 are hammers?**

There are 3 hammers out of the 10 tools. "3 out of 10" is called a *ratio.*

A *ratio* compares two numbers by division.

"3 out of 10" can be written in 3 ways:

$\frac{3}{10}$       **3 to 10**       **3:10**

**Example 1:**

The ratio of triangles to circles is $\frac{2}{5}$, or 2 to 5, or 2:5.

The ratio of all figures to squares is $\frac{11}{4}$, or 11:4, or 11 to 4. Do not write $\frac{11}{4}$ as a mixed number!

**Example 2:**

The ratio of blue parts to all parts is $\frac{13}{20}$.

The ratio of blue parts to orange parts is 13:7.

The ratio of all parts to blue parts is 20 to 13.

# EXERCISES

**1.** For 4 hearts there are ____ diamonds.

**2.** The ratio of hearts to diamonds is ____ to ____.

Use with exercises 1–2.

Write each ratio, using a colon (:).

**3.** arrows to all figures

**4.** arrows to circles

**5.** circles to arrows

**6.** all figures to circles

Use with exercises 3–6.

Write each ratio as a fraction.

**7.** red parts to all parts

**8.** blue parts to all parts

**9.** all parts to white parts

**10.** red parts to white parts

Use with exercises 7–10.

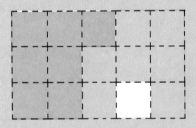

Draw a picture to represent each ratio.

**11.** The ratio of circles to squares is 4:3.

**12.** 3 out of 8 parts are shaded.

EXTRA PRACTICE page 495, set 63

## SKILLS REVIEW

Multiply. Write each answer in simplest form.

**13.** $\frac{3}{4} \times \frac{3}{5}$

**14.** $\frac{3}{4} \times \frac{4}{5}$

**15.** $\frac{7}{9} \times \frac{3}{10}$

**16.** $\frac{5}{12} \times \frac{4}{5}$

**17.** $1\frac{5}{6} \times 1\frac{1}{3}$

**18.** $1\frac{1}{2} \times 3\frac{2}{3}$

**19.** $5\frac{1}{2} \times 1\frac{2}{5}$

**20.** $1\frac{4}{5} \times 3\frac{1}{4}$

# WRITING AND INTERPRETING RATIOS

**A rug is 9 feet wide and 12 feet long. What is the ratio of the width to the length?**

**Example 1:** Compare 9 feet to 12 feet.

| Write the ratio in fraction form. | Simplify as with fractions. | When both measurements are in the same unit, we can omit the unit. |
|---|---|---|
| $\dfrac{9 \text{ feet}}{12 \text{ feet}}$ | $\dfrac{\overset{3}{\cancel{9}} \text{ feet}}{\underset{4}{\cancel{12}} \text{ feet}}$ | $\dfrac{3}{4}$ |

The ratio is 3 to 4.

**Example 2:** Compare 9 feet to 4 yards.

You are comparing two similar measurements, lengths. You should first express both measurements in the same unit.

| Write the ratio in fraction form. | Change to the same unit, and simplify. | Since both measurements are in the same unit, omit the unit. |
|---|---|---|
| solution a: $\dfrac{9 \text{ feet}}{4 \text{ yards}}$ | $\dfrac{\overset{3}{\cancel{9}} \text{ feet}}{\underset{4}{\cancel{12}} \text{ feet}}$ | $\dfrac{3}{4}$ |
| solution b: $\dfrac{9 \text{ feet}}{4 \text{ yards}}$ | $\dfrac{3 \text{ yards}}{4 \text{ yards}}$ | $\dfrac{3}{4}$ |

A ratio that compares two unlike measurements (such as the number of miles traveled to the number of gallons of gas used) is called a **rate**. A rate is usually written so that the denominator is 1 unit.

**Example 3:** Write the ratio of 330 miles to 10 gallons as a rate.

$$\frac{330 \text{ miles}}{10 \text{ gallons}} = \frac{(330 \div 10) \text{ miles}}{(10 \div 10) \text{ gallons}}$$

$$= \frac{33 \text{ miles}}{1 \text{ gallon}} \text{ or } 33 \text{ mi/gal}$$

Read: **33 miles** *per* **gallon.**

**Example 4:** Write the ratio $36 for 8 hours as a rate.

$$\frac{\$36}{8 \text{ hours}} = \frac{\$(36 \div 8)}{(8 \div 8) \text{ hours}}$$

$$= \frac{\$4.50}{1 \text{ hour}} \text{ or } \$4.50/\text{hour} \quad \text{Read:} \quad \$4.50 \text{ per hour.}$$

## EXERCISES

First express both amounts in the same unit, and then simplify the ratio.

**1.** 3 gallons to 4 quarts

**2.** 32 oz:2 lb

**3.** 5 c to 3 pt

**4.** 3 yd:5 ft

**5.** $\frac{1}{2}$ ft: 5 in.

**6.** 3 ft to $1\frac{1}{3}$ yd

**7.** 3 hours to 120 minutes

**8.** 1 nickel:2 dimes

**9.** 12 pennies:1 dime

**10.** 3 dozen roses to 8 roses

**11.** 1 year:4 months

**12.** 7 days:3 weeks

**13.** 2 weeks:10 days

Express each ratio as a rate.

**14.** 50 miles in 2 hours

**15.** 600 gallons in 30 minutes

**16.** $42 for 3 blouses

**17.** 27¢ for 3 pencils

**18.** $4 for 2 tickets

**19.** $2.40 for 6 flowers

**20.** 12°F in 6 hours

**21.** $40 for 8 hours

**22.** $60 for 4 hours

**23.** 150 words in 3 minutes

**24.** 12 lb in 6 weeks

**25.** $3.87 for 3 lb

**26.** $15 for 3 ounces

Ed Hoppe Photography

Write two ratios to compare the number of chairs to the number of tables.

**For 6 chairs there are 3 tables.** $\dfrac{6}{3}$ **and** $\dfrac{2}{1}$ **For every 2 chairs there is 1 table.**

The ratios $\frac{6}{3}$ and $\frac{2}{1}$ are **equivalent ratios** because they can be used to compare the same group of objects.

**Equivalent ratios result in equal cross products.**

**Example 1:** $\dfrac{6}{3} \diagdown\hspace{-1em}\diagup \dfrac{2}{1}$ $\longrightarrow 3 \times 2 = 6$
$\longrightarrow 6 \times 1 = 6$   $\dfrac{6}{3} = \dfrac{2}{1}$

A **proportion** states that two ratios are equivalent. $\frac{6}{3} = \frac{2}{1}$ is a proportion.

**Example 2:** Write two ratios comparing the number of squares to the number of triangles. Then write a proportion.

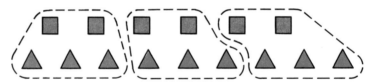

$\dfrac{6}{9}$   $\dfrac{2}{3}$   $\dfrac{6}{9} = \dfrac{2}{3}$

The following examples show two methods for determining if a proportion is true.

**Example 3:** Is the proportion $\frac{4}{3} = \frac{8}{6}$ true?

You can reduce $\frac{8}{6}$ to lowest terms.

$$\dfrac{8}{6} = \dfrac{8 \div 2}{6 \div 2} = \dfrac{4}{3}$$

$$\dfrac{4}{3} = \dfrac{4}{3}$$

$\frac{4}{3} = \frac{8}{6}$ is a true proportion.

**Example 4:** Is the proportion $\frac{3}{4} = \frac{9}{10}$ true?

You can use cross products.

$\dfrac{3}{4} \diagdown\hspace{-1em}\diagup \dfrac{9}{10}$ $\longrightarrow 4 \times 9 = 36$
$\longrightarrow 3 \times 10 = 30$

36 is not equal to 30.

$\frac{3}{4} = \frac{9}{10}$ is not a true proportion.

# EXERCISES

Write two ratios. Then write a proportion for the following drawings:

**1.**

squares to circles

**2.**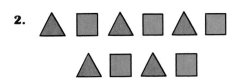

triangles to squares

In exercises 3–12, determine if each proportion is true by simplifying the ratios.

**3.** $\frac{2}{3} = \frac{4}{6}$

**4.** $\frac{3}{2} = \frac{9}{12}$

**5.** $\frac{12}{6} = \frac{4}{2}$

**6.** $\frac{4}{5} = \frac{12}{15}$

**7.** $\frac{20}{15} = \frac{8}{6}$

**8.** $\frac{8}{2} = \frac{6}{4}$

**9.** $\frac{10}{6} = \frac{6}{3}$

**10.** $\frac{10}{8} = \frac{15}{12}$

**11.** $\frac{30}{20} = \frac{10}{4}$

**12.** $\frac{2}{6} = \frac{4}{8}$

In exercises 13–22, determine if each proportion is true by using cross products.

**13.** $\frac{6}{8} = \frac{3}{4}$

**14.** $\frac{14}{2} = \frac{3}{1}$

**15.** $\frac{4}{8} = \frac{2}{4}$

**16.** $\frac{2}{4} = \frac{3}{6}$

**17.** $\frac{10}{4} = \frac{5}{2}$

**18.** $\frac{6}{9} = \frac{1}{3}$

**19.** $\frac{4}{3} = \frac{8}{5}$

**20.** $\frac{7}{21} = \frac{1}{3}$

**21.** $\frac{25}{15} = \frac{4}{3}$

**22.** $\frac{3}{6} = \frac{12}{6}$

EXTRA PRACTICE page 495, set 64

## CHECKPOINT

Write the indicated ratios.

**1.**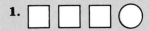

squares to circles

**2.** 2 yards to 5 feet

Write each ratio as a rate.

**3.** 120 miles in 3 hours

**4.** $20 for 5 hours

**5.** Is $\frac{2}{3} = \frac{10}{12}$ a true proportion?

# SOLVING PROPORTIONS BY TABLES

Mary Elenz Tranter

**Notepaper is on sale at 2 pads for $1. How many pads can you buy for $3?**

You can use a proportion to solve the problem.

2 pads for $1    $\dfrac{2}{1} = \dfrac{?}{3}$    how many pads for $3

**Example 1:** Solve the proportion $\frac{2}{1} = \frac{?}{3}$.

You can use equivalent ratios to complete a table.

|  |  | $2 \times 2$ | $3 \times 2$ |
|---|---|---|---|
| **Pads** ⟶ | 2 | 4 | 6 |
| **Dollars** ⟶ | 1 | 2 | 3 |
|  |  | $2 \times 1$ | $3 \times 1$ |

So $? = 6$.

You can buy 6 pads for $3.

NOTE: It is a good idea to use cross products to check.

$\dfrac{2}{1} \times \dfrac{6}{3} \longrightarrow \begin{matrix} 6 \\ 6 \end{matrix}$ ✔

**Example 2:** Solve $\frac{5}{4} = \frac{25}{?}$.

|  | $2 \times 5$ | $3 \times 5$ | $4 \times 5$ | $5 \times 5$ |
|---|---|---|---|---|
| 5 | 10 | 15 | 20 | 25 |
| 4 | 8 | 12 | 16 | 20 |
|  | $2 \times 4$ | $3 \times 4$ | $4 \times 4$ | $5 \times 4$ |

So $? = 20$.

**Example 3:** Solve $\frac{18}{?} = \frac{6}{8}$.

|  | $2 \times 6$ | $3 \times 6$ |
|---|---|---|
| 6 | 12 | 18 |
| 8 | 16 | 24 |
|  | $2 \times 8$ | $3 \times 8$ |

So $? = 24$.

# EXERCISES

Solve each proportion by copying and completing the table.

**1.** $\dfrac{2}{3} = \dfrac{[?]}{9}$

**2.** $\dfrac{6}{5} = \dfrac{30}{[?]}$

**3.** $\dfrac{135}{3} = \dfrac{[?]}{9}$

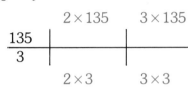

**4.** $\dfrac{5}{4} = \dfrac{[?]}{12}$

**5.** $\dfrac{16}{[?]} = \dfrac{4}{3}$

**6.** $\dfrac{1}{3} = \dfrac{[?]}{15}$

**7.** $\dfrac{3}{2} = \dfrac{15}{[?]}$

**8.** $\dfrac{[?]}{25} = \dfrac{6}{5}$

EXTRA PRACTICE page 496, set 65

## SKILLS REVIEW

Divide. Simplify each answer.

**9.** $\dfrac{1}{2} \div \dfrac{1}{3}$

**10.** $\dfrac{3}{4} \div \dfrac{5}{8}$

**11.** $\dfrac{5}{6} \div \dfrac{5}{8}$

**12.** $\dfrac{2}{3} \div \dfrac{4}{9}$

**13.** $1\dfrac{1}{2} \div \dfrac{3}{4}$

**14.** $2\dfrac{3}{5} \div 1\dfrac{3}{10}$

**15.** $1\dfrac{1}{4} \div \dfrac{3}{5}$

**16.** $2\dfrac{1}{8} \div 3\dfrac{3}{4}$

Jerry Reschke

**Dan raked 2 yards in 3 hours. At that rate, how long will it take him to rake 8 yards?**

**Read:** *Given:* 2 yards in 3 hours

*To find:* the time needed for 8 yards

**Plan:** Solve the proportion $\frac{2}{3} = \frac{8}{\boxed{?}}$.

**Compute:**

|  | $2 \times 2$ | $3 \times 2$ | $4 \times 2$ |
|---|---|---|---|
| **yards** $\longrightarrow 2$ | 4 | 6 | 8 |
| **hours** $\longrightarrow 3$ | 6 | 9 | 12 |
|  | $2 \times 3$ | $3 \times 3$ | $4 \times 3$ |

**Answer:** It will take 12 hours to rake 8 yards.

**Check:** Use cross products.

$$\frac{2}{3} \times \frac{8}{12} \longrightarrow \begin{array}{l} 3 \times 8 = 24 \\ 2 \times 12 = 24 \end{array} \ \vee$$

# EXERCISES

**1.**

SHIRTS
2 for $15.00

How many shirts can you buy if you have $30 to spend?

**2.**

PAINT 2 gallons for $25.00

What is the cost of 6 gallons of paint?

**3.** Justin drove 45 miles in one hour. At that rate, how far will he travel in 4 hours?

**4.** Marimarlene drove 83 miles in 2 hours. At that rate, how far will she travel in 4 hours?

**5.** Corn is on sale at 3 cans for $1. How many cans could you buy with $4?

**6.** A used-book store offers a 2-for-1 trade: You receive one book for each two books you trade in. How many books should you bring to trade if there are 3 books you want?

**7.** Cindy can knit 5 pairs of mittens from 2 packages of yarn. How many pairs of mittens can she make from 6 packages?

**8.** Bryan works 7 nights every 2 weeks. At that rate, how many nights will he work in 10 weeks?

**9.** The ratio of boys to girls in a class is 3:4. If there are 12 boys, how many girls are in the class?

**10.** 4 out of 7 dentists surveyed preferred Brusher's Toothpaste. If 21 dentists were surveyed, how many preferred Brusher's?

**11.** It costs 25¢ for each $\frac{1}{2}$ hour at a parking meter. How much money should Bambi put into the meter if she plans on leaving the car parked for 2 hours?

**12.** 6 servings of hot chicken salad require $\frac{1}{2}$ cup of shredded cheddar cheese. How much cheese should be used for 18 servings?

Brent Jones

**Tricia purchased 10 plants at the rate of 2 for $3. What did the plants cost her?**

You can use a proportion to solve the problem.

**Example 1:** Solve the proportion $\frac{2}{3} = \frac{10}{?}$.

$$\frac{2}{3} = \frac{10}{?} \quad \begin{array}{l}\longleftarrow \textbf{ number of plants} \\ \longleftarrow \textbf{ cost}\end{array}$$

You can solve a proportion by using equivalent fractions. Remember that you can multiply or divide both the numerator and the denominator of a fraction by any nonzero number to get an equivalent fraction.

**By what number can you multiply 2 to get 10? You know $2 \times 5 = 10$. So multiply *both* 3 and 2 by 5.**

$$\frac{2}{3} = \frac{2 \times 5}{3 \times 5} = \frac{10}{15}$$

The 10 plants cost $15.

You can check by using cross products.

$$\frac{2}{3} \times \frac{10}{15} \begin{array}{l}\longrightarrow 30 \\ \longrightarrow 30\end{array} \quad \checkmark$$

**Example 2:** Solve the proportion $\frac{5}{3} = \frac{20}{?}$.

**You know $5 \times 4 = 20$.**

$$\frac{5 \times 4}{3 \times 4} = \frac{20}{12}$$

So $? = 12$.

**Example 3:** Solve the proportion $\frac{?}{4} = \frac{12}{16}$.

**You know $16 \div 4 = 4$. So divide both 12 and 16 by 4.**

$$\frac{12}{16} = \frac{12 \div 4}{16 \div 4} = \frac{3}{4}$$

So $? = 3$.

**Example 4:** Solve the proportion $\frac{15}{12} = \frac{?}{8}$.

First simplify $\frac{15}{12}$.

$$\frac{15}{12} = \frac{15 \div 3}{12 \div 3} = \frac{5}{4}$$

$$\frac{5}{4} = \frac{?}{8} \longleftarrow \text{ the new proportion to be solved}$$

You know $4 \times 2 = 8$.

$$\frac{5 \times 2}{4 \times 2} = \frac{10}{8}$$

So $? = 10$.

## EXERCISES

Solve these proportions by using equivalent fractions.

1. $\frac{2}{3} = \frac{?}{12}$

2. $\frac{5}{3} = \frac{15}{?}$

3. $\frac{8}{5} = \frac{?}{10}$

4. $\frac{?}{3} = \frac{30}{15}$

5. $\frac{4}{?} = \frac{16}{4}$

6. $\frac{2}{?} = \frac{8}{20}$

7. $\frac{3}{5} = \frac{?}{15}$

8. $\frac{3}{2} = \frac{27}{?}$

9. $\frac{3}{6} = \frac{?}{2}$

10. $\frac{?}{3} = \frac{14}{6}$

11. $\frac{4}{5} = \frac{?}{20}$

12. $\frac{8}{?} = \frac{20}{15}$

13. $\frac{9}{12} = \frac{3}{?}$

14. $\frac{4}{?} = \frac{12}{45}$

15. $\frac{6}{5} = \frac{?}{30}$

16. $\frac{?}{10} = \frac{12}{40}$

17. $\frac{12}{5} = \frac{24}{?}$

18. $\frac{18}{?} = \frac{27}{15}$

19. $\frac{?}{2} = \frac{28}{8}$

20. $\frac{12}{3} = \frac{?}{2}$

21. $\frac{?}{18} = \frac{6}{27}$

22. $\frac{5}{12} = \frac{10}{?}$

23. $\frac{15}{10} = \frac{?}{2}$

24. $\frac{20}{?} = \frac{4}{3}$

25. $\frac{15}{12} = \frac{5}{?}$

26. $\frac{3}{?} = \frac{2}{12}$

27. $\frac{6}{?} = \frac{12}{10}$

28. $\frac{15}{4} = \frac{?}{8}$

29. $\frac{?}{3} = \frac{14}{21}$

30. $\frac{7}{?} = \frac{14}{18}$

31. $\frac{9}{8} = \frac{36}{?}$

32. $\frac{10}{9} = \frac{30}{?}$

33. $\frac{15}{?} = \frac{25}{10}$

34. $\frac{1}{2} = \frac{4}{?}$

35. $\frac{?}{3} = \frac{4}{12}$

36. $\frac{3}{2} = \frac{36}{?}$

37. $\frac{8}{?} = \frac{4}{5}$

38. $\frac{6}{4} = \frac{?}{8}$

39. $\frac{8}{14} = \frac{4}{?}$

40. $\frac{?}{4} = \frac{9}{2}$

41. $\frac{15}{?} = \frac{5}{2}$

42. $\frac{24}{16} = \frac{?}{4}$

43. $\frac{35}{14} = \frac{5}{?}$

44. $\frac{27}{45} = \frac{?}{5}$

45. $\frac{12}{48} = \frac{?}{4}$

EXTRA PRACTICE page 496, set 66

# 8.7 SOLVING PROPORTIONS BY CROSS PRODUCTS

Norma Morrison

**Shock absorbers are on sale at 2 for \$41, including the price for installing them. You need 8 shock absorbers for your 2 cars. What will the 8 shocks cost?**

You can use a proportion to solve the problem.

**Example 1:** Use cross products to solve the proportion $\frac{41}{2} = \frac{?}{8}$.

$$\frac{41}{2} = \frac{?}{8}$$
$$2 \times ? = 41 \times 8$$
$$2 \times ? = 328$$

**The question you have to answer is: What number times 2 equals 328? To find out, divide 328 by 2.**

$$328 \div 2 = 164$$

So $? = 164$.

8 shock absorbers will cost \$164.

**Example 2:** Solve the proportion $\frac{6}{16} = \frac{3}{?}$.

$$\frac{6}{16} = \frac{3}{?}$$
$$16 \times 3 = 6 \times ?$$
$$48 = 6 \times ? \quad \textbf{What number times 6 equals 48?}$$
$$48 \div 6 = 8 \quad \textbf{To find out, divide 48 by 6.}$$

So $? = 8$.

**Example 3:** Solve the proportion $\frac{6}{?} = \frac{10}{25}$.

$$\frac{6}{?} = \frac{10}{25}$$
$$? \times 10 = 6 \times 25$$
$$? \times 10 = 150 \quad \textbf{What number times 10 equals 150?}$$
$$150 \div 10 = 15 \quad \textbf{To find out, divide 150 by 10.}$$

So $? = 15$.

# EXERCISES

Solve each proportion by using cross products.

**1.** $\frac{10}{2} = \frac{?}{1}$  **2.** $\frac{6}{27} = \frac{2}{?}$  **3.** $\frac{?}{3} = \frac{4}{1}$  **4.** $\frac{9}{2} = \frac{?}{6}$

**5.** $\frac{?}{8} = \frac{12}{32}$  **6.** $\frac{32}{6} = \frac{48}{?}$  **7.** $\frac{?}{3} = \frac{10}{15}$  **8.** $\frac{9}{7} = \frac{27}{?}$

**9.** $\frac{?}{3} = \frac{20}{6}$  **10.** $\frac{21}{14} = \frac{3}{?}$  **11.** $\frac{?}{8} = \frac{3}{4}$  **12.** $\frac{32}{24} = \frac{4}{?}$

**13.** $\frac{3}{?} = \frac{9}{18}$  **14.** $\frac{?}{2} = \frac{21}{6}$  **15.** $\frac{3}{9} = \frac{?}{18}$  **16.** $\frac{4}{5} = \frac{?}{20}$

**17.** $\frac{9}{6} = \frac{3}{?}$  **18.** $\frac{?}{1} = \frac{12}{2}$  **19.** $\frac{12}{5} = \frac{24}{?}$  **20.** $\frac{8}{7} = \frac{?}{14}$

**21.** $\frac{4}{3} = \frac{20}{?}$  **22.** $\frac{5}{?} = \frac{30}{12}$  **23.** $\frac{?}{3} = \frac{35}{15}$  **24.** $\frac{4}{2} = \frac{?}{10}$

**25.** $\frac{12}{4} = \frac{24}{?}$  **26.** $\frac{11}{5} = \frac{22}{?}$  **27.** $\frac{?}{2} = \frac{40}{16}$  **28.** $\frac{3}{?} = \frac{24}{64}$

*EXTRA PRACTICE page 496, set 67*

## CHECKPOINT

**1.** Solve the proportion by completing the table: $\frac{7}{3} = \frac{?}{9}$.

$$\begin{array}{c|c|c|} 7 & & \\ \hline 3 & & \\ \end{array}$$

**2.** Solve by using equivalent fractions: $\frac{?}{2} = \frac{12}{24}$.

**3.** Solve by using cross products: $\frac{5}{?} = \frac{45}{36}$.

Solve.

**4.** 10 pencils cost $1. How many pencils could you buy with $3?

237

Bruce Wellman/Picture Group

**A team had a win-loss ratio of 4:3. If 8 games were won, how many were lost?**

**Read:**   *Given:*   win-loss ratio of 4:3;

8 games won

*To find:*   number of games lost

**Plan:**   Solve the proportion   $\frac{4}{3} = \frac{8}{?}$.

**Compute:**

$$\frac{4}{3} = \frac{8}{?}$$
$$3 \times 8 = 4 \times ?$$
$$24 = 4 \times ?$$

What number times 4 equals 24? To find out, divide 24 by 4.

$$24 \div 4 = 6$$

So $? = 6$.

**Answer:**   6 games were lost.

**Check:**   $\frac{4}{3} \times \frac{8}{6} \longrightarrow \begin{array}{c} 24 \\ 24 \end{array} \Big\} \; \checkmark$

## EXERCISES

**1.**

What will 9 pairs cost?

**2.**

What will 15 pounds cost?

**3.** Mary drove 80 miles in 2 hours. At that rate, how long will it take her to drive 240 miles?

**4.** 3 out of 5 freshmen voted for Greg Lynn for class president. How many of the 600 freshmen voted for Greg?

**5.** Becky caught 2 fish for every 1 hook she lost. How many fish did she catch if she lost 3 hooks?

**6.** 4 bars of soap cost $0.79. How much will 20 bars cost?

**7.** A car can travel 125 miles on 5 gallons of gas. At that rate, how much gas will it use to go 500 miles?

**8.** 3 pounds of oranges cost $1.29. How much will 12 pounds cost?

**9.** Band members could put $2 out of every $5 they collected into a fund for a trip. If $1500 was put in the fund, how much did they collect?

**10.** A car used 2 gallons of gas to travel 64 miles. At that rate, how far could the car travel using 6 gallons of gas?

**11.** Jim can read 20 pages of a novel in 30 minutes. At that rate, how long will it take him to read 30 pages?

**12.** Gelatin is on sale at 5 boxes for $1. How many boxes could you buy for $3?

EXTRA PRACTICE page 497, set 68

## MATH NOTE

The ratio of hamsters to parakeets in a pet store was 4 to 3. 7 hamsters were sold, and 7 new parakeets arrived at the store. The ratio of hamsters to parakeets was then 3 to 4. How many hamsters and how many parakeets were originally in the store?

# ENLARGING AND REDUCING

T. Rumreich/Picture Group

8 in.

6 in.

The picture of the bird's head could be *enlarged* to be made into a wall poster. It could be *reduced* to fit onto a postage stamp.

**Example 1:** Enlarge the picture by a ratio of 3:2.

new figure    original figure

For every 2 units of the original figure, there are 3 units in the new figure.

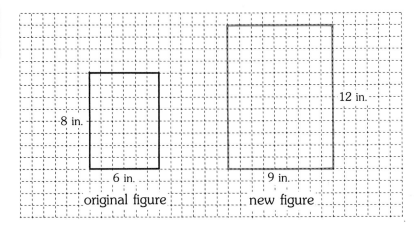

8 in.

6 in.

original figure

12 in.

9 in.

new figure

**Example 2:** Reduce the picture by a ratio of 1:2.

new figure    original figure

For every 2 units of the original figure, there is 1 unit in the new figure.

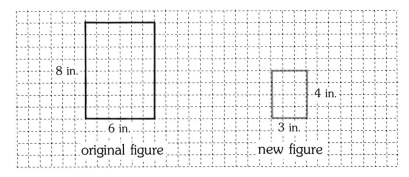

8 in.

6 in.

original figure

4 in.

3 in.

new figure

Notice that in each ratio, the number for the *new* figure is written first, and the number for the *original* figure is written second.

## EXERCISES

Copy each figure and draw the indicated enlargement or reduction.

**1.**

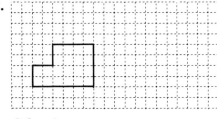

3:1 enlargement

**2.**

1:2 reduction

**3.**

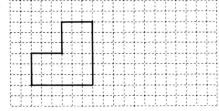

1:3 reduction

**4.**

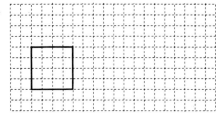

2:1 enlargement

**5.**

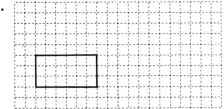

1:3 reduction

**6.**

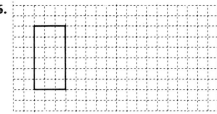

2:3 reduction

**7.**

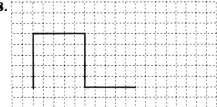

3:2 enlargement

**8.**

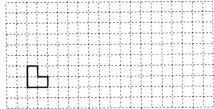

3:5 reduction

*EXTRA PRACTICE page 497, set 69*

**Similar figures** have the same shape but do not have to be the same size. The ratios of corresponding sides of two similar figures are equal.

**Example 1:** Triangles *ABC* and *DEF* are similar figures.

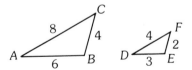

The corresponding sides are: $\overline{AB} \longleftrightarrow \overline{DE}$, $\overline{AC} \longleftrightarrow \overline{DF}$, and $\overline{BC} \longleftrightarrow \overline{EF}$.

$$\frac{AB}{DE} = \frac{6}{3} = \frac{2}{1}$$

$$\frac{BC}{EF} = \frac{4}{2} = \frac{2}{1} \qquad \text{All the ratios are equal.}$$

$$\frac{AC}{DF} = \frac{8}{4} = \frac{2}{1}$$

If two figures are similar, you can use proportions to find the missing length of a side.

**Example 2:**

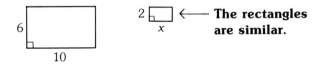

The rectangles are similar.

Use the proportion $\frac{6}{2} = \frac{10}{?}$ to find length *x*.

$$6 \times \boxed{?} = 2 \times 10$$
$$6 \times \boxed{?} = 20$$

What number times 6 equals 20?

To find out, divide 20 by 6.

$$20 \div 6 = 3\frac{2}{6} = 3\frac{1}{3}$$

So $\boxed{?} = 3\frac{1}{3}$.

# EXERCISES

For these two similar figures, find the indicated ratios. Then write the ratios in lowest terms.

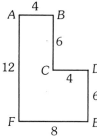

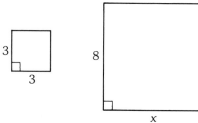

**1.** $\dfrac{AB}{GH}$     **2.** $\dfrac{DE}{JK}$     **3.** $\dfrac{AF}{GL}$     **4.** $\dfrac{FE}{LK}$     **5.** $\dfrac{BC}{HI}$     **6.** $\dfrac{CD}{IJ}$

Find the missing length for each pair of similar figures.

**7.**

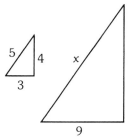

**8.**

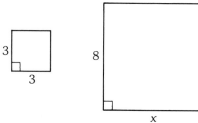

**9.**

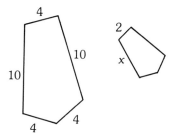

**10.**

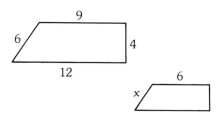

**11.**

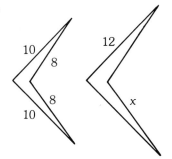

**12.**

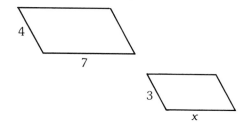

EXTRA PRACTICE page 498, set 70

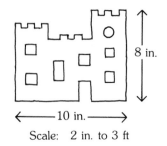

Scale: 2 in. to 3 ft

Elaine Wicks, O.S.F./Taurus

**Some students are designing a prop for a school play. They have drawn the picture above. Each 2 inches of the drawing stands for 3 feet of the prop. How high will the castle be? How wide?**

A *scale drawing* compares a length on a drawing to a real length. You can solve a proportion to find the real length.

**Example 1:** on the drawing $\longrightarrow$ $\dfrac{2 \text{ in.}}{3 \text{ ft}} = \dfrac{8 \text{ in.}}{\boxed{?} \text{ ft}}$ real length $\longrightarrow$

$2 \times \boxed{?} = 3 \times 8$

$2 \times \boxed{?} = 24$

What number times 2 equals 24? To find out, divide 24 by 2.

$24 \div 2 = 12$

So $\boxed{?} = 12$.

$\dfrac{2 \text{ in.}}{3 \text{ ft}} = \dfrac{10 \text{ in.}}{\boxed{?} \text{ ft}}$

$2 \times \boxed{?} = 3 \times 10$

$2 \times \boxed{?} = 30$

What number times 2 equals 30? To find out, divide 30 by 2.

$30 \div 2 = 15$

So $\boxed{?} = 15$.

The castle will be 12 feet high and 15 feet wide.

**Example 2:** In a scale drawing, $\frac{1}{4}$ inch stands for 2 feet. How long is a line in the drawing if the real length is 16 feet?

on the drawing $\longrightarrow$ $\dfrac{\frac{1}{4} \text{ inch}}{2 \text{ feet}} = \dfrac{\boxed{?} \text{ inches}}{16 \text{ feet}}$ real length $\longrightarrow$

$2 \times \boxed{?} = \dfrac{1}{4} \times 16$

$2 \times \boxed{?} = 4$

What number times 2 equals 4? To find out, divide 4 by 2.

$4 \div 2 = 2$

So $\boxed{?} = 2$ inches.

## EXERCISES

Measure the straight-line distances on the map to the nearest $\frac{1}{4}$ inch.

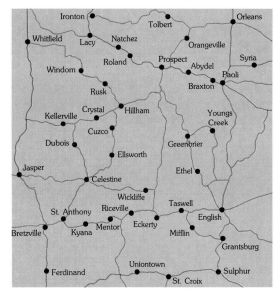

Scale: 1 in. to 20 mi

1. Measure the distance between Eckerty and Taswell. About how many miles is this?

2. Measure the distance between Lacy and Braxton. About how many miles is this?

3. About how many miles is it from Greenbrier to Prospect?

4. How far is it from Paoli to Sulphur?

A scale often used by interior decorators is $\frac{1}{4}$ inch to 1 foot. Use this scale to answer the following questions.

5. What length would represent a room 20 feet long?

6. What length would represent a width of 18 feet?

7. On a drawing, the kitchen is $1\frac{1}{2}$ inches wide. What is the real width?

8. A closet is 1 inch wide on a drawing. What is the real width?

Measure each insect to the nearest $\frac{1}{4}$ inch.

9. Cornfield Ant

Scale: 1 in. to $\frac{1}{2}$ in.

How long is the ant?

10. Two-Spotted Lady Bug

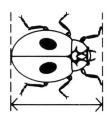

Scale: 1 in. to $\frac{1}{4}$ in.

How long is the lady bug?

EXTRA PRACTICE page 498, set 71

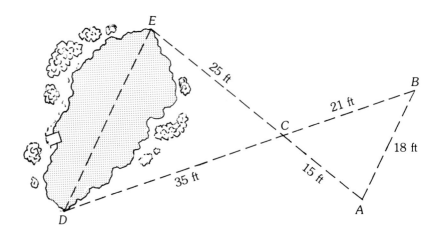

**A surveyor took the measurements shown. △ABC is similar to △EDC. What is the length of the pond?**

**Read:**   *Given:*   the two triangles are similar;
$AB = 18$ ft, $BC = 21$ ft, $AC = 15$ ft,
$DC = 35$ ft, $EC = 25$ ft

*To find:*   the length of the pond (*DE*)

**Plan:**   Solve a proportion to find the missing length.

**Compute:**   $\dfrac{DC}{BC} = \dfrac{35}{21} = \dfrac{5}{3}$ or $\dfrac{EC}{AC} = \dfrac{25}{15} = \dfrac{5}{3}$

$$\dfrac{?}{18} = \dfrac{5}{3}$$

$? \times 3 = 18 \times 5$
$? \times 3 = 90$

What number times 3 equals 90?
To find out, divide 90 by 3.

$90 \div 3 = 30$

So ? = 30.

**Answer:**   The pond is 30 feet long.

**Check:**   $\dfrac{5}{3} \times \dfrac{30}{18} \longrightarrow 3 \times 30 = 90$
$\longrightarrow 5 \times 18 = 90$  ✔

# EXERCISES

**1.**

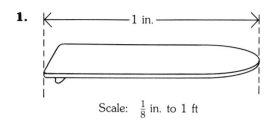

Scale: $\frac{1}{8}$ in. to 1 ft

What is the real length represented by the scale drawing?

**2.**

SALE!
6 greeting cards for $1.50

How many cards can you buy with $6.00?

**3.** A football team has won 8 out of their first 9 games. At that rate, how many games would they win if they play 18 games?

**4.** In an encyclopedia, a picture of an insect is 4 inches long. If the picture of the insect was enlarged by a 3:1 ratio, how long is the insect in real life?

**5.** A picture of a bumblebee was reduced by a ratio of 1:2. What is the wingspan of the bumblebee if the photo shows it to be $\frac{3}{4}$ inch?

**6.** A map uses the scale 1 inch to 21 miles. A $1\frac{1}{2}$-inch length is how many miles?

**7.** A map was drawn to the scale of 1 inch to 5 miles. If the distance between two towns is $2\frac{1}{2}$ inches on the map, how far apart are they?

**8.** The floor plan for a house was drawn to the scale of $\frac{1}{8}$ inch to 1 foot. If the scale drawing is $1\frac{1}{2}$ inches long, how long is the kitchen?

**9.** In a book, an illustration of the planet Mars was drawn to the scale of 1 inch to 2100 miles. If the diameter of the picture is 2 inches, what is the diameter of Mars?

**10.** A scale is $\frac{1}{4}$ inch to 1 foot. If a room measures 12 feet by 16 feet, what dimensions would you draw the floor plan?

**11.** 2 pounds of carrots cost $0.69. How much will 8 pounds cost?

**12.** A photograph measuring $3\frac{1}{2}$ inches wide and $4\frac{3}{8}$ inches high is enlarged so that its width is 8 inches. How high is the enlargement?

*EXTRA PRACTICE page 498, set 72*

P. Beck/FPG

A bricklayer builds and repairs walls, arches, fireplaces, and chimneys. The bricklayer reads a blueprint to find out the designer's plans and then decides the layout to be used.

Where the designer has called for an opening, such as a door or a window, the bricklayer will fit the bricks by cutting them with a hammer and chisel.

Use the blueprint drawing below to answer the following:

**1.** Starting at the left, how many feet of brick should be laid until the first window is reached?

**2.** How many feet in from the right is the start of the first window space?

**3.** How many feet of space are needed for the door?

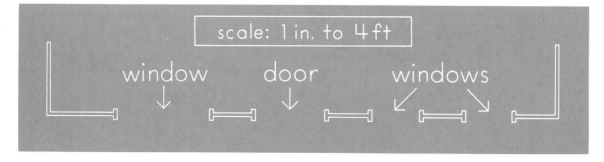

A bricklayer must know how to mix the mortar that is used to hold bricks together. For each 1 part of cement used, 1 part of lime is used and 6 parts of sand are used.

You use 10 pounds of cement. Use proportions to find the amounts needed.

**4.** How much lime should you use?

**5.** How much sand should you use?

Complete.

Words to choose from:  *similar, ratio, scale drawing, proportion.*

**1.** A _____ compares two numbers by division.                                    8.1

**2.** A _____ states that two ratios are equivalent.                                8.3

**3.** _____ figures have the same shape but not neces-                              8.10
sarily the same size.

**4.** A picture drawn to a certain ratio is a _____.                                8.11

Write each ratio in lowest terms.                                                          8.1

**5.**

pens : pencils

**6.**

all figures to squares

First express both amounts in the same unit, and then simplify the ratio.                 8.2

**7.** 7 feet to 3 yards                    **8.** 3 pounds to 40 ounces

**9.** 1 foot to 15 inches                  **10.** 3 nickels to 4 dimes

Express each ratio as a rate.

**11.** 324 miles on 18 gallons             **12.** $50 for 8 hours

**13.** $10.60 for 4 weeks                  **14.** 324 miles in 8 hours

Is each proportion true?                                                                   8.3

**15.** $\frac{1}{2} = \frac{3}{5}$         **16.** $\frac{6}{5} = \frac{12}{10}$          **17.** $\frac{4}{6} = \frac{10}{15}$

**249**

Solve each proportion by copying and completing the table.

**18.** $\frac{2}{1} = \frac{8}{[?]}$

**19.** $\frac{[?]}{8} = \frac{3}{2}$

Solve the proportions by using equivalent fractions.

**20.** $\frac{[?]}{4} = \frac{2}{1}$        **21.** $\frac{3}{4} = \frac{6}{[?]}$        **22.** $\frac{16}{12} = \frac{[?]}{3}$

**23.** $\frac{2}{[?]} = \frac{18}{27}$        **24.** $\frac{6}{[?]} = \frac{12}{32}$        **25.** $\frac{15}{9} = \frac{[?]}{3}$

Solve the proportions by using cross products.

**26.** $\frac{5}{3} = \frac{[?]}{9}$        **27.** $\frac{15}{3} = \frac{25}{[?]}$        **28.** $\frac{[?]}{3} = \frac{28}{12}$

**29.** $\frac{4}{5} = \frac{[?]}{15}$        **30.** $\frac{3}{6} = \frac{[?]}{20}$        **31.** $\frac{2}{8} = \frac{3}{[?]}$

**32.**

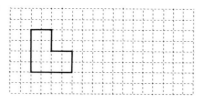

Draw a 3:2 enlargement.

**33.**

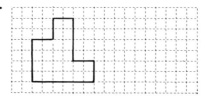

Draw a 1:2 reduction.

**34.**

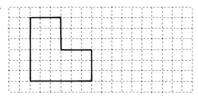

Draw a 2:3 reduction.

**35.**

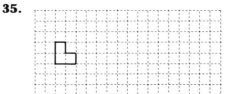

Draw a 3:1 enlargement.

**250**

Use the similar figures to find x.

**36.**

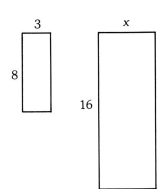

**37.**

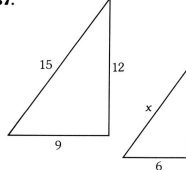

**38.**

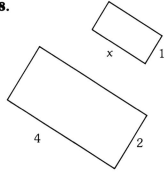

**39.**

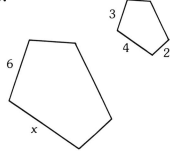

**40.** How long is the room?

**41.** How wide is the room?

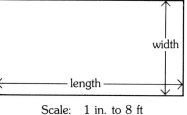

Scale:   1 in. to 8 ft

Solve.

**42.** A map is drawn to the scale of 1 inch to 20 miles. A distance of 85 miles is what length on the map?

**43.** A photograph 3 inches wide and 5 inches high is enlarged to a height of 12 inches. How wide is the enlargement?

**44.** If 2 birthstone rings cost $148, what would 6 rings cost?

*CHAPTER REVIEW*

**1.** ○○○□□△△△△△

Write the ratio of all figures to circles.

**2.** First express both amounts in the same unit, and then simplify the following ratio:   2 hours to 30 minutes.

**3.** Express the following ratio as a rate:   69 miles to 3 gallons.

**4.** Is each proportion true?

a. $\dfrac{5}{4} = \dfrac{15}{12}$

b. $\dfrac{7}{4} = \dfrac{20}{12}$

**5.** Solve the proportion by copying and completing the table.   $\dfrac{?}{28} = \dfrac{5}{4}$

Solve the proportions by using equivalent fractions.

**6.** $\dfrac{6}{9} = \dfrac{?}{12}$

**7.** $\dfrac{12}{8} = \dfrac{6}{?}$

**8.** $\dfrac{8}{?} = \dfrac{4}{3}$

Solve the proportions by using cross products.

**9.** $\dfrac{9}{4} = \dfrac{?}{12}$

**10.** $\dfrac{15}{10} = \dfrac{12}{?}$

**11.** $\dfrac{6}{15} = \dfrac{?}{25}$

**12.**

Draw a 3:1 enlargement.

**13.**

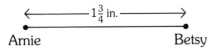

Use the similar figures to find x.

**14.** ←———— $1\frac{3}{4}$ in. ————→

Arnie                    Betsy

Scale:   1 in. to 20 mi.

How far apart do Arnie and Betsy live?

Use proportions to solve.

**15.** 2 pens cost $0.89. How much will 10 pens cost?

**16.** 4 items sell for $12. What would 5 items sell for?

Write a percent for the colored portion of each square.

1.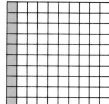

2.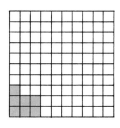

3.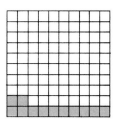

Change each percent to a fraction in lowest terms.

**4.** 87%        **5.** 50%        **6.** 32%        **7.** 4%

Change each percent to a decimal.

**8.** 33%        **9.** 20%        **10.** 97%        **11.** 6%

Change to a percent.

**12.** $\frac{56}{100}$        **13.** 0.05        **14.** $\frac{2}{5}$        **15.** 2

Solve.

**16.** 12 is what percent of 80?

**17.** 14 is 20% of what number?

**18.** Find 20% of 60.

**19.** During a sale, a watch sold for $83.30. If the sale price was 85% of the regular price, what was the regular price?

**20.** A basketball player completed 3 out of 5 free throws. What percent of the player's free throws were completed?

**21.** What is the sale price of a $12 cassette tape if there is a 10% discount?

**22.** What is the commission on sales of $15,000 if the rate of commission is 8%?

**23.** What is the total cost of a $36 radio if there is a 5% sales tax?

**THE MEANING OF PERCENT**

Camerique

The building industry uses 75 out of every 100 pieces, or 75%, of the lumber produced in the United States.

The symbol % is read "percent." **Percent** means "hundredths," "out of each hundred," or "for every hundred." You can think of percents as follows:

| Percent | Think |
|---------|-------|
| 3% | 3 parts out of each 100 parts |
| 25% | 25 parts out of each 100 parts |
| 100% | 100 parts out of each 100 parts |
| 110% | 110 parts for every 100 parts |

**Example 1:** Change each percent to a fraction in lowest terms.

a. $10\% = \dfrac{10}{100}$     b. $3\% = \dfrac{3}{100}$     c. $84\% = \dfrac{84}{100}$

    $= \dfrac{1}{10}$                                     $= \dfrac{21}{25}$

**Example 2:** Change each percent to a decimal.

a. $30\% = \dfrac{30}{100}$     b. $3\% = \dfrac{3}{100}$     c. $66\% = \dfrac{66}{100}$

    $= 0.3$                $= 0.03$              $= 0.66$

Another way to change a percent to a decimal is to move the decimal point two places to the left and drop the percent sign. This shortcut is very helpful when changing percents greater than 100% and fractional percents.

**Example 3:** Change each percent to a decimal.

a. $72\% = .72\% = 0.72$        b. $125\% = 1.25\% = 1.25$

c. $23.5\% = .23\,5\% = 0.235$     d. $0.5\% = .00\,5\% = 0.005$

# EXERCISES

Write a percent for the colored portion of each square.

**1.**     **2.**     **3.**     **4.**

Write as a percent.

**5.** 27 out of each 100    **6.** $\frac{18}{100}$    **7.** $\frac{8}{100}$    **8.** 107 for every 100

Solve.

**9.** Candice Haines earns $175 today for every $100 she earned ten years ago. What percent of her earnings then are her earnings now?

**10.** Jubal Trapp saves $15 out of every $100 he earns. What percent of his earnings does he save?

Change each percent to a fraction in lowest terms.

**11.** 95%    **12.** 35%    **13.** 25%    **14.** 70%    **15.** 1%    **16.** 53%

**17.** 90%    **18.** 4%    **19.** 15%    **20.** 48%    **21.** 88%    **22.** 50%

Change each percent to a decimal.

**23.** 62%    **24.** 17%    **25.** 47%    **26.** 28%    **27.** 8%    **28.** 16%

**29.** 6%    **30.** 40%    **31.** 11%    **32.** 35%    **33.** 76%    **34.** 60%

**35.** 45.6%    **36.** 12.2%    **37.** 350%    **38.** 175%    **39.** 2.2%    **40.** 0.8%

Change each percent to a decimal.

**Example:**   a. $\frac{1}{2}\% = 0.5\%$

$$= .00\,5\% = 0.005$$

b. $24\frac{2}{5}\% = 24.4\%$

$$= .24\,4\% = 0.244$$

**41.** $\frac{1}{5}\%$    **42.** $2\frac{1}{4}\%$    **43.** $\frac{3}{4}\%$    **44.** $\frac{3}{10}\%$    **45.** $43\frac{4}{5}\%$

*EXTRA PRACTICE page 499, set 73*

## 9.2 DECIMALS AND FRACTIONS AS PERCENTS

Photri

People cause $\frac{9}{10}$ of all forest fires. What percent is that?

**Example 1:** $\dfrac{9}{10} = \dfrac{9 \times 10}{10 \times 10} = \dfrac{90}{100} = 90\%$

90% of all forest fires are caused by people.

**Example 2:** Change 0.86 to a percent.

$0.86 = \dfrac{86}{100} = 86\%$

Another way to change a decimal to a percent is to move the decimal point two places to the right and include the percent sign.

**Example 3:**

a. $1.9 = 1\,90\% = 190\%$

b. $0.003 = 0\,00.3\% = 0.3\%$

c. $2\dfrac{3}{5} = 2\dfrac{6}{10}$

$\quad = 2.6$ —— Include a 0.

$\quad = 2\,60\%$

$\quad = 260\%$

# EXERCISES

Write as a fraction with a denominator of 100.

**1.** $\frac{1}{5}$　　**2.** 0.3　　**3.** $\frac{7}{20}$　　**4.** 0.75　　**5.** $\frac{3}{25}$　　**6.** 0.07

Change to a percent.

**7.** 0.85　　**8.** 0.6　　**9.** 0.2　　**10.** 0.25　　**11.** 0.03

**12.** 0.17　　**13.** 0.09　　**14.** 0.4　　**15.** 0.42　　**16.** 0.61

**17.** $\frac{4}{100}$　　**18.** $\frac{87}{100}$　　**19.** $\frac{9}{25}$　　**20.** $\frac{19}{20}$　　**21.** $\frac{3}{5}$

**22.** $\frac{6}{100}$　　**23.** $\frac{2}{5}$　　**24.** $\frac{33}{50}$　　**25.** $\frac{8}{10}$　　**26.** $\frac{1}{2}$

**27.** 1.4　　**28.** 2.67　　**29.** 1　　**30.** $1\frac{1}{4}$　　**31.** $3\frac{2}{5}$

**Example:** $\frac{1}{3} = 0.3333\ \cdots$

$$= 0\ 33.33\ \cdots\ \%$$

$$= 33.\overline{3}\%\ \text{(often written } 33\frac{1}{3}\%)$$

**32.** $\frac{2}{3}$　　　　**33.** $1\frac{1}{3}$　　　　**34.** $1\frac{2}{3}$　　　　**35.** $\frac{1}{6}$

Copy and complete each table.

| | Fraction | Decimal | Percent | | Fraction | Decimal | Percent |
|---|---|---|---|---|---|---|---|
| **36.** | $\frac{3}{4}$ | — | — | **37.** | $\frac{3}{25}$ | — | — |
| **38.** | — | 0.7 | — | **39.** | — | 0.04 | — |
| **40.** | $\frac{4}{5}$ | — | — | **41.** | — | 0.55 | — |

Solve.

**42.** Forests cover 0.3 of all the land on earth. What percent is that?

**43.** Forests cover $\frac{1}{10}$ of the land in North Dakota. What percent is that?

EXTRA PRACTICE page 499, set 74

## 9.3 FINDING A PERCENT OF A GIVEN NUMBER

S. Berkowitz/Taurus

**A car's radiator holds 15 quarts. For the car's radiator to contain 40% antifreeze, how many quarts of antifreeze should be used?**

To solve percent problems use the proportion

$$\frac{\text{part}}{\text{whole}} = \frac{\text{percent amount}}{100}$$

**Example 1:**  Find 40% of 15.

$$\frac{\text{part} \longrightarrow \boxed{?}}{\text{whole} \longrightarrow 15} = \frac{40 \longleftarrow \text{percent amount}}{100 \longleftarrow 100}$$

$\boxed{?} \times 100 = 15 \times 40$  **Find the cross products.**

$\boxed{?} \times 100 = 600$  **What number times 100 equals 600?**

$600 \div 100 = 6$  **To find out, divide 600 by 100.**

**So $\boxed{?} = 6$.**

So, 6 quarts of antifreeze should be used.

The problem could also be solved by writing the percent as a decimal and using the rule

percent × whole = part

**Example 2:**  Find 40% of 15.

$$0.4 \times 15 = \boxed{?}$$

**Use the decimal** ⬆  $6 = \boxed{?}$
**form for the percent.**

## EXERCISES

Find each number.

1. 45% of 40   2. 60% of 10   3. 25% of 36   4. 20% of 55

5. 50% of 24   6. 75% of 24   7. 84% of 50   8. 6% of 800

258

Solve.

**9.** What number is 40% of 30?

**10.** What number is 29% of 200?

**11.** What number is 35% of 140?

**12.** What number is 9% of 200?

**13.** What number is 90% of 170?

**14.** What number is 125% of 60?

**15.** What number is 100% of 35?

**16.** What number is 18% of 760?

**17.** What number is 5% of 36?

**18.** What number is 4% of 8.2?

**19.** What number is 12.5% of 45?

**20.** What number is 0.5% of 125?

**21.** What number is 4.5% of 70?

**22.** What number is 275% of 30.5?

**23.** What number is 150% of 8?

**24.** What number is 2.5% of 300?

**25.** What number is $\frac{1}{2}$% of 40?

**26.** What number is $10\frac{3}{5}$% of 50?

**27.** What number is $33\frac{1}{3}$% of 3?

**28.** What number is $66\frac{2}{3}$% of 15?

EXTRA PRACTICE page 499, set 75

## CALCULATOR NOTE

Some calculators have a %  key. To find 18% of 30, use the following key sequence:

ENTER                    DISPLAY

**30**  ×   **18**  %      *5.4*

If your calculator does not have a percent key, use the alternate method.

ENTER                    DISPLAY

**30**  ×   **0.18**  =      *5.4*

Use a calculator to check your answers to the exercises.

Schiappa/Picture Group

**Homeowners in Clark County have to pay a property tax that is 4% of the value of their property. What is the tax on property valued at $68,000?**

**Read:**  *Given:*  4% tax; $68,000 property value

*To find:*  amount of tax

**Plan:**  Find 4% of 68,000.

**Compute:**

$$\frac{\boxed{?}}{68,000} = \frac{4}{100}$$

$\boxed{?} \times 100 = 68,000 \times 4$   **Find the cross products.**

$\boxed{?} \times 100 = 272,000$   **What number times 100 equals 272,000?**

$272,000 \div 100 = 2720$   **To find out, divide 272,000 by 100.**

So $\boxed{?} = 2720.$

**Answer:**  The property tax is $2720.

**Check:**  You can use the alternate method to check the result.

$0.04 \times 68,000 = \boxed{?}$

$2720 = \boxed{?}$  ✔

## EXERCISES

**1.** Bill's health insurance will pay 80% of the cost of his hospital bill. The hospital bill was $1675. How much of the bill will be paid by the insurance company?

**2.** The Federal Housing Authority requires that the minimum window area be 10% of the floor area. If the floor area is 225 square feet, what is the minimum window area?

**3.** How much is a 15% tip on a bill for $25?

**4.** About 70% of a person's body weight is water. If a person weighs 115 pounds, how much of that weight is water?

**5.** Hannah wants to put 20% down on a video recorder. The recorder costs $995. How much is the down payment?

**6.** Michael spends 30% of his income for rent. His monthly income is $1200. How much does he pay each month in rent?

**7.** The retail price of a ski jacket is 175% of the wholesale price. If the wholesale price is $72, what is the retail price?

**8.** About 28.2% of the population is under 18 years of age. Out of every 500 persons, about how many are under 18 years of age?

**9.** Fran saves 15% of the money she earns. She earns $25 a week. How much does she save each week?

**10.** Women make up $51\frac{3}{5}\%$ of the labor force. Out of every 500 workers, about how many are women?

## SKILLS REVIEW

Find each answer.

| | | | | | | | |
|---|---|---|---|---|---|---|---|
| **11.** | $\begin{array}{r} 96 \\ +72 \\ \hline \end{array}$ | **12.** | $\begin{array}{r} 105 \\ +\ 83 \\ \hline \end{array}$ | **13.** | $\begin{array}{r} 107 \\ -\ 92 \\ \hline \end{array}$ | **14.** | $\begin{array}{r} 380 \\ -\ 76 \\ \hline \end{array}$ |
| **15.** | $\begin{array}{r} 5.2 \\ +0.9 \\ \hline \end{array}$ | **16.** | $\begin{array}{r} 6.3 \\ +5.7 \\ \hline \end{array}$ | **17.** | $\begin{array}{r} 12.1 \\ -\ 0.8 \\ \hline \end{array}$ | **18.** | $\begin{array}{r} 10.61 \\ -\ 5.2 \\ \hline \end{array}$ |
| **19.** | $\begin{array}{r} 2460 \\ +\ 983 \\ \hline \end{array}$ | **20.** | $\begin{array}{r} 956 \\ -705 \\ \hline \end{array}$ | **21.** | $\begin{array}{r} 9.07 \\ +0.78 \\ \hline \end{array}$ | **22.** | $\begin{array}{r} 6.08 \\ -2.8 \\ \hline \end{array}$ |

McMichael/Picture Group

**An apple that weighs 175 grams contains about 147 grams of water. What percent of the apple is water?**

**Example 1:**   147 is what percent of 175?

$$\frac{\text{part} \longrightarrow 147}{\text{whole} \longrightarrow 175} = \frac{\boxed{?} \longleftarrow \text{percent amount}}{100 \longleftarrow 100}$$

$175 \times \boxed{?} = 147 \times 100$   **Find the cross products.**

$175 \times \boxed{?} = 14{,}700$   **175 times what number equals 14,700? To find out, divide 14,700 by 175.**

$14{,}700 \div 175 = 84$

So $\boxed{?} = 84.$

84% of the apple is water.

You could also solve the problem by using the rule

percent × whole = part

**Example 2:**   147 is what percent of 175?

$\boxed{?} \times 175 = 147$   **What number times 175 equals 147?**

$147 \div 175 = 0.84$   **To find out, divide 147 by 175.**

So $\boxed{?} = 0.84. \longrightarrow 84\%$   **Change the decimal to a percent.**

## EXERCISES

Solve.

1. 4 is what percent of 16?

2. 12 is what percent of 80?

3. 3 is what percent of 15?

4. 7 is what percent of 25?

5. 28 is what percent of 80?

6. 14 is what percent of 20?

7. 24 is what percent of 240?

8. 27 is what percent of 45?

9. 13 is what percent of 25?

10. 90 is what percent of 150?

11. 34 is what percent of 200?

12. 45 is what percent of 90?

13. 48 is what percent of 160?

14. 60 is what percent of 80?

15. 42 is what percent of 120?

16. 86 is what percent of 200?

17. 23 is what percent of 115?

18. 105 is what percent of 300?

19. 9 is what percent of 6?

20. 32.5 is what percent of 26?

21. 17.64 is what percent of 420?

22. 0.175 is what percent of 35?

23. 1 is what percent of 3?

24. 2 is what percent of 3?

25. One cup of skim milk contains about 300 milligrams of calcium. The recommended daily allowance (RDA) of calcium is 1200 milligrams. What percent of the RDA of calcium is in a cup of skim milk?

*EXTRA PRACTICE page 500, set 76*

---

## CALCULATOR NOTE

To check your results to problems like those above, multiply the *whole* by your answer and see if the part is the result.

**Example:** 21 is what percent of 84?   Answer:   25%

|  | ENTER | | | | DISPLAY |
|---|---|---|---|---|---|
| **Check:** | **84** | ×  | **25** | %  | *21* |

**Liz received 57 votes for class president. If 95 votes were cast, what percent of the votes did she receive?**

**Read:**   *Given:*   Liz got 57 votes. 95 votes were cast.

   *To find:*   What percent of the votes did Liz get?

**Plan:**   57 is what percent of 95?

**Compute:**
$$\frac{57}{95} = \frac{\boxed{?}}{100}$$

$95 \times \boxed{?} = 57 \times 100$   **Find the cross products.**

$95 \times \boxed{?} = 5700$   **What number times 95 equals 5700?**

$5700 \div 95 = 60$   **To find out, divide 5700 by 95.**

So $\boxed{?} = 60$.

**Answer:**   Liz received 60% of the votes.

**Check:**   A good way to check this problem is to find 60% of 95.

$0.6 \times 95 = 57$

⌐This agrees with the given information.

So, 60% is correct.   ✔

# EXERCISES

1. Liz answered 48 out of 50 questions correctly. What percent is that?

2. A machine produced 50 parts. 3 of the parts were defective. What percent of the parts were defective?

3. Of 750 people polled, 630 preferred Brand X. What percent of the people preferred Brand X?

4. The Larsons spend $55 a week for food. If the Larsons earn $137.50 a week, what percent of their earnings is spent on food?

5. There are 5600 registered voters in Clay County. 3500 people voted in the last election. What percent of the registered voters voted?

6. Steve answered 23 out of 25 questions on the math test correctly. What percent of the questions did he answer correctly?

7. A car's highway mileage is 30 miles to the gallon. Its city mileage is 25 miles to the gallon. What percent of the city mileage is the highway mileage?

8. For every 200 people in the United States, 11 are between the ages of 10 and 14. What percent of the population is between the ages of 10 and 14?

9. 268 out of each 400 television sets sold last year were color sets. What percent of the television sets were color?

10. The Salvation Army collected $15,700. Their goal was $20,000. What percent of their goal did they reach?

EXTRA PRACTICE page 500, set 77

## SKILLS REVIEW

Find each answer.

11. $\begin{array}{r} 36 \\ \times 9 \\ \hline \end{array}$

12. $9\overline{)36}$

13. $\begin{array}{r} 180 \\ \times 15 \\ \hline \end{array}$

14. $15\overline{)180}$

15. $\begin{array}{r} 5.06 \\ \times 2.2 \\ \hline \end{array}$

16. $2.2\overline{)5.06}$

17. $\begin{array}{r} 4.095 \\ \times 1.3 \\ \hline \end{array}$

18. $1.3\overline{)4.095}$

19. $\begin{array}{r} 506 \\ \times 115 \\ \hline \end{array}$

20. $115\overline{)506}$

21. $\begin{array}{r} 6.2 \\ \times 0.186 \\ \hline \end{array}$

22. $6.2\overline{)0.186}$

## FINDING THE WHOLE, GIVEN THE PART AND THE PERCENT

Jim Whitmer

**A shop advertised that you could save $6 if you bought a shirt during the 20%-off sale. What was the original cost of the shirt?**

**Example 1:** 6 is 20% of what number?

$$\frac{\text{part}}{\text{whole}} = \frac{\text{percent amount}}{100}$$

$$\frac{6}{?} = \frac{20}{100}$$

$? \times 20 = 6 \times 100$    **Find the cross products.**

$? \times 20 = 600$    **What number times 20 equals 600?**

$600 \div 20 = 30$    **To find out, divide 600 by 20.**

So $? = 30$.

The shirt originally cost $30. Another way to solve the problem is to write the percent as a decimal and use the rule

percent × whole = part

**Example 2:** 6 is 20% of what number?

Use the decimal ⟶ $0.2 \times ? = 6$    0.2 times what number equals 6?
form for the percent.    $6 \div 0.2 = 30$    To find out, divide 6 by 0.2.

So $? = 30$.
↑
**original cost**

## EXERCISES

Solve.

**1.** 9 is 15% of what number?

**2.** 7 is 25% of what number?

**3.** 9 is 20% of what number?

**4.** 10 is 5% of what number?

**5.** 4 is 25% of what number?

**6.** 3 is 15% of what number?

**7.** 100 is 25% of what number?

**8.** 6 is 30% of what number?

**9.** 66 is 150% of what number?

**10.** 18 is 5% of what number?

**11.** 3 is 0.5% of what number?

**12.** 63 is $15\frac{3}{4}$% of what number?

Find the original cost of each item.

| 15% off | |
| --- | --- |
| Item | Amount off |
| **13.** jeans | $3 |
| **15.** jacket | $6 |
| **17.** sweater | $3.60 |
| **19.** boots | $5.70 |

| 20% off | |
| --- | --- |
| Item | Amount off |
| **14.** slacks | $6 |
| **16.** belt | $2 |
| **18.** robe | $4.40 |
| **20.** hat | $3.60 |

*EXTRA PRACTICE page 500, set 78*

## CHECKPOINT

Change to a fraction or a mixed numeral. Simplify.

**1.** 84%  **2.** 70%  **3.** 2%  **4.** 115%  **5.** 0.3%

Change to a decimal.

**6.** 92%  **7.** 80%  **8.** 1%  **9.** 125%  **10.** 0.5%

Change to a percent.

**11.** 0.6  **12.** $\frac{1}{5}$  **13.** 0.02  **14.** $7\frac{1}{2}$  **15.** 0.007

Solve.

**16.** Find 18% of 54.  **17.** 67.5 is 15% of what number?  **18.** 8 is what percent of 25?

**19.** About 43% of a person's body weight is muscle. If a person weighs 120 pounds, what amount of that weight is muscle?

**20.** Bone makes up about 21 pounds of a 120-pound person's body weight. What percent of that person's body weight is bone?

**267**

Jacqueline Durand

Evan works at a department store. Since he is an employee, he has to pay only **80%** of the price of anything he buys in the store. He has **$24** to buy a pair of roller skates. What is the price of the most expensive pair of skates he can buy?

**Read:** *Given:* pays 80%; has $24

*To find:* original price of the skates

**Plan:** 24 is 80% of what number?

**Compute:**

$$\frac{24}{\boxed{?}} = \frac{80}{100}$$

$\boxed{?} \times 80 = 24 \times 100$   Find the cross products.

$\boxed{?} \times 80 = 2400$   What number times 80 equals 2400?

$2400 \div 80 = 30$   To find out, divide 2400 by 80.

So $\boxed{?} = 30$.

**Answer:** He can buy a $30 pair of skates.

**Check:** Is 80% of 30 equal to 24?

$0.8 \times 30 = 24$ ✔

## EXERCISES

1. Insurance covered all but 30% of the cost of repairing a car. If the owner had to pay $258, how much did it cost to repair the car?

2. The Hidalgos want to be able to make a 20% down payment on a house. They have saved $13,600. How expensive a house can they buy?

3. A manufacturer knows that only 92% of the parts a machine produces are usable. To fill an order for 4600 usable parts, how many parts must the machine produce?

4. Mark bought an old car for $300. He intends to repair it and sell it for a profit. If he wants his purchase price to be 30% of the selling price, what should the selling price be?

5. During a sale, a bicycle sold for $157.25. If the sale price was 85% of the regular price, what was the regular price?

6. Midville's population of 8800 is 110% of last year's population. What was the population last year?

7. A family had to pay a property tax that was 2.5% of the value of their property. They paid $1450 in tax. What was the value of their property?

8. A bank pays 10.5% a year in interest on one kind of savings account. How much would you have to have in the account to get $63 in yearly interest?

EXTRA PRACTICE page 501, set 79

## MATH NOTE

What do you call a cold-weather jogger?

To find the answer:

1. Change each fraction or decimal to a percent.

2. Match the percent to a letter in the code box.

3. Write the letter on the blank.

Code Box

| | |
|---|---|
| A=0.5% | E=5% |
| I=25% | L=0.25% |
| N=20% | P=50% |
| R=125% | S=2.5% |
| T=12.5% | W=2% |

0.02    $\frac{1}{4}$    0.2    $\frac{1}{8}$    $\frac{1}{20}$    1.25

____   ____   ____   ____   ____   ____

0.025    $\frac{1}{2}$    $1\frac{1}{4}$    0.25    $\frac{1}{5}$    0.125    0.05    $\frac{5}{4}$

____   ____   ____   ____   ____   ____   ____   ____

**What is the total cost of a $149 record turntable if there is a 6% sales tax?**

To find the total cost:

1. Find the amount of tax.

2. Add the tax to the original cost.

**Example:**

Step 1:   Find 6% of 149.

$$\frac{\boxed{?}}{149} = \frac{6}{100}$$

So $\boxed{?} = 8.94.$ ⟵ **tax**

Step 2:   Add.

$149 + 8.94 = 157.94$ ⟵ **total cost**

The total cost of the turntable is $157.94.

# EXERCISES

Given the price and the percent of the sales tax, find the total cost.

**1.** $25, 6%      **2.** $54, 5%      **3.** $125, 5%      **4.** $35.50, 6%

**5.** $76, 5.5%      **6.** $350, 6%      **7.** $84, 4%      **8.** $68, $4\frac{1}{2}$%

What is the total cost of each item if there is a 5% sales tax?

**9.** headphones, $23

**10.** cassette tape, $5

**11.** speakers, $230

**12.** receiver, $167.80

**13.** tape deck, $109

**14.** radio, $59

EXTRA PRACTICE page 501, set 80

As a result of inflation, a bag of groceries that cost $24.20 last month now costs $25.41. What is the percent of increase in the cost of the groceries?

To find the percent of decrease or increase, find the amount of change by subtracting, and then solve the following proportion:

$$\frac{\text{amount of change}}{\text{original number}} = \frac{\text{percent amount}}{100}$$

**Example:** Find the percent of increase from $24.20 to $25.41.

Subtract to find the amount of change.

$$25.41 - 24.20 = 1.21$$   The amount of change is an increase of $1.21.

Solve the proportion.

$$\frac{1.21}{24.20} = \frac{?}{100}$$

$$24.20 \times ? = 1.21 \times 100 \quad \text{Find the cross products.}$$

$$24.20 \times ? = 121$$

$$121 \div 24.20 = 5$$

$$\text{So } ? = 5.$$

The percent of increase is 5%. ⟵ The answer must always state either increase or decrease.

Find the percent of increase or decrease.

1. from 5 to 6                    2. from 25 to 29

3. from 15 to 12                  4. from 600 to 450

5. from 540 to 675               6. from 1200 to 1050

7. Last year Tim's monthly rent was $320. This year his monthly rent is $368. What is the percent of change from last year to this year?

8. The Sims' electric bill was $55 in May but $60.50 in June. What was the percent of change from May to June?

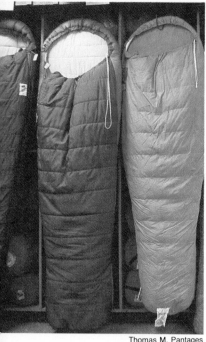

Thomas M. Pantages

**A $90 sleeping bag is on sale at a 15% discount. What is the sale price of the sleeping bag?**

To find the sale price:

1. Find the amount of the discount.

2. Subtract the discount from the original price.

**Example 1:**

Step 1:   Find 15% of 90.

$$\frac{\boxed{?}}{90} = \frac{15}{100}$$

So $\boxed{?} = 13.50$.

↑ —— **amount of discount**

Step 2:   Subtract.   **$90 - 13.50 = 76.50$**

↑ ——**sale price**

The sale price is $76.50.

If there is a 15% discount, then you are paying $100\% - 15\%$, or 85%, of the original cost. So, another way to find the sale price is to find 85% of $90.

**Example 2:**   Find 85% of 90.

$$\frac{\boxed{?}}{90} = \frac{85}{100}$$

$\boxed{?} \times 100 = 90 \times 85$   **Find the cross products.**

$\boxed{?} \times 100 = 7650$   **What number times 100 equals 7650? To find out, divide 7650 by 100.**

$7650 \div 100 = 76.50$

So $\boxed{?} = 76.50$.

The sale price is $76.50.

# EXERCISES

Given the original price and the percent of discount, find the amount of the discount and the sale price.

**1.** $50, 20%         **2.** $60, 15%         **3.** $50, 15%         **4.** $75, 15%

**5.** $9.50, 20%       **6.** $185, 30%        **7.** $112.50, 20%     **8.** $8.95, 20%

Given the original price and the percent of discount, find the sale price.

**9.** $45, 9%          **10.** $118, 25%       **11.** $450, 12%       **12.** $25, 16%

**13.** $23.50, 30%     **14.** $74.50, 20%     **15.** $126, 18%       **16.** $2580, 15%

**17.** A store offers a 20% discount on the following items. Find the sale price of each item.
tent, $250
backpack, $28
sleeping bag, $52

**18.** The store offers a 15% discount on the following items. What is the sale price of each item?
flashlight, $18
first-aid kit, $35
compass, $9

Find the total cost.

**Example:**   original price $30; discount 15%; sales tax 6%

1.  $\dfrac{?}{30} = \dfrac{15}{100}$

    $? = 4.50$

    ↑

    **discount**

2.      30
       − 4.50
        25.50

        ↑

    **sale price**

3.  $\dfrac{?}{25.50} = \dfrac{6}{100}$

    $? = 1.53$

    ↑

    **sales tax**

4.      25.50
       + 1.53
        27.03

        ↑

    **total cost**

| Original price | Percent of discount | Percent of sales tax |
|---|---|---|
| **19.** $127 | 20% | 5% |
| **20.** $299 | 25% | 4% |
| **21.** $8.50 | 20% | 5% |
| **22.** $22.75 | 20% | 5% |

EXTRA PRACTICE page 501, set 81

| **COMMISSIONS** |

Brent Jones

A salesperson is often paid on **commission.** A salesperson that has sales of $650 and receives a 14% commission would be paid 14% of $650.

**Example:** Find 14% of 650.

$$\frac{\boxed{?}}{650} = \frac{14}{100}$$

$\boxed{?} \times 100 = 650 \times 14$    **Find the cross products.**

$\boxed{?} \times 100 = 9100$    **What number times 100**

$9100 \div 100 = 91$    **equals 9100? To find out, divide 1900 by 100.**

So $\boxed{?} = 91$.

The salesperson would be paid $91.

## EXERCISES

Copy and complete.

| | Sales | Rate of commission | Amount of commission |
|---|---|---|---|
| **1.** | $550 | 20% | ___ |
| **2.** | $780 | 15% | ___ |
| **3.** | $1550 | 6% | ___ |
| **4.** | $4000 | ___ | $200 |
| **5.** | ___ | 20% | $460 |

Solve.

**6.** What is the commission on sales of $1500 if the rate of commission is 12%?

**7.** A real-estate agency charges a 6.5% commission rate. If the agency sells the Chinns' house for $72,000, how much commission must the Chinns pay to the agency?

EXTRA PRACTICE page 502, set 82

SPORTS STATISTICS

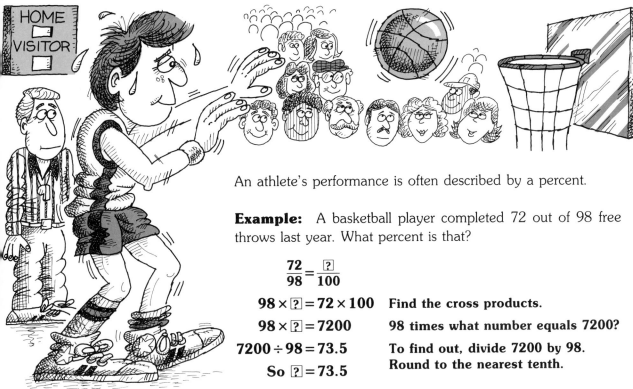

An athlete's performance is often described by a percent.

**Example:** A basketball player completed 72 out of 98 free throws last year. What percent is that?

$$\frac{72}{98} = \frac{\boxed{?}}{100}$$

| | |
|---|---|
| $98 \times \boxed{?} = 72 \times 100$ | **Find the cross products.** |
| $98 \times \boxed{?} = 7200$ | **98 times what number equals 7200?** |
| $7200 \div 98 = 73.5$ | **To find out, divide 7200 by 98.** |
| So $\boxed{?} = 73.5$ | **Round to the nearest tenth.** |

The player made 73.5% of the free throws.

## EXERCISES

If necessary, round to the nearest tenth when dividing.

1. A baseball player has a 0.340 batting average. What percent is that?

2. A field-goal kicker made 5 out of 6 field-goal attempts. What percent is that?

3. A basketball player completed 5 out of 7 free throws. What percent is that?

4. A quarterback completed 11 out of 15 passes in a game. What percent of the passes were completed?

5. A basketball player makes 0.42 of her field-goal attempts. What percent of her field-goal attempts does she make?

6. A basketball player makes 0.62 of his free-throw attempts. What percent of his free-throw attempts does he make?

*EXTRA PRACTICE page 502, set 83*

A real-estate agent helps people buy and sell property. The agent shows property that is for sale and looks for property for clients to buy. Most agents work for an agency or a company. When property is sold, the real-estate company receives a commission, which is figured as a percent of the selling price. The agent then receives a percent of this commission.

Horan/Picture Group

A real-estate company sold a house for $78,800. The company's commission is 6% of the selling price of the house. The real-estate agent receives 55% of the company's commission. How much money will the real-estate agent receive for selling the house?

**6% of 78,800 = 4728** ⟵ **the real-estate company's commission**

**55% of 4728 = 2600.4**

The real-estate agent will receive $2600.40.

Find how much money the real-estate agent would receive, given the selling price of the property, the real-estate company's commission rate, and the percent the real-estate agent receives of the commission.

**1.** $65,400; 6%; 55%  **2.** $80,000; 6.5%; 50%

**3.** $136,000; 6%; 58%  **4.** $250,000; 6%; 50%

# CHAPTER REVIEW

**1.** % means (hundredths, hundreds).　　　　　　　　　　　　　9.1

**2.** Sales tax is (added to, subtracted from) the cost of an item.　　　9.9

**3.** The amount of discount is (added to, subtracted from) the original price
of an item.　　9.10

Write a percent for the colored portion of each square.　　　　　9.1

**4.** 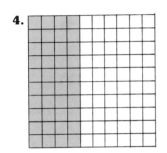　　**5.** 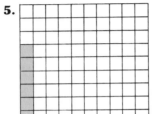　　**6.**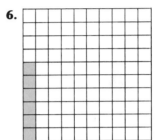

**7.** 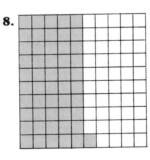　　**8.** 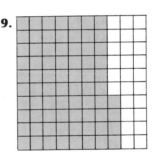　　**9.**

Change each percent to a fraction in lowest terms.

**10.** 36%　　　**11.** 10%　　　**12.** 2%　　　**13.** 13%

Change each percent to a decimal.

**14.** 48%　　　**15.** 67%　　　**16.** 30%　　　**17.** 4%

**18.** 125%　　　**19.** 12.2%　　　**20.** 150%　　　**21.** 0.5%

Copy and complete the table.

| | Fraction | Decimal | Percent | |
|---|---|---|---|---|
| **22.** | —— | —— | 3% | 9.1 |
| **23.** | —— | 0.4 | —— | 9.2 |
| **24.** | $\frac{1}{2}$ | —— | —— | |
| **25.** | —— | 0.27 | —— | |
| **26.** | —— | 0.06 | —— | |
| **27.** | $\frac{1}{20}$ | —— | —— | |

Change to a percent.

**28.** 6.3        **29.** 0.002        **30.** 5.4        **31.** $3\frac{1}{5}$

**32.** What number is 50% of 24?        9.3

**33.** What number is 100% of 160?

**34.** What number is 65% of 11?

**35.** 21 is what percent of 84?        9.5

**36.** 2.8 is what percent of 56?

**37.** 0.72 is what percent of 12?

**38.** 4 is 25% of what number?        9.7

**39.** 63 is 60% of what number?

Given the price and the percent of sales tax, find the total cost.        9.9

**40.** $100, 5%        **41.** $185, 6%        **42.** $215, 5%

**43.** $55, 6%        **44.** $30, 5.5%        **45.** $112.80, 5%

Given the original price and the percent of discount, find the sale price.  9.10

**46.** $80, 20%          **47.** $249, 25%          **48.** $125, 15%

**49.** $35, 15%          **50.** $8.50, 20%          **51.** $215.50, 20%

Copy and complete the table.  9.11

| Sales | Rate of commission | Amount of commission |
|-------|-------------------|---------------------|
| **52.** $3320 | 5% | ____ |
| **53.** $5200 | 8% | ____ |
| **54.** $23,100 | 6% | ____ |
| **55.** $56,800 | 8% | ____ |

Solve.

**56.** The Clarks' dinner bill was $55. If they left a 15% tip, how much did they leave for a tip?  9.4

**57.** On one airline flight, 92 out of 115 available seats were sold. What percent of the seats were sold?  9.6

**58.** If you answered 28 out of 35 questions on a test correctly, what percent of the questions did you answer correctly?

**59.** The property tax in one city is 4% of the value of the property. If the Millers paid $3120 in tax, what was the value of their property?  9.8

**60.** What is the total cost of a $469 video recorder if there is a 6% sales tax?  9.9

**61.** An appliance store was having a 20%-off sale. A dishwasher regularly sold for $259. What was the sale price of the dishwasher?  9.10

**62.** What is the commission on sales of $1600 if the commission rate is 15%?  9.11

**63.** A quarterback completed 17 out of 25 passes in a game. What percent is that?  9.12

Write a percent for the colored portion of each square.

**1.** 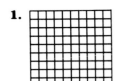   **2.** 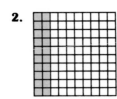   **3.**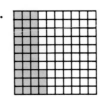

Change each percent to a fraction in lowest terms.

**4.** 63%          **5.** 30%          **6.** 5%          **7.** 24%

Change each percent to a decimal.

**8.** 47%          **9.** 10%          **10.** 3%          **11.** 48%

Change to a percent.

**12.** $\frac{1}{4}$          **13.** 0.03          **14.** 1.56          **15.** $2\frac{1}{2}$

Solve.

**16.** Find 36% of 250.

**17.** What number is 35% of 180?

**18.** 2.2 is what percent of 44?

**19.** 17 is 20% of what number?

**20.** What is the total cost of a $145 tape deck if there is a 5% sales tax?

**21.** What is the sale price of a $120 bicycle if there is a 15% discount?

**22.** What is the commission on sales of $550 if the commission rate is 16%?

**23.** A quarterback completed 15 out of 20 passes in a game. What percent is that?

**24.** Out of 500 parts a machine produced, 6 were defective. What percent of the parts were defective?

**25.** A bank pays 6.5% a year in interest. How much would you have to have in an account to get $130 in yearly interest?

For each segment below, find the length in millimeters. Then rewrite the same length, using centimeters.

**1.** ——————————————— **2.** ——————————

Draw line segments with the following lengths:

**3.** 2.5 cm **4.** 63 mm

Choose the most reasonable measurement.

**5.** length of a baseball bat
50 cm   1 m   0.7 km

**6.** width of a sidewalk
2 km   2 cm   2 m

**7.** weight of an orange
200 mg   200 g   200 kg

**8.** weight of a vitamin tablet
100 mg   100 g   100 kg

**9.** capacity of a can of motor oil
10 L   1 L   100 mL

**10.** capacity of a can of soup
300 mL   3 L   30 mL

**11.** temperature on a cold winter day
55°F   63°F   5°F

**12.** temperature of boiling water
212°C   85°C   100°C

Copy and complete.

**13.** 410 m = ___ km     **14.** 3.1 m = ___ cm     **15.** 28 cm = ___ mm

**16.** 8.1 km = ___ m     **17.** 279 cm = ___ m     **18.** 84 mm = ___ cm

**19.** 670 g = ___ kg     **20.** 58 kg = ___ g     **21.** 700 mg = ___ g

**22.** 28 g = ___ mg     **23.** 6 L = ___ mL     **24.** 925 mL = ___ L

Solve.

**25.** Diane swam 900 meters. Jason swam 0.7 kilometer. Who swam farther? By how much?

**26.** Nathan feeds his dog 2 cans of dog food each day. If one can contains 182 grams of food, how many kilograms of food does the dog eat per day?

**281**

This ruler can be used to measure lengths in **centimeters** and in **millimeters**.

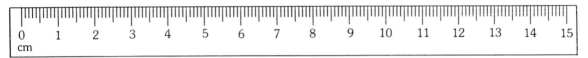

1 centimeter (cm) is the distance between each pair of numbered marks. Each centimeter is divided into 10 equal spaces. So each small space is 0.1 cm.

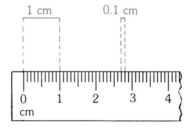

1 millimeter (mm) is the distance across each small space.

That is, 1 mm = 0.1 cm.

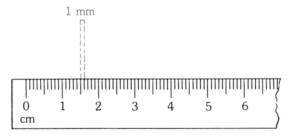

When you use a metric ruler to measure a length, you can express the measurement in millimeters and in centimeters.

**Example:**

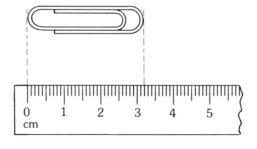

The length of the paper clip is 32 mm, or 3.2 cm.

## EXERCISES

Choose the most reasonable measurement.

**1.** length of a pencil
   19 cm   19 mm   1.9 cm

**2.** width of a dime
   20 cm   1.7 cm   37 mm

**3.** width of a quarter
   24 mm   4.4 cm   24 cm

**4.** thickness of a nickel
   2 mm   2 cm   1.2 cm

**5.** length of a dollar bill
   15.6 cm   96 mm   11 cm

**6.** length of a sewing needle
   32 mm   32 cm   13.2 cm

For each segment below, find the length in millimeters. Then rewrite the same length, using centimeters.

**7.** ⎯⎯⎯⎯⎯⎯⎯⎯⎯⎯⎯⎯⎯⎯⎯

**8.** ⎯⎯⎯⎯⎯⎯⎯⎯⎯⎯⎯⎯⎯⎯⎯⎯⎯

**9.** ⎯⎯⎯⎯⎯⎯⎯⎯⎯⎯⎯⎯⎯⎯

**10.** ⎯⎯⎯⎯⎯⎯

**11.** ⎯⎯⎯⎯⎯⎯⎯⎯⎯⎯⎯⎯⎯⎯⎯⎯⎯⎯⎯⎯⎯

**12.** ⎯⎯⎯⎯⎯⎯⎯⎯⎯⎯⎯⎯⎯⎯⎯⎯

Draw line segments with the following lengths:

**13.** 29 mm

**14.** 61 mm

**15.** 7.4 cm

**16.** 3.9 cm

**17.** 10.2 cm

**18.** 56 mm

**19.** 1.7 cm

**20.** 89 mm

*EXTRA PRACTICE page 502, set 84*

The basic unit of length in the metric system is the **meter.** Prefixes are used with the word *meter* to name other units of length. The meanings of these prefixes are related to the place values used for numbers.

| place values | thousand | hundred | ten | one | tenth | hundredth | thousandth |
|---|---|---|---|---|---|---|---|
| prefix | kilo | hecto | deka | (none) | deci | centi | milli |
| metric units of length | kilometer (km) | hectometer (hm) | dekameter (dam) | meter (m) | decimeter (dm) | centimeter (cm) | millimeter (mm) |

1 km  = 1000 m

1 hm  = 100 m

1 dam = 10 m

1 dm  = 0.1 m

1 cm  = 0.01 m

1 mm  = 0.001 m

The most commonly used units of length are the **meter,** the **millimeter,** the **centimeter,** and the **kilometer.**

1 m

The distance from a doorknob to the floor is about 1 **meter.**

 1 mm   The thickness of this macrame cord is about 1 **millimeter.**

1 cm

| 1 | ABC 2 | DEF 3 |
|---|---|---|

The width of a push button on a telephone is about 1 **centimeter.**

1 km

The distance of 5 city blocks is about 1 **kilometer.**

## EXERCISES

Choose the correct answer.

**1.** A kilometer is (10, 100, 1000) meters.   **2.** A meter is (10, 100, 1000) centimeters.

**3.** A meter is (10, 100, 1000) millimeters.

Complete each statement with *mm, cm, m,* or *km* so that the statement is reasonable.

**4.** The length of a cross-country ski trail is 10 ___.

**5.** The length of a swimming pool is 25 ___.

**6.** The width of camera film is 35 ___.

**7.** The width of a small pearl earring is 3 ___.

**8.** The length of a bus route is 55 ___.

**9.** The length of a building lot is 50 ___.

**10.** The length of a tablecloth is 213 ___.

**11.** The height of a person is 176 ___.

**12.** The length of a bike route is 20 ___.

**13.** The thickness of a stereo headphone wire is 3 ___.

Copy and complete.

**14.** 1 km = ___ m

**15.** 1 m = ___ cm

**16.** 1 cm = ___ m

**17.** 1 mm = ___ m

**18.** 1 m = ___ km

**19.** 1 m = ___ mm

Choose the most reasonable measurement.

**20.** length of a car key
   75 cm   15 mm   5 cm

**21.** length of a baseball bat
   107 mm   107 cm   10.7 m

**22.** height of a volleyball net
   20 cm   8 m   2 m

**23.** length of a straight pin
   5.5 cm   24 mm   96 mm

**24.** thickness of a pencil
   8 mm   18 cm   0.5 m

**25.** height of a bowling pin
   0.75 m   38 cm   125 mm

**26.** height of the Statue of Liberty
   46 m   4.6 m   4.6 km

**27.** length of the Mississippi River
   3779 km   37.79 km   3779 m

**28.** length of a canoe
   5 m   150 cm   20 m

**29.** height of the Washington Monument
   169 m   1.69 m   1.69 km

EXTRA PRACTICE page 503, set 85

# EQUIVALENT METRIC MEASUREMENTS

Photri

**The bike path through the park is 5.6 km long. How many meters long is the path?**

**Example 1:**   5.6 km = ___ m

**1 km = 1000 m**

**When you change from a larger unit to a smaller unit, the number of units increases. So you multiply.**

**5.6 × 1000 = 5 600.**

5.6 km = 5600 m

The bike path is 5600 m long.

**Example 2:**   249 cm = ___ m

**1 m = 100 cm**

**When you change from a smaller unit to a larger unit, the number of units decreases. So you divide.**

**249 ÷ 100 = 2.49**

249 cm = 2.49 m

**Example 3:**   125 mm = ___ cm

**1 cm = 10 mm**

**When you change from a smaller unit to a larger unit, the number of units decreases. So you divide.**

**125 ÷ 10 = 12.5**

125 mm = 12.5 cm

## EXERCISES

Complete each statement, using *multiply* or *divide*.

**1.** When changing from km to m, _____ by 1000.

**2.** When changing from cm to mm, _____ by 10.

**3.** When changing from cm to m, _____ by 100.

**4.** When changing from m to km, _____ by 1000.

**5.** When changing from mm to cm, _____ by 10.

**6.** When changing from m to cm, _____ by 100.

Copy and complete.

**7.** 1 cm = ___ mm

**8.** 1 m = ___ cm

**9.** 1 km = ___ m

**10.** 2.9 cm = ___ mm

**11.** 85 mm = ___ cm

**12.** 8.9 m = ___ cm

**13.** 125 cm = ___ m

**14.** 9.2 km = ___ m

**15.** 1250 m = ___ km

**16.** 30 km = ___ m

**17.** 7.9 cm = ___ mm

**18.** 198 cm = ___ m

**19.** 1258 m = ___ km

**20.** 45 mm = ___ cm

**21.** 8.1 m = ___ cm

**22.** 10.6 cm = ___ mm

**23.** 6.2 km = ___ m

**24.** 857.8 m = ___ km

**25.** 122 mm = ___ cm

**26.** 72 cm = ___ m

**27.** 275 m = ___ cm

**28.** 1.68 m = ___ cm

**29.** 7050 m = ___ km

**30.** 10.5 m = ___ cm

**31.** 35 cm = ___ mm

**32.** 7 mm = ___ cm

**33.** 0.7 km = ___ m

**34.** 258.1 cm = ___ m

**35.** 130.6 cm = ___ mm

**36.** 28 m = ___ cm

*EXTRA PRACTICE page 503, set 86*

*SKILLS REVIEW*

Multiply.

**37.** 28
$\times 0.6$

**38.** 7.2
$\times 0.5$

**39.** 0.85
$\times 2.3$

**40.** 204
$\times 0.19$

Divide.

**41.** $8\overline{)4.024}$

**42.** $1.5\overline{)48}$

**43.** $0.35\overline{)1.148}$

**44.** $2.4\overline{)0.912}$

You can solve the problems in this section by using addition, subtraction, multiplication, or division. Sometimes you must change all the given measurements to the same unit before you compute. Sometimes you must change the computed answer to another unit in order to answer the question.

Rentmeester/FPG

Rentmeester/FPG

**The women's Olympic record in the high jump is 2.02 m. The men's Olympic record in the high jump is 2.36 m. How many centimeters higher is the men's record?**

**Read:** *Given:* women's record, 2.02 m;
men's record, 2.36 m

*To find:* number of centimeters difference

**Plan:** Subtract 2.02 from 2.36 to find the difference in meters. Then change the difference from meters to centimeters.

**Compute:**
$$
\begin{array}{r}
2.3\ 6 \\
-2.0\ 2 \\
\hline
0.3\ 4
\end{array}
\quad 0.34\ \text{m} = 34\ \text{cm}
$$

**Answer:** The men's record is 34 cm higher.

**Check:**
$$
\begin{array}{r}
2.3\ 6 \\
-2.0\ 2 \\
\hline
0.3\ 4 \\
2.3\ 6
\end{array}
\quad \text{Add.} \quad \checkmark
$$

## EXERCISES

1. Darlene's old skis were 150 cm long. Her new skis are 175 cm long. How many centimeters longer are her new skis?

2. Last year Michael was 159 cm tall. This year he is 171 cm tall. How many centimeters did he grow during the year?

3. Bill's bike odometer read 1443.2 km at the start of the trip. At the end of the trip it read 1525.1 km. How many kilometers did he ride?

4. Each curtain panel requires 75 cm of fabric. How many meters of fabric are required for 8 curtain panels?

5. Gloria wants to run 2 km. How many times must she run around a 100-meter running track?

6. The length of the swimming pool is 25 m. How many laps equal 1 kilometer?

7. Fabric sells for $4.95 per meter. How much will 3.5 m cost? Round your answer to the nearest cent.

8. A plant hanger needs 8 pieces of macrame cord, each measuring 1.75 m long. How many plant hangers can be made from 50 meters of cord?

---

## CHECKPOINT

For each segment below, find the length in millimeters. Then rewrite the same length, using centimeters.

1. _____

2. _____

Complete each statement with *mm, cm, m,* or *km* so that the statement is reasonable.

3. The width of a washing machine is 75 ___.

4. The length of a living-room rug is 5 ___.

5. The length of a bridge over a river is 0.8 ___.

Copy and complete.

6. 8.5 cm = ___ mm

7. 16 km = ___ m

8. 5.3 m = ___ cm

Solve.

9. Each runner in a relay ran 400 m. How many kilometers did the 4 team members run in the relay?

289

The most commonly used units of mass (commonly called weight) in the metric system are the **kilogram,** the **gram,** and the **milligram.**

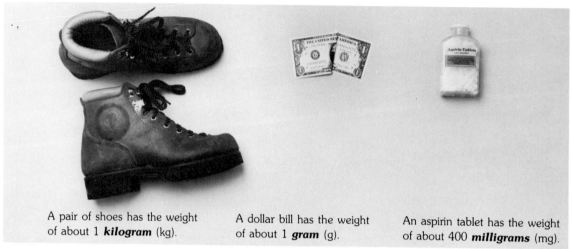

A pair of shoes has the weight of about 1 **kilogram** (kg).

A dollar bill has the weight of about 1 **gram** (g).

An aspirin tablet has the weight of about 400 **milligrams** (mg).

Ed Hoppe Photography

**Example 1:**  4.8 kg = ___ g

**1 kg = 1000 g**

**When you change from a larger unit to a smaller unit, the number of units increases. So you multiply.**

**4.8 × 1000 = 4 800.**
4.8 kg = 4800 g

**Example 2:**  1200 mg = ___ g

**1 g = 1000 mg**

**When you change from a smaller unit to a larger unit, the number of units decreases. So you divide.**

**1200 ÷ 1000 = 1.200**
1200 mg = 1.2 g

# EXERCISES

Complete each statement with *mg, g,* or *kg* so that the statement is reasonable.

**1.** The weight of an empty suitcase is 5 ___.     **2.** The weight of a vitamin tablet is 500 ___.

**3.** The weight of a slice of bread is 23 ___.

**4.** The weight of a baseball is 145 ___.

**5.** The weight of an automobile is 900 ___.

**6.** The weight of a toothbrush is 28 ___.

Choose the most reasonable measurement.

**7.** weight of a box of cereal
   3.4 kg   340 mg   340 g

**8.** weight of an apple
   100 mg   100 g   100 kg

**9.** weight of an egg
   28 g   28 kg   28 mg

**10.** weight of a brick
   2.4 kg   24 g   24 mg

**11.** weight of a refrigerator
   140 kg   140 g   140 mg

**12.** weight of a loaf of bread
   200 mg   500 g   2 kg

Copy and complete.

**13.** 1000 g = ___ kg

**14.** 1200 mg = ___ g

**15.** 5800 g = ___ kg

**16.** 1800 g = ___ kg

**17.** 765 g = ___ kg

**18.** 150 kg = ___ g

**19.** 16.5 kg = ___ g

**20.** 1750 mg = ___ g

**21.** 125 kg = ___ g

**22.** 800 g = ___ mg

**23.** 12.1 kg = ___ g

**24.** 5000 mg = ___ g

**25.** 7.88 kg = ___ g

**26.** 4080 g = ___ kg

**27.** 15 250 mg = ___ g

EXTRA PRACTICE page 503, set 87

## SKILLS REVIEW

Complete the table.

| | Fraction or mixed number | Decimal | Percent |
|---|---|---|---|
| **28.** | $\frac{2}{5}$ | ___ | ___ |
| **29.** | ___ | 0.83 | ___ |
| **30.** | ___ | ___ | 9% |
| **31.** | ___ | 0.025 | ___ |

The metric units of capacity that are used most often are the *liter* (L) and the ***milliliter*** (mL).

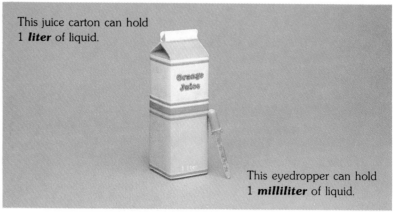

This juice carton can hold 1 *liter* of liquid.

Orange Juice

This eyedropper can hold 1 *milliliter* of liquid.

Kenji Kerins

**Example 1:** 1750 mL = ____ L

**1 L = 1000 mL**

**When you change from a smaller unit to a larger unit, the number of units decreases. So you divide.**

**1750 ÷ 1000 = 1.750**

1750 mL = 1.75 L

**Example 2:** 2.5 L = ____ mL

**1 L = 1000 mL**

**When you change from a larger unit to a smaller unit, the number of units increases. So you multiply.**

**2.5 × 1000 = 2 500**

2.5 L = 2500 mL

## EXERCISES

Complete each statement with *mL* or *L* so that the statement is reasonable.

**1.** The capacity of an automobile gasoline tank is 50 ____.

**2.** The capacity of a bottle of shampoo is 300 ____.

**3.** The capacity of a juice glass is 150 ____.

**4.** The capacity of a can of house paint is 4 ____.

Choose the most reasonable measurement.

**5.** capacity of a cup of soup
200 mL  2 L  0.2 mL

**6.** capacity of a bucket
8 mL  8 L  80 L

**7.** capacity of a teapot
100 L  10 L  2.5 L

**8.** capacity of a thermos
1.5 L  15 L  150 mL

**9.** capacity of a barrel of oil
170 L  170 mL  17 L

**10.** capacity of a cream pitcher
2.4 L  24 mL  0.24 L

**11.** capacity of a glass of milk
3.3 L  300 mL  33 mL

**12.** capacity of a soup spoon
10 mL  75 mL  2 mL

**13.** capacity of a soup pot
16 L  16 mL  0.16 L

**14.** capacity of an aquarium
60 L  0.6 L  60 mL

Copy and complete.

**15.** 1 L = ____ mL

**16.** 3.6 L = ____ mL

**17.** 785 mL = ____ L

**18.** 2150 mL = ____ L

**19.** 12 L = ____ mL

**20.** 50.5 L = ____ mL

**21.** 1200 mL = ____ L

**22.** 900 mL = ____ L

**23.** 2.3 L = ____ mL

**24.** 1900 mL = ____ L

**25.** 3.6 L = ____ mL

**26.** 7 L = ____ mL

**27.** 1.55 L = ____ mL

**28.** 2.08 L = ____ mL

**29.** 295 mL = ____ L

*EXTRA PRACTICE page 504, set 88*

## MATH NOTE

How can you measure exactly 6 liters, using a 4-L container and a 9-L container and nothing else?

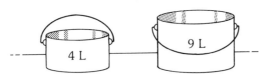

You can solve the problems in this section by using addition, subtraction, multiplication, or division. Sometimes you must change all the given measurements to the same unit before you compute. Sometimes you must change the computed answer to another unit in order to answer the question.

**The Gossetts heated 4 L of apple cider to serve at the ice-skating party. If each mug holds 250 mL, how many servings of hot apple cider can be served?**

**Read:**  *Given:*   4 L of hot apple cider

Each mug holds 250 mL.

*To find:*   How many 250-mL servings are in 4 L?

**Plan:**  First change 4 L to milliliters.

Then divide that number of milliliters by 250.

**Compute:**  **4 L = 4000 mL**

$$
\begin{array}{r}
16 \\
250\overline{)4000} \\
250\phantom{0} \\
\hline
1500 \\
1500 \\
\hline
0
\end{array}
$$

**Answer:** The Gossetts can serve 16 mugs of hot apple cider.

**Check:**

$$\begin{array}{r} 16 \\ \times\,250 \\ \hline 800 \\ 32\phantom{00} \\ \hline 4000 \end{array}$$ ✔

## EXERCISES

1. Mrs. Kraeger mailed a package weighing 1.6 kg. If the contents of the package weighed 1.45 kg, how much did the box and the wrapping weigh?

2. Each can of motor oil holds 1000 mL of oil. How many liters are in a case containing 12 cans?

3. One granola bar weighs 29.7 g. How much do 6 granola bars weigh?

4. How many 250-mL servings can be poured from a 2-L container of juice?

5. The total weight of the raisins in 6 individual boxes is 255 g. What is the weight of the raisins in each box?

6. A delivery company charges $0.82 per kilogram to deliver packages. How much would it charge to deliver a 2.5-kg package?

7. A car has a 60-L gas tank. If the car averages 12 kilometers per liter, how far can the car travel on a full tank?

8. The Taylor family car traveled 975 km on 75 L of gas. How many kilometers per liter does their car average?

9. Linda will fill a 24-L aquarium, using a 2-L teakettle. How many times will she have to fill the teakettle in order to fill the aquarium?

10. A pharmacist had a 1.5-L container of cough medicine. How many 300-mL bottles of cough medicine can be filled from the container?

*EXTRA PRACTICE page 504, set 89*

## SKILLS REVIEW

Solve.

11. What number is 7% of 95?

12. What number is 120% of 80?

13. 12 is what percent of 240?

14. 80 is what percent of 400?

15. 25 is 25% of what number?

16. 300 is 150% of what number?

# TEMPERATURE—CELSIUS AND FAHRENHEIT

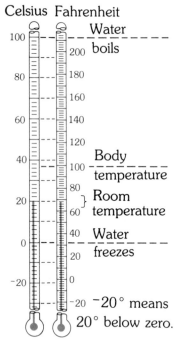

Celsius Fahrenheit

Water boils

Body temperature

Room temperature

Water freezes

−20° means 20° below zero.

Thermometers can be marked with different scales. On the **Celsius scale,** temperature is measured in degrees Celsius (°C). On the **Fahrenheit scale,** temperature is measured in degrees Fahrenheit (°F). The Celsius scale is a metric scale. The Fahrenheit scale is nonmetric.

Grant Heilman

# EXERCISES

What is the most reasonable outdoor temperature for each of the following?

**1.** ice-skating
−10°C   10°C   25°C

**2.** sledding
39°F   50°F   20°F

**3.** snow skiing
15°C   −5°C   10°C

**4.** ice fishing
40°F   35°F   10°F

**5.** water skiing
27°C   10°C   80°C

**6.** swimming
175°F   82°F   40°F

**7.** a snowy day
6°C   16°C   −6°C

**8.** a rainy day
60°F   15°F   20°F

**9.** a desert at noon
45°C   95°C   105°C

**10.** a hot summer day
35°F   195°F   93°F

What is the most reasonable temperature for each of the following?

**11.** inside a hot oven
82°C   200°C   100°C

**12.** boiling water
100°F   212°F   150°F

**13.** a glass of iced tea
5°C   40°C   ⁻10°C

**14.** a cup of hot tea
200°F   95°F   70°F

**15.** inside a freezer
⁻18°C   12°C   28°C

**16.** room temperature
22°F   68°F   155°F

**17.** normal body temperature
98°C   37°C   9°C

**18.** a person with a fever
102°F   40°F   130°F

**19.** inside a refrigerator
35°C   3°C   10°C

**20.** a glass of cold milk
98°F   38°F   28°F

Air temperature feels colder to exposed skin when there is wind. The combined effect of air temperature and wind speed is the windchill.

Use the windchill chart to answer the following:

**21.** The thermometer reading is 0°C. The wind speed is 25 km/h (25 kilometers per hour). What is the windchill?

**22.** The windchill is ⁻30°C. The thermometer reading is ⁻15°C. What is the wind speed?

**23.** The wind speed is 40 km/h. The windchill is ⁻24°C. What is the thermometer reading?

Windchill Chart

| Wind speed (km/h) | Thermometer reading (°C) | | | | | | | | |
|---|---|---|---|---|---|---|---|---|---|
| | 0 | ⁻5 | ⁻10 | ⁻15 | ⁻20 | ⁻25 | ⁻30 | ⁻35 | ⁻40 |
| | Windchill (°C) (equivalent temperature) | | | | | | | | |
| Calm | 0 | ⁻5 | ⁻10 | ⁻15 | ⁻20 | ⁻25 | ⁻30 | ⁻35 | ⁻40 |
| 10 | ⁻4 | ⁻10 | ⁻15 | ⁻21 | ⁻27 | ⁻32 | ⁻38 | ⁻43 | ⁻49 |
| 15 | ⁻8 | ⁻14 | ⁻20 | ⁻26 | ⁻32 | ⁻38 | ⁻45 | ⁻51 | ⁻57 |
| 20 | ⁻10 | ⁻17 | ⁻23 | ⁻30 | ⁻37 | ⁻43 | ⁻50 | ⁻56 | ⁻63 |
| 25 | ⁻12 | ⁻19 | ⁻26 | ⁻33 | ⁻40 | ⁻47 | ⁻54 | ⁻61 | ⁻68 |
| 30 | ⁻14 | ⁻21 | ⁻28 | ⁻36 | ⁻43 | ⁻50 | ⁻57 | ⁻64 | ⁻71 |
| 35 | ⁻16 | ⁻23 | ⁻30 | ⁻38 | ⁻45 | ⁻52 | ⁻60 | ⁻67 | ⁻74 |
| 40 | ⁻17 | ⁻24 | ⁻32 | ⁻39 | ⁻47 | ⁻54 | ⁻62 | ⁻69 | ⁻77 |
| 45 | ⁻18 | ⁻25 | ⁻33 | ⁻41 | ⁻48 | ⁻56 | ⁻64 | ⁻71 | ⁻79 |
| 50 | ⁻19 | ⁻26 | ⁻34 | ⁻42 | ⁻50 | ⁻57 | ⁻65 | ⁻73 | ⁻81 |
| 55 | ⁻19 | ⁻27 | ⁻35 | ⁻43 | ⁻51 | ⁻59 | ⁻67 | ⁻74 | ⁻82 |
| 60 | ⁻20 | ⁻28 | ⁻36 | ⁻44 | ⁻52 | ⁻60 | ⁻68 | ⁻76 | ⁻83 |

*EXTRA PRACTICE page 504, set 90*

Nuncio/FPG

**1.** Tony earns $390 a week. How much will he earn in 52 weeks?

**2.** Mr. Thorpe wants to buy an $85,000 house. How much money is needed to make a 20% down payment?

**3.** The total bill for your groceries is $14.18. How much change should you receive from a $25 check?

**4.** The labor charge for repairing John's car was $64.75 for 3.5 hours of work. How much did the mechanic charge per hour for labor?

**5.** If a liter of water weighs 1 kilogram, how much do 90 liters of water in an aquarium weigh?

**6.** Laura's car gets 14 kilometers per liter. How many liters of gasoline will be needed for a 1470-kilometer trip?

**7.** Jim's car traveled 444 kilometers on 37 liters of gas. How many kilometers per liter does the car get?

8. On a camping trip, each person needs about 1000 g of dried food every day. How many kilograms of dried food are needed for 4 persons on a 3-day trip?

9. A beginning hiker can carry about 25% of his or her body weight in a backpack. If a beginning hiker weighs 56 kg, how many kilograms can that person carry in a backpack?

10. Michael worked $3\frac{1}{2}$ hours a day for 5 days. How many hours did he work in all?

11. A recipe calls for 0.5 liter of milk for each serving. How many liters of milk are needed for 6 servings?

12. Mary bought 4 meters of fabric. She used 2.75 meters of the fabric to make a dress. How many meters were left over?

13. Gail bought 0.3 kilogram of walnuts, 0.25 kilogram of cashews, and 0.5 kilogram of peanuts. What was the total weight of the purchase?

14. A plane has 32 rows of seats. 24 rows are in the non-smoking section. What percent of the rows of seats are for non-smokers?

---

*MATH NOTE*

The small cubes weigh the same and the large cubes weigh the same. If one large cube weighs 4 g more than two small cubes, find the weight of a large cube.

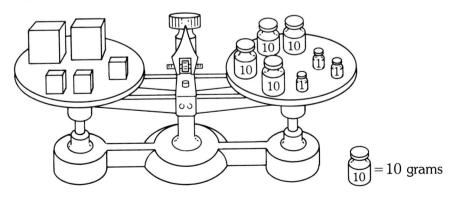

= 10 grams        = 1 gram

**299**

Tool-and-die makers can shape a block of metal into a precise metal tool or part. For shaping, they use boring machines, milling machines, lathes, drilling machines, and grinding machines. To make precise measurements, they use instruments such as a micrometer or a Vernier caliper. Tool-and-die makers read blueprints and other drawings that show the overall sizes and shapes of the metal tools or parts.

Use the drawing to find each of the following:

1. distance from left edge of part to center of hole A

2. distance from bottom edge of part to center of hole B

3. distance between centers of holes A and B

4. width of part

5. length of part

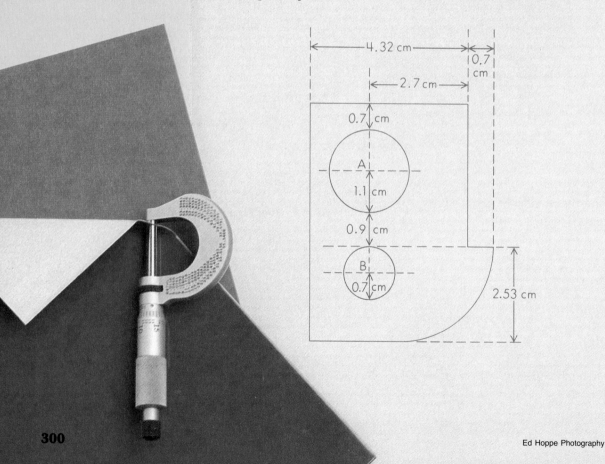

300

Which lettered choice best matches each numbered item?

a. mm    b. g    c. °C    d. m    e. L    f. cm    g. kg

h. milli    i. kilo    j. mL    k. °F    l. km    m. centi    n. mg

**1.** meter          **2.** centimeter       10.2

**3.** millimeter       **4.** kilometer

**5.** thousand     **6.** hundredth     **7.** thousandth

**8.** gram     **9.** kilogram     **10.** milligram     10.5

**11.** liter     **12.** milliliter     10.6

**13.** degrees Celsius     **14.** degrees Fahrenheit     10.8

For each segment below, find the length in millimeters. Then rewrite the same length, using centimeters.     10.1

**15.** —————————————

**16.** ———————————————————

**17.** ——————————

Draw line segments with the following lengths:

**18.** 6.3 cm          **19.** 41 mm

Choose the most reasonable measurement.     10.2

**20.** length of a pencil         **21.** length of a bathtub
     19 cm   19 mm   19 km        0.8 m   150 cm   180 mm

**22.** distance from Denver to Colo-     **23.** length of a car
     rado Springs                   50 cm   5 m   50 m
     12 m   112 km   1112 mm

Copy and complete.

10.3

**24.** 8.3 cm = ___ mm     **25.** 6.7 km = ___ m     **26.** 295 cm = ___ m

Choose the most reasonable measurement.

10.5

**27.** weight of a hamburger bun
60 kg   60 mg   60 g

**28.** weight of a vitamin tablet
10 g   100 mg   1 kg

**29.** weight of a bowling ball
6 kg   600 g   26 kg

Copy and complete.

**30.** 2.65 kg = ___ g     **31.** 406 g = ___ kg     **32.** 3050 g = ___ kg

Choose the most reasonable measurement.

10.6

**33.** capacity of an automobile gas
tank
65 L   16.5 L   165 mL

**34.** capacity of a water pitcher
2.5 L   250 mL   25 L

**35.** capacity of a teaspoon
5 mL   5 L   0.5 L

Copy and complete.

**36.** 1500 mL = ___ L     **37.** 45 L = ___ mL     **38.** 3.8 L = ___ mL

Choose the most reasonable temperature.

10.8

**39.** room temperature
20°C   72°C   160°C

**40.** boiling water
100°F   212°F   32°F

Solve.

**41.** John wants to run 3 km. How many laps must he run on
a 300-m track?

10.4

**42.** One slice of cheese weighs 28 g. How much do 12 slices
weigh?

10.7

**43.** A thermos holds 2 L. How many 250-mL servings does
it contain?

For each segment below, find the length in millimeters. Then rewrite the same length, using centimeters.

**1.** ——————————— **2.** ———————————

Draw line segments with the following lengths:

**3.** 3.9 cm

**4.** 84 mm

Choose the most reasonable measurement.

**5.** length of a pen
1.4 cm   14 cm   14 mm

**6.** length of this page
23.5 cm   23 km   23 mm

**7.** weight of a kitchen stove
90 kg   90 g   900 mg

**8.** weight of a 10-speed bike
15 kg   150 g   15 mg

**9.** capacity of a drinking glass
300 mL   3 L   1300 mL

**10.** capacity of an aquarium
48 mL   48 L   0.48 L

**11.** temperature of boiling water
100°F   32°F   212°F

**12.** temperature of an ice cube
0°C   32°C   100°C

Copy and complete.

**13.** 857 m = ___ km

**14.** 16.4 cm = ___ mm

**15.** 342 cm = ___ m

**16.** 5.1 km = ___ m

**17.** 192 mm = ___ cm

**18.** 1449 m = ___ km

**19.** 1200 mg = ___ g

**20.** 2400 g = ___ kg

**21.** 4.1 kg = ___ g

**22.** 16 L = ___ mL

**23.** 756 mL = ___ L

**24.** 1.8 L = ___ mL

Solve.

**25.** David is 185 cm tall. Bonnie is 1.7 m tall. Who is taller? By how much?

**26.** Every day Jessica feeds her cat 1 can of cat food. If each can contains 182 grams of food, how many kilograms of food does the cat eat per week?

# CUMULATIVE REVIEW

Write each ratio in lowest terms.

☐ ☐ ◯ ◯ ◯ ◯ ▽ ▽ ▽ ▽

**1.** squares to triangles

**2.** all figures to circles

First express both amounts in the same unit, and then simplify the ratio.

**3.** 6 feet to 3 yards

**4.** 20 cups to 1 pint

Express each ratio as a rate.

**5.** 360 miles on 12 gallons

**6.** $20 for 4 hours

Is each proportion true?

**7.** $\frac{8}{4} = \frac{2}{1}$

**8.** $\frac{1}{3} = \frac{2}{5}$

**9.** $\frac{12}{18} = \frac{4}{6}$

**10.** $\frac{4}{5} = \frac{8}{10}$

Solve the proportion by completing the table.

**11.** $\frac{2}{3} = \frac{10}{[?]}$ $\quad \dfrac{2}{3}$ |——|——|——|——|——

Solve the proportions by using equivalent fractions.

**12.** $\frac{2}{5} = \frac{[?]}{10}$

**13.** $\frac{4}{[?]} = \frac{8}{4}$

**14.** $\frac{[?]}{2} = \frac{3}{6}$

**15.** $\frac{2}{4} = \frac{16}{[?]}$

Solve the proportions by using cross products.

**16.** $\frac{2}{5} = \frac{6}{[?]}$

**17.** $\frac{[?]}{8} = \frac{9}{24}$

**18.** $\frac{1}{[?]} = \frac{8}{60}$

**19.** $\frac{7}{10} = \frac{[?]}{50}$

**20.** Draw a 2 to 1 enlargement.

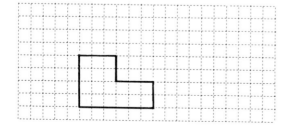

**21.** Draw a 1 to 3 reduction.

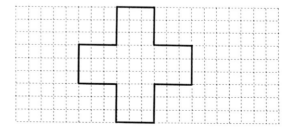

Use the similar figures to find x.

**22.**

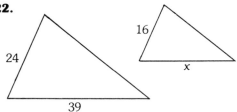

**23.**

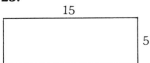

**24.** How long is the car?
**25.** What is the height of the car?

Scale: 1 in. to 1.6 yd

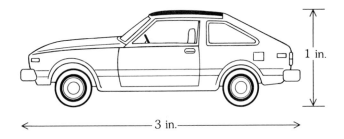

Solve.

**26.** While Clare is at rest, her heart beats 18 times in 15 seconds. How many times would it beat in 60 seconds?

**27.** A map is drawn to the scale of 1 inch to 25 miles. A distance of 230 miles is what length on the map?

Write a percent for the colored portion of each square.

**28.**

**29.**

Copy and complete the table.

| | Fraction | Decimal | Percent |
|---|---|---|---|
| **30.** | $\frac{3}{4}$ | —— | —— |
| **31.** | —— | 0.5 | —— |
| **32.** | —— | —— | 51% |

Solve.

**33.** What number is 45% of 80?

**34.** 130 is what percent of 200?

**35.** 28 is 35% of what number?

305

Given the price and the percent of sales tax, find the total cost.

**36.** $50, 6%

**37.** $28, 5%

Given the original price and the percent of discount, find the sale price.

**38.** $32, 20%

**39.** $12.90, 10%

Solve.

**40.** Mr. Bell's commission rate is 10%. What is his commission on sales of $5870?

**41.** A basketball player makes 0.52 of her free-throw attempts. What percent of her free-throw attempts does she make?

For each segment below, find the length in centimeters.

**42.** _____

**43.** _____

Copy and complete.

**44.** 24 cm = ___ mm

**45.** 5.3 m = ___ cm

Choose the most reasonable measurement.

**46.** length of a paper clip
31 mm   31 cm   3.1 m

**47.** height of a person
1800 cm   1.8 m   180 m

**48.** weight of a person
75 g   75 mg   75 kg

**49.** weight of a peach
190 mg   190 g   190 kg

**50.** capacity of a tablespoon
150 mL   15 mL   1.5 mL

**51.** capacity of a gasoline can
380 mL   38L   3.8 L

Choose the most reasonable temperature.

**52.** room temperature
10°C   20°C   30°C

**53.** a bowl of soup
50°C   10°C   100°C

Solve.

**54.** Matt gives his fish 4 g of food each day. How long will a 100-g box of fish food last?

**55.** A car traveled 490 kilometers on 70 liters of gas. How many kilometers per liter does the car average?

CUMULATIVE REVIEW

Choose the best answer.

1. The number of square units a figure contains is called the (perimeter, area, volume).

2. The distance around a polygon is called the (perimeter, area, volume).

3. The number of cubic units a solid figure contains is called the (perimeter, area, volume).

Solve.

4. Using the formula, find the perimeter of a rectangle with a length of 12 meters and a width of 7 meters.

5. Find the area of a rectangle with a length of 18 feet and a width of 10 feet.

6. Find the circumference of a circle with a diameter of 14 inches. Use $\frac{22}{7}$ for $\pi$.

7. Find the area of a circle with a radius of 10 feet. Use 3.14 for $\pi$.

Use the right triangular prism to find the following:

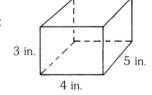

3 in.

5 in.

4 in.

8. volume

9. surface area

10. Find the area of a triangle with a base of 8 meters and a height of 6 meters.

11.

How many faces are there in the figure above? How many edges?

12.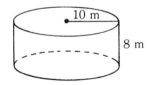

10 m

8 m

Find the volume of the cylinder. Use 3.14 for $\pi$.

13. How many square feet of carpet will Sam need to cover a floor shaped like a rectangle that is 12 feet long and 10 feet wide?

J. Zimmerman/FPG

**A volleyball coach wants to mark the boundary lines of a volleyball court with tape. If the court is 60 feet long and 30 feet wide, how many feet of tape will the coach need?**

The distance around a polygon is called the **perimeter.**

**To find the perimeter of a polygon, add the lengths of all the sides.**

**Example 1:** Find the perimeter of the volleyball court.

```
  60
  60
  30
+ 30
 180
```

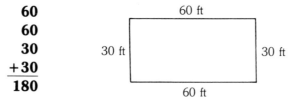

The coach will need 180 feet of tape.

**Example 2:** Find the perimeter of the polygon.

```
  15
  15
+ 15
  45
```

The perimeter is 45 feet.

**Example 3:** Find the perimeter of the polygon.

```
  2.1
  2.1
  3.8
  4.2
  5.7
+ 4.2
 22.1
```

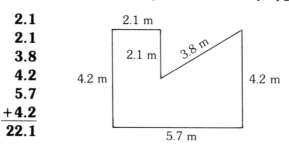

The perimeter is 22.1 meters.

# EXERCISES

Find the perimeter of each polygon.

**1.**
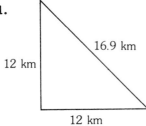
16.9 km
12 km
12 km

**2.**
6 m
8 m
8 m
6 m

**3.**
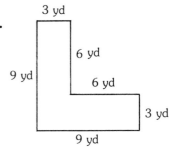
3 yd
6 yd
9 yd
6 yd
3 yd
9 yd

**4.**
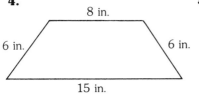
8 in.
6 in.
6 in.
15 in.

**5.**
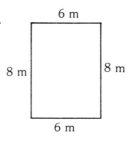
9 m
8 m
8 m
5 m   5 m

**6.**
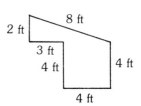
2 ft
8 ft
3 ft
4 ft
4 ft
4 ft

**7.**
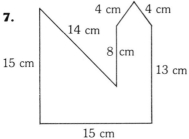
4 cm   4 cm
14 cm
8 cm
15 cm
13 cm
15 cm

**8.**
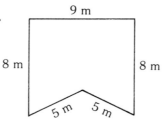
8.2 m
3.9 m
3.9 m
8.2 m

**9.**
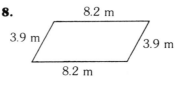
15 yd   15 yd
15 yd   15 yd
15 yd

**10.**
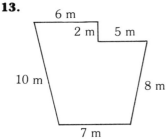
7 m   7 m
1 m   1 m
2.5 m   2.5 m
9 m

**11.**
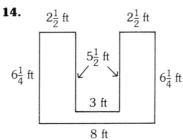
7 yd   7 yd
7 yd   7 yd
7 yd   7 yd

**12.**
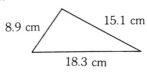
8.9 cm   15.1 cm
18.3 cm

**13.**
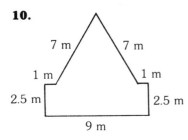
6 m
2 m   5 m
10 m   8 m
7 m

**14.**
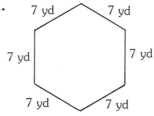
$2\frac{1}{2}$ ft   $2\frac{1}{2}$ ft
$5\frac{1}{2}$ ft
$6\frac{1}{4}$ ft   $6\frac{1}{4}$ ft
3 ft
8 ft

**15.**
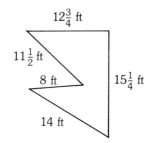
$12\frac{3}{4}$ ft
$11\frac{1}{2}$ ft
8 ft
$15\frac{1}{4}$ ft
14 ft

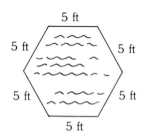

5 ft

5 ft       5 ft

5 ft       5 ft

5 ft

**A landscaper will install stone edging around the sides of a reflecting pool. The pool is shaped like a regular hexagon, each side 5 feet long. How many feet of edging does the landscaper need?**

**Example 1:** Find the perimeter of the reflecting pool.

**5 + 5 + 5 + 5 + 5 + 5 = 30**

The landscaper needs 30 feet of edging.

A **formula** may be used to find the perimeter of a regular polygon. In the formula below, each letter is suggested by key words in the following rule: *The perimeter of a regular polygon equals the number of sides times the length of each side.*

$$P \qquad = \qquad n \qquad \times \qquad l$$

**perimeter of a regular polygon    number of sides    length of each side.**

**Example 2:** Find the perimeter of the reflecting pool, using the formula.

$$P = n \times l$$
$$= 6 \times 5$$
$$= 30$$

The landscaper needs 30 feet of edging.

A formula may also be used to find the perimeter of a **rectangle.** The formula may be expressed two ways.

$$P \;=\; 2 \;\times\; (l \;+\; w) \qquad \text{or} \qquad P \;=\; (2 \;\times\; l) \;+\; (2 \;\times\; w)$$

perimeter      length   width       perimeter     length       width

**Example 3:** Find the perimeter of the rectangular pool.

64 ft (width)

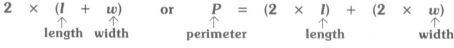

164 ft (length)

$$P = 2 \times (l + w) \qquad\qquad \text{or} \qquad\qquad P = (2 \times l) + (2 \times w)$$
$$= 2 \times (164 + 64) \qquad\qquad\qquad\qquad\qquad = (2 \times 164) + (2 \times 64)$$
$$= 2 \times 228 \qquad\qquad\qquad\qquad\qquad\qquad\quad = 328 + 128$$
$$= 456 \qquad\qquad\qquad\qquad\qquad\qquad\qquad\quad = 456$$

The perimeter of the pool is 456 feet.

# EXERCISES

Find the perimeter of each regular polygon, using the formula.

**1.**
15 m

**2.**
6 ft

**3.**
12 yd

**4.**
9 km

Find the perimeter of each rectangle, using the formula.

**5.**
5 ft
11 ft

**6.**
12 yd
8 yd

**7.**
3.1 m
7.5 m

**8.**
110 ft
100 ft

Given the length of one side, find the perimeter of each square.

**Example:** 7 ft

A square is a regular polygon with 4 sides. So the formula $P = n \times l$ for the perimeter of a regular polygon can be used to find a more specific formula for the perimeter of a square: $P = 4 \times l$ (also written $P = 4 \times s$).

$P = 4 \times l$   **Use the perimeter formula for a square.**

$\quad = 4 \times 7$   **Substitute 7 for $l$.**

$\quad = 28$

The perimeter of the square is 28 feet.

**9.** 9 ft

**10.** 45 in.

**11.** 125 km

Given the length and the width, find the perimeter of each rectangle.

**12.** $l = 8$ ft, $w = 6$ ft

**13.** $l = 15$ m, $w = 12$ m

**14.** $l = 8\frac{1}{2}$ ft, $w = 6\frac{1}{2}$ ft

Given the number of sides ($n$) and the length of each side ($l$), find the perimeter of each regular polygon.

**15.** $n = 4$, $l = 6$ ft

**16.** $n = 5$, $l = 6\frac{1}{3}$ yd

**17.** $n = 3$, $l = 45$ m

**18.** $n = 6$, $l = 12$ km

**19.** $n = 8$, $l = 4\frac{1}{2}$ in.

**20.** $n = 5$, $l = 1.6$ m

EXTRA PRACTICE page 505, set 91

A. Schofield/Valan Photos

**The diameter of a ferris wheel is 45 feet. When Lisa goes around once on the ferris wheel, how far will she travel?**

The distance around any circle is called the **circumference.** If the circumference of any circle is divided by the diameter of that circle, the answer will always be about 3.14 or $\frac{22}{7}$. To name this ratio of circumference to diameter $(\frac{C}{d})$, we use the Greek letter $\pi$ (called *pi*). Therefore, we can write $\frac{C}{d} = \pi$. This leads to the following formula:

$$C = \pi \times d$$

circumference     pi     diameter

**Example 1:** How far will Lisa travel? Use 3.14 for $\pi$.

$C = \pi \times d$

  $= 3.14 \times 45$

  $= 141.3$

Lisa will travel 141.3 feet.

Since the diameter is two times the radius, we can write $2 \times r$ in place of *d*. This gives $C = \pi \times 2 \times r$. Usually we write

$$C = 2 \times \pi \times r$$

circumference     pi     radius

**Example 2:** Find the circumference of a circle with a radius of 7 meters. Use $\frac{22}{7}$ for $\pi$.

$C = 2 \times \pi \times r$

  $= 2 \times \dfrac{22}{7} \times 7$

  $= 44$

The circumference of the circle is 44 meters.

# EXERCISES

Find the diameter if the radius of each circle is as follows:

**1.** 6 m          **2.** 4 ft          **3.** 12 in.          **4.** 9 cm          **5.** 3 yd

Find the radius if the diameter of each circle is as follows:

**6.** 10 cm          **7.** 16 ft          **8.** 100 in.          **9.** 2 m          **10.** 15 ft

Find the circumference of each circle. Use 3.14 for $\pi$.

**11.**
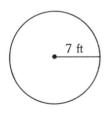
6 m

**12.**
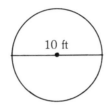
10 ft

**13.**

7.5 in.

**14.** radius:  3 yd          **15.** diameter:  20 mm          **16.** radius:  9 in.

**17.** diameter:  18 mm          **18.** radius:  5 ft          **19.** diameter:  6.8 m

Find the circumference of each circle. Use $\frac{22}{7}$ for $\pi$.

**20.**
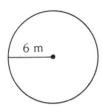
7 ft

**21.**
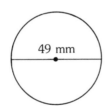
49 mm

**22.**
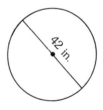
42 in.

**23.** radius:  14 yd          **24.** diameter:  21 ft          **25.** radius:  $3\frac{1}{2}$ in.

**26.** diameter:  28 cm          **27.** radius:  $10\frac{1}{2}$ yd          **28.** diameter:  35 ft

Solve.

**29.** The diameter of a shot put circle is 7 feet. What is the circumference? Use $\frac{22}{7}$ for $\pi$.

**30.** The radius of a circular trampoline is 6.75 feet. What is the circumference? Use 3.14 for $\pi$.

*EXTRA PRACTICE page 505, set 92*

Connie and P.C. Peri

**Jim wants to cover his patio with 1-foot-square tiles. The patio is 13 feet long and 10 feet wide. How many tiles will Jim need?**

The amount of surface enclosed by a figure is called its **area.** Area is measured in **square units.** Here are two examples of square units.

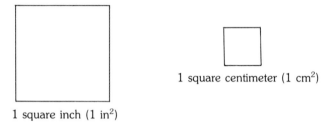

1 square inch (1 in$^2$)    1 square centimeter (1 cm$^2$)

Jim needs to find the area of his patio in square feet (ft$^2$).

**Example 1:** Find how many 1-foot-square tiles Jim will need. Count the square units inside the figure.

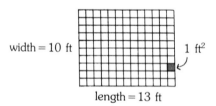

width = 10 ft          1 ft$^2$

length = 13 ft

There are 130 squares inside the figure. Each square is 1 square foot. Jim needs 130 tiles to cover the patio.

**Example 2:** Find how many 1-foot-square tiles are needed to cover a floor that is 15 feet long and 6 feet wide.

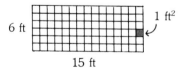

6 ft          1 ft$^2$

15 ft

There are 90 squares inside the figure. Each square is 1 square foot. So 90 tiles are needed to cover the floor.

# EXERCISES

What square unit does each symbol stand for?

**1.** $cm^2$      **2.** $ft^2$      **3.** $m^2$      **4.** $in^2$      **5.** $yd^2$

Find the number of square units in each rectangle.

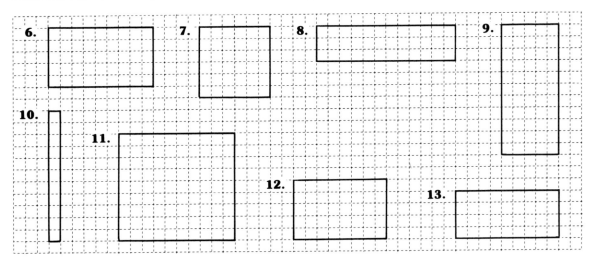

Draw rectangles having the following lengths and widths. Then draw in the square units to show the number of square inches in each rectangle.

**14.** $l=3$ in., $w=2$ in.        **15.** $l=5$ in., $w=1$ in.

**16.** $l=4$ in., $w=4$ in.        **17.** $l=6$ in., $w=3$ in.

## SKILLS REVIEW

Compute. Simplify.

**18.** $\begin{array}{r} \frac{3}{8} \\ +\frac{2}{8} \\ \hline \end{array}$      **19.** $\begin{array}{r} \frac{7}{9} \\ -\frac{4}{9} \\ \hline \end{array}$      **20.** $\begin{array}{r} \frac{1}{2} \\ +\frac{1}{4} \\ \hline \end{array}$      **21.** $\begin{array}{r} \frac{5}{6} \\ -\frac{1}{3} \\ \hline \end{array}$      **22.** $\begin{array}{r} \frac{3}{4} \\ +\frac{2}{3} \\ \hline \end{array}$

**23.** $\begin{array}{r} 8\frac{5}{6} \\ -3\frac{1}{6} \\ \hline \end{array}$      **24.** $\begin{array}{r} 5\frac{1}{4} \\ +2\frac{3}{8} \\ \hline \end{array}$      **25.** $\begin{array}{r} 2\frac{2}{3} \\ -1\frac{1}{4} \\ \hline \end{array}$      **26.** $\begin{array}{r} 4\frac{5}{8} \\ +2\frac{5}{6} \\ \hline \end{array}$      **27.** $\begin{array}{r} 9\frac{1}{2} \\ -3\frac{3}{4} \\ \hline \end{array}$

**AREAS OF RECTANGLES AND PARALLELOGRAMS**

Jacqueline Durand

**Luisa built a tabletop in the shape of a rectangle. The top was 6 feet long and 3 feet wide. What was the area of the tabletop?**

The area of a rectangle is equal to the length times the width. (Be sure the length and the width are in the same unit of measure.)

$$A \;=\; l \;\times\; w$$

area of rectangle / length width

**Example 1:** Find the area of Luisa's tabletop.

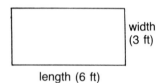

width (3 ft)

length (6 ft)

$A = l \times w$

$\quad = 6 \times 3$

$\quad = 18$

We say:  The area is 18 square feet.

We write:  $A = 18 \text{ ft}^2$

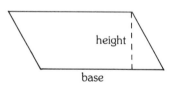

height

base

A parallelogram can be rearranged to form a rectangle.

The height is the distance between the bases, measured along a line perpendicular to the bases.

The area of a parallelogram is equal to the base times the height.

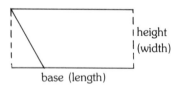

height (width)

base (length)

$$A \;=\; b \;\times\; h$$

area of parallelogram / base height

**Example 2:** Find the area of a parallelogram with a base of 8 feet and a height of 5 feet.

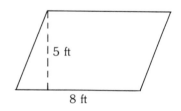

5 ft

8 ft

$A = b \times h$

$\quad = 8 \times 5$

$\quad = 40$

The area of the parallelogram is 40 ft$^2$.

## EXERCISES

Find the area of each rectangle, given the length and the width.

**1.** $l = 7$ ft, $w = 3$ ft      **2.** $l = 10$ m, $w = 9$ m      **3.** $l = 12$ in., $w = 2$ in.

**4.** $l = 15$ yd, $w = 3$ yd      **5.** $l = 18$ ft, $w = 15$ ft      **6.** $l = 42$ in., $w = 19$ in.

Find the area of each square, given the length of one side. (Hint: The sides of a square have the same length, so the area formula is often written as $A = s \times s$ or $A = s^2$.)

**7.** 4 ft      **8.** 6 in.      **9.** 8 yd      **10.** 10 m

**11.** 12 ft      **12.** 9 yd      **13.** 15 in.      **14.** 2.6 m

Find the area of each parallelogram, given the length of the base and the height.

**15.** $b = 5$ in., $h = 4$ in.      **16.** $b = 10$ ft, $h = 3$ ft      **17.** $b = 12$ yd, $h = 8$ yd

**18.** $b = 15$ m, $h = 9$ m      **19.** $b = 20$ in., $h = 16$ in.      **20.** $b = 25$ ft, $h = 14$ ft

Find the area of each figure.

**21.**
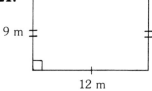
9 m
12 m

**22.**
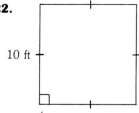
10 ft

**23.**
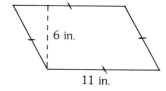
6 in.
11 in.

**24.**
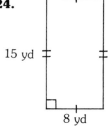
15 yd
8 yd

**25.**
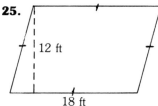
12 ft
18 ft

**26.**
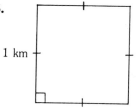
1 km

Solve.

**27.** Juan's yard is rectangular in shape. It is 125 feet long and 67 feet wide. What is the area?

**28.** One piece of a patchwork quilt is shaped like a parallelogram. The base is 8 inches, and the height is 6 inches. What is the area?

EXTRA PRACTICE page 505, set 93

# AREAS OF TRIANGLES AND TRAPEZOIDS

K. Scholz/H. Armstrong Roberts

A clipper ship carried sails of different shapes. Some were shaped like triangles. Others were shaped like trapezoids.

Think of the area of a triangle as one-half the area of a parallelogram.

The area of a triangle (shaded area) is one-half the area of a parallelogram.

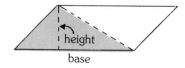

$$A \; = \; \frac{1}{2} \; \times \; b \; \times \; h$$

area of triangle · · · base · · · height

**Example 1:**  Find the area of the sail below.

$$A = \frac{1}{2} \times b \times h$$

$$= \frac{1}{2} \times 12 \times 20$$

$$= 120$$

The area of the sail is 120 ft$^2$.

20 ft

12 ft

Think of the area of a trapezoid as one-half the area of a parallelogram.

The area of an entire parallelogram is $(b_1 + b_2) \times h$. The area of a trapezoid (shaded area) is $\frac{1}{2} \times (b_1 + b_2) \times h$.

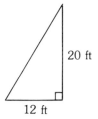

base$_1$    base$_2$

height

base$_2$ + base$_1$

$$A \; = \; \frac{1}{2} \; \times \; (b_1 \; + \; b_2) \; \times \; h$$

area of trapezoid · · · base$_1$ · · base$_2$ · · height

**Example 2:**  Find the area of the sail below.

$$A = \frac{1}{2} \times (b_1 + b_2) \times h$$

$$= \frac{1}{2} \times (40 + 36) \times 12$$

$$= \frac{1}{2} \times 76 \times 12$$

$$= 456$$

The area of the sail is 456 ft$^2$.

36 ft

12 ft

40 ft

# EXERCISES

State the base(s) and the height of each figure. Then find its area in square units.

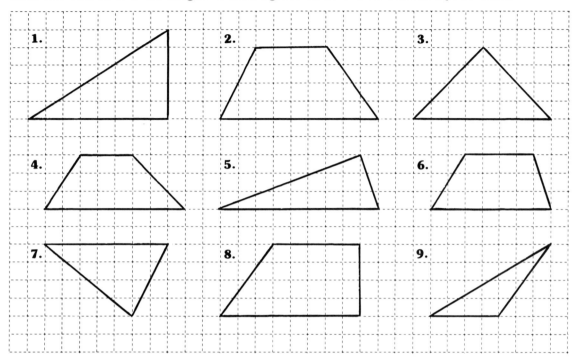

Given the base and the height, find the area of each triangle.

**10.** $b=6$ ft, $h=3$ ft
**11.** $b=12$ m, $h=6$ m
**12.** $b=10$ in., $h=8$ in.

**13.** $b=9$ cm, $h=8$ cm
**14.** $b=16$ ft, $h=1$ ft
**15.** $b=20$ in., $h=6$ in.

**16.** $b=45$ m, $h=4$ m
**17.** $b=8$ yd, $h=6$ yd
**18.** $b=0.4$ km, $h=0.2$ km

Given the two bases and the height, find the area of each trapezoid.

**19.** $h=3$ in.
$b_1=2$ in.
$b_2=4$ in.

**20.** $h=9$ ft
$b_1=5$ ft
$b_2=6$ ft

**21.** $h=10$ m
$b_1=8$ m
$b_2=2$ m

Solve.

**22.** A piece of stained glass is shaped like a triangle. The base is 4 inches, and the height is 6 inches. What is the area?

**23.** A piece of stained glass is shaped like a trapezoid. One base is $3\frac{1}{2}$ inches and the other base is $5\frac{1}{2}$ inches. The height is 4 inches. What is the area?

EXTRA PRACTICE page 506, set 94

Brian Seed/Photo Trends

**The center ring of a three-ring circus has a 20-foot radius. What is the area of the center ring?**

The area of a circle equals $\pi$ times the square of the radius. (The *square of the radius* is the radius times itself.) The formula for the area of a circle is

$$A = \pi \times r^2 \longleftarrow r^2 \text{ means } r \times r.$$

area of circle $\uparrow$

radius squared $\uparrow$

**Example 1:** Find the area of the center ring. Use 3.14 for $\pi$.

$A = \pi \times r^2$

$\quad = 3.14 \times 20 \times 20$

$\quad = 1256$

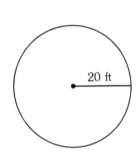

20 ft

The area of the center ring is 1256 ft$^2$.

Besides the center ring, the circus has two smaller rings. Each ring has a radius of 14 feet.

**Example 2:** Find the area of each smaller ring. Use $\frac{22}{7}$ for $\pi$.

$A = \pi \times r^2$

$\quad = \frac{22}{7} \times 14 \times 14$

$\quad = 616$

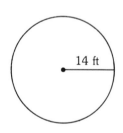

14 ft

The area of each smaller ring is 616 ft$^2$.

Sometimes the diameter of a circle is given. Remember that the *radius* is one-half the *diameter.*

**Example 3:** Find the area of a circle with a diameter of 18 inches. Use 3.14 for $\pi$.

$A = \pi \times r^2$

$\quad = 3.14 \times 9 \times 9$    Since $d = 18$ inches, $r = 9$ inches.

$\quad = 254.34$

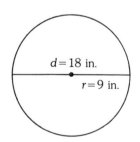

$d = 18$ in.

$r = 9$ in.

The area of the circle is 254.34 in$^2$.

## EXERCISES

Find the radius of each circle, given the following diameters.

**1.** 12 ft  **2.** 16 m  **3.** 4 m  **4.** 10 cm

**5.** 18 yd  **6.** 8 in.  **7.** 2 km  **8.** 20 ft

Find $r^2$.

**9.** $r=3$  **10.** $r=6$  **11.** $r=4$  **12.** $r=10$

**13.** $r=8$  **14.** $r=12$  **15.** $r=20$  **16.** $r=15$

**17.**

Find the area of the circle.
Use 3.14 for $\pi$.

**18.**

Find the area of the circle.
Use $\frac{22}{7}$ for $\pi$.

Find the area of each circle. Use 3.14 for $\pi$.

**19.** $r=9$ m  **20.** $d=2$ ft  **21.** $r=12$ in.  **22.** $d=16$ yd

Find the area of each circle. Use $\frac{22}{7}$ for $\pi$.

**23.** $d=14$ ft  **24.** $r=21$ in.  **25.** $d=28$ yd  **26.** $r=42$ m

EXTRA PRACTICE page 506, set 95

---

## CHECKPOINT

**1.** Find the perimeter of a square, each side having a length of 12 meters.

**2.** Find the circumference of a circle with a diameter of 5 cm. Use 3.14 for $\pi$.

Find the area. Use 3.14 for $\pi$.

**3.**

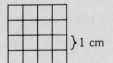

**4.**

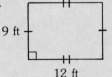

**5.**

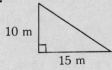

**6.**

R. Smith/H. Armstrong Roberts

Gary Tighe/FPG

Frank Siteman/Taurus

Identify each object in the pictures above. Each object matches the shape of a **solid figure** below.

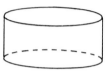  

**Cylinder**   **Rectangular solid**   **Cube**

**Example 1:** Each object pictured above is an example of which solid figure?

The oil storage tank is an example of a cylinder. The stereo receiver is an example of a rectangular solid. The die is an example of a cube.

Other solid figures include the following:

**Pyramid**   **Cone**   **Sphere**   **Triangular prism**

A rectangular solid has 6 sides, called *faces,* and 12 *edges.*

Each face of a rectangular solid is a rectangle.

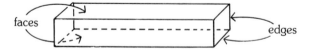

faces                                    edges

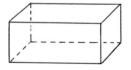

**Example 2:** Find the number of faces and the number of edges in the figure. (Dashed lines are used to show edges that could not be seen on a real object.)

There are 6 faces and 12 edges in the figure.

# EXERCISES

In each figure, how many faces are there? How many edges?

**1.**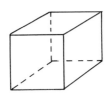

**2.**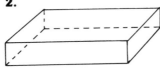

**3.**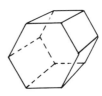

**4.**

**5.**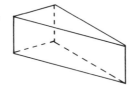

**6.**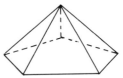

Identify the type of solid figure shown.

**7.**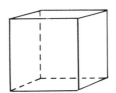

**8.**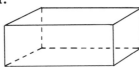

**9.**

**10.**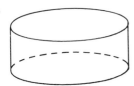

**11.**

**12.**

**13.** Draw the pattern below. Cut along the solid lines, and fold along the dashed lines. Use tape to hold the solid figure together. What type of solid figure do you have?

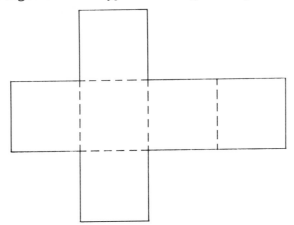

323

Paul Morin/Photo Trends

**A company makes wooden blocks with square faces. Each edge is 1 inch long. Such blocks are called cubic inches. How many blocks can be packed into a box 6 inches long, 4 inches wide, and 3 inches high?**

The amount of space that a solid figure encloses is called its *volume.* Volume is measured in **cubic units.**

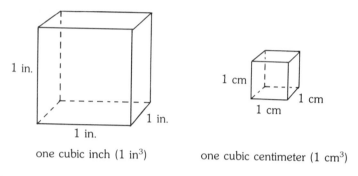

one cubic inch (1 in³)    one cubic centimeter (1 cm³)

**Example 1:** How many 1-cubic-inch blocks will the box hold?

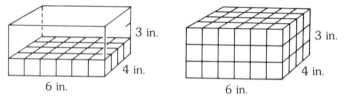

Each layer has 6 rows of 4 blocks each. So, each layer has 24 blocks. Since there are 3 layers, the box will hold 72 blocks.

**Example 2:** How many 1-cubic-inch blocks will the rectangular solid hold?

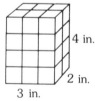

Each layer has 3 rows of 2 blocks each. So, each layer has 6 blocks. Since there are 4 layers, the rectangular solid will hold 24 blocks.

# EXERCISES

What unit of volume does each symbol stand for?

**1.** $m^3$           **2.** $in^3$           **3.** $cm^3$           **4.** $ft^3$           **5.** $yd^3$

Find the number of cubes needed to fill each rectangular solid. The first layer of cubes is shown to give you a hint.

**6.**
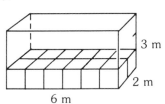
3 m, 2 m, 6 m

**7.**
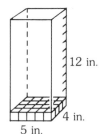
12 in., 4 in., 5 in.

**8.**
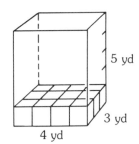
5 yd, 3 yd, 4 yd

**9.**
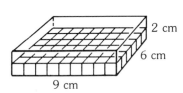
2 cm, 6 cm, 9 cm

**10.**
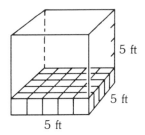
5 ft, 5 ft, 5 ft

**11.**
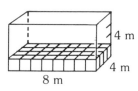
4 m, 4 m, 8 m

**12.**
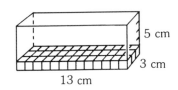
5 cm, 3 cm, 13 cm

**13.**
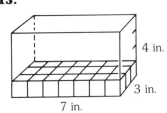
4 in., 3 in., 7 in.

**14.**
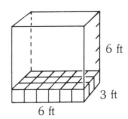
6 ft, 3 ft, 6 ft

## SKILLS REVIEW

Compute. Simplify.

**15.** $\frac{1}{3} \times \frac{2}{5}$       **16.** $\frac{3}{8} \div \frac{1}{9}$       **17.** $\frac{2}{9} \times 3$       **18.** $10 \div \frac{5}{9}$

**19.** $1\frac{1}{2} \times 2\frac{2}{3}$       **20.** $\frac{6}{7} \div 4\frac{1}{2}$       **21.** $3\frac{1}{5} \times \frac{1}{8}$       **22.** $2\frac{2}{5} \div 4\frac{2}{3}$

Paul Morin/Photo Trends

**Barb built a storage chest in industrial arts class. The chest was 4 feet long, 2 feet wide, and 2 feet high. What was the volume of the storage chest?**

The storage chest is an example of a **right prism.** A prism has 2 *bases* that are congruent polygons. The other faces of a right prism are rectangles.

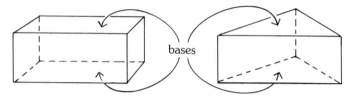

bases

*Right rectangular prism*          *Right triangular prism*

The volume of any prism is equal to the area of one base *B* times the height *h*.

$$V = B \times h$$

volume of    area of    height
prism        one base

**Example 1:**  Find the volume of the storage chest.

$V = B \times h$          $B = 4 \times 2$, **because the area of a**
$\quad = (4 \times 2) \times 2$   **rectangle equals** $l \times w$.
$\quad = 16$

We say:  The volume equals 16 cubic feet.

We write:  $V = 16 \text{ ft}^3$

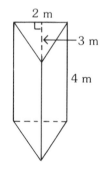

**Example 2:**  Find the volume of a 4-meter-high right triangular prism.

$V = B \times h$
$\quad = (\frac{1}{2} \times 2 \times 3) \times 4$   $B = \frac{1}{2} \times 2 \times 3$, **because the area of a triangle equals** $\frac{1}{2} \times b \times h$.
$\quad = 12$

The volume of the triangular prism is 12 m³.

# EXERCISES

Find the volume.

1.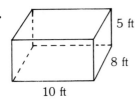
5 ft
8 ft
10 ft

2.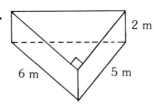
2 m
6 m
5 m

3.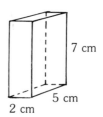
7 cm
5 cm
2 cm

4.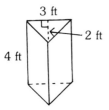
3 ft
2 ft
4 ft

5.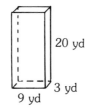
20 yd
3 yd
9 yd

6.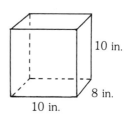
10 in.
10 in.
8 in.

Find the volume of each rectangular prism, given the length, the width, and the height.

7. $l=12$ ft
$w=10$ ft
$h=4$ ft

8. $l=15$ m
$w=8$ m
$h=6$ m

9. $l=11$ cm
$w=9$ cm
$h=3$ cm

10. $l=6$ ft
$w=6$ ft
$h=6$ ft

11. $l=3$ yd
$w=2$ yd
$h=1$ yd

12. $l=25$ m
$w=5$ m
$h=2$ m

13. $l=20$ cm
$w=18$ cm
$h=12$ cm

14. $l=10$ in.
$w=10$ in.
$h=10$ in.

15. $l=2.6$ m
$w=1.8$ m
$h=3.2$ m

16. $l=10$ cm
$w=8.5$ cm
$h=4.3$ cm

17. $l=10\frac{1}{2}$ ft
$w=9\frac{1}{3}$ ft
$h=5\frac{1}{4}$ ft

18. $l=4\frac{1}{2}$ in.
$w=4\frac{1}{2}$ in.
$h=4\frac{1}{2}$ in.

Solve.

19. Mary wants to pack a carton 3 feet long, 2 feet wide, and 1 foot high with cubes that are 1 ft$^3$ in volume. How many cubes can she fit into the carton?

20. A concrete form is shaped like a right triangular prism. If the area of the base is 8 ft$^2$ and the height is 3 ft, how many cubic feet of concrete will it take to fill the form?

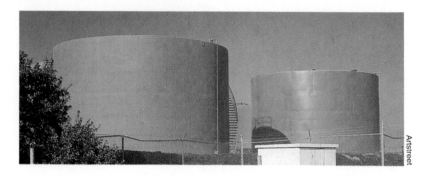

An oil storage tank is 30 feet high and the base (bottom) has a radius of 20 feet. What is the volume of the tank?

The tank is an example of a **cylinder.** To find the volume of a cylinder, multiply the area of the base by the height.

area of the base

$$V = \pi \times r^2 \times h$$

volume of cylinder    pi    radius squared    height

**Example 1:** Find the volume of the storage tank. Use 3.14 for $\pi$.

$V = \pi \times r^2 \times h$

$\quad = 3.14 \times 20 \times 20 \times 30$

$\quad = 37{,}680$

The volume of the storage tank is 37,680 ft$^3$.

**Example 2:** Find the volume of a cylinder with a diameter of 14 m and a height of 20 m. Remember, the radius is half the diameter. Use $\frac{22}{7}$ for $\pi$.

$V = \pi \times r^2 \times h$

$\quad = \frac{22}{7} \times 7 \times 7 \times 20$

$\quad = 3080$

The volume of the cylinder is 3080 m$^3$.

30 ft

20 ft

base

14 m

20 m

# EXERCISES

Find the volume of each cylinder. Use 3.14 for $\pi$.

**1.**
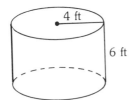
4 ft  6 ft

**2.**
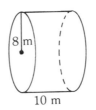
8 m  10 m

**3.**
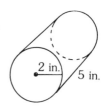
2 in.  5 in.

**4.**
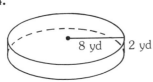
8 yd  2 yd

**5.**
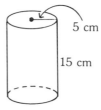
5 cm  15 cm

**6.**

10 ft  9 ft

Find the volume of each cylinder, given the radius and the height. Use 3.14 for $\pi$.

**7.** $r=3$ m
$h=6$ m

**8.** $r=12$ in.
$h=9$ in.

**9.** $r=8$ ft
$h=10$ ft

**10.** $r=12$ cm
$h=7$ cm

**11.** $r=2$ ft
$h=8$ ft

**12.** $r=10$ yd
$h=4$ yd

**13.** $r=18$ in.
$h=10\frac{1}{2}$ in.

**14.** $r=7$ m
$h=3$ m

**15.** $r=2.6$ cm
$h=1.5$ cm

Find the volume of each cylinder, given the height and the radius or the diameter. Use $\frac{22}{7}$ for $\pi$. (Remember that the radius is half the diameter.)

**16.** $d=14$ cm
$h=5$ cm

**17.** $d=14$ in.
$h=3$ in.

**18.** $r=7$ ft
$h=20$ ft

**19.** $r=28$ m
$h=10$ m

**20.** $r=7$ cm
$h=12$ cm

**21.** $d=42$ in.
$h=5$ in.

Solve.

**22.** What is the volume of a mailing tube that has a radius of 2 inches and a height of 9 inches? Use 3.14 for $\pi$.

**23.** An aluminum can has a diameter of 6 inches and a height of 7 inches. What is the volume? Use $\frac{22}{7}$ for $\pi$.

EXTRA PRACTICE page 506, set 96

**329**

The stage crew built a large storage box. The box was 6 feet long, 4 feet wide, and 3 feet deep. How many square feet of plywood did they need?

The **surface area** of a solid is the total area of its faces.

**Example 1:** Find the surface area of the storage box.

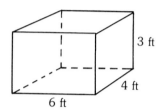

3 ft

4 ft

6 ft

| Part of the box | Area |
|---|---|
| front | $6 \times 3 = 18$ ft$^2$ |
| back | $6 \times 3 = 18$ ft$^2$ |
| top | $6 \times 4 = 24$ ft$^2$ |
| bottom | $6 \times 4 = 24$ ft$^2$ |
| left | $4 \times 3 = 12$ ft$^2$ |
| right | $4 \times 3 = 12$ ft$^2$ |
| | total area    108 ft$^2$ |

The stage crew needed 108 ft$^2$ of plywood.

**Example 2:** Find the surface area of the tent.

| Part of the tent | Area | |
|---|---|---|
| front (triangle) | $\frac{1}{2} \times 12 \times 8 = 48$ ft$^2$ | **Use the formula** |
| back (triangle) | $\frac{1}{2} \times 12 \times 8 = 48$ ft$^2$ | $A = \frac{1}{2} \times b \times h.$ |
| bottom | $12 \times 7 \ = 84$ ft$^2$ | |
| left | $10 \times 7 \ = 70$ ft$^2$ | |
| right | $10 \times 7 \ = 70$ ft$^2$ | |
| | total area    320 ft$^2$ | |

10 ft

8 ft

7 ft

12 ft

The surface area of the tent is 320 ft$^2$.

**330**

# EXERCISES

Find the surface area of each right prism.

**1.**

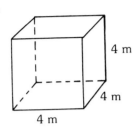

4 m
4 m
4 m

**2.**

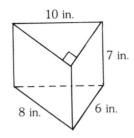

10 in.
7 in.
8 in.
6 in.

**3.**

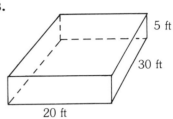

5 ft
30 ft
20 ft

**4.**

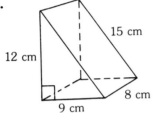

15 cm
12 cm
8 cm
9 cm

**5.**

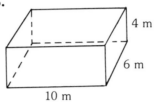

4 m
6 m
10 m

**6.**

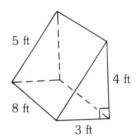

5 ft
4 ft
8 ft
3 ft

**7.**

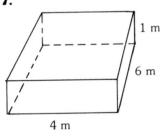

1 m
6 m
4 m

**8.**

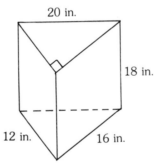

20 in.
18 in.
12 in.
16 in.

**9.**

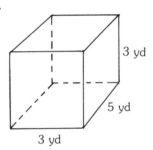

3 yd
5 yd
3 yd

---

## MATH NOTE

In which cube is the number of units of *volume* the same as the number of units of *surface area*?

2 cm

4 cm

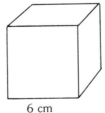

6 cm

EXTRA PRACTICE page 507, set 97

Leonard Harris/Leo de Wys Inc.

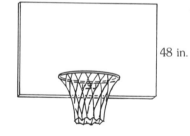

72 in.

48 in.

**Toni made a rectangular basketball backboard with a length of 72 inches and a width of 48 inches. What is the area of the backboard?**

**Read:**   *Given:*   The backboard is 72 inches long and 48 inches wide.

*To find:*   area of the backboard

**Plan:**   To find the area of a rectangle, which operation can be used? You must multiply the length by the width.

**Compute:**   $A = l \times w$
$= 72 \times 48$
$= 3456$

**Answer:**   The area of the backboard is 3456 in$^2$.

**Check:**   Use an estimate.

$70 \times 50 = 3500$   ✔

# EXERCISES

1. Mario decided to put in a new driveway shaped like a rectangle. He wanted to make it 30 feet long and 12 feet wide. How many feet of lumber did he need to build a form around the driveway?

2. What is the area of the driveway mentioned in exercise 1?

3. Mario put a barrel filled with flowers next to his driveway. If the top of the barrel is a circle with a 30-inch diameter, what is the circumference? Use 3.14 for $\pi$.

4.

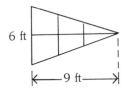

6 ft

9 ft

The triangle on a shuffleboard court has a base of 6 feet and a height of 9 feet. What is the area?

5. The face-off circle on a hockey rink has a radius of 15 feet. What is the area? Use 3.14 for $\pi$.

6.

2 ft

4 ft

3 ft

To bury a time capsule, the freshman class of Piedmont High School dug a hole 3 feet long, 2 feet wide, and 4 feet deep. How many cubic feet of dirt did they remove?

7.

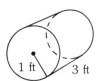

1 ft    3 ft

The time capsule was shaped like a cylinder. The radius of the base was 1 foot, and the height was 3 feet. What was the volume? Use 3.14 for $\pi$.

EXTRA PRACTICE page 507, set 98

A knowledge of perimeter, area, and volume can be very useful to a farmer. The following problems show situations in which a farmer might need to know about these topics.

Use with exercise 1.

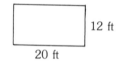

12 ft

20 ft

**1.** If a farmer builds a fence to make the rectangular pen at the left, how many feet of fencing will be needed? Does the farmer need to find area, perimeter, or volume?

**2.** A farmer builds a corncrib that is circular and has a 10-foot diameter. If the sides of the corncrib are made of chicken wire, how many feet of chicken wire will the farmer need? Use 3.14 for $\pi$.

Use with exercise 4.

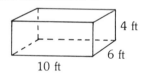

4 ft

6 ft

10 ft

**3.** A rectangular field is 150 yards long and 85 yards wide. What is the area?

**4.** A tank is in the shape of a rectangular prism. It is 10 feet long, 6 feet wide, and 4 feet deep. What is the volume of the tank?

Use with exercise 5.

25 ft

10 ft

**5.** A silo used for storage is a cylinder. The height is 25 feet and the radius of the base is 10 feet. What is the volume of the silo? Use 3.14 for $\pi$.

Use with exercise 6.

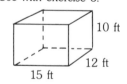

10 ft

12 ft

15 ft

**6.** The inside of the toolshed shown needs to be painted, including the floor. How many square feet must be painted? (You will need to find the area of the front, the back, the ceiling, the floor, and the right and left sides.)

Complete.

1. The distance around a polygon is called the _____.  11.1

2. The distance around a circle is called the _____.  11.3

3. The amount of surface enclosed by a figure is called the _____.  11.4

4. The amount of space that a solid figure encloses is called the _____.  11.9

5. The total area of the faces of a solid is called the _____ _____.  11.12

Find the perimeter of each polygon.  11.1

**6.**

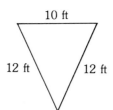
10 ft
12 ft    12 ft

**7.**

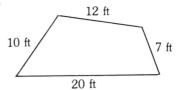
12 ft
10 ft    7 ft
20 ft

**8.**

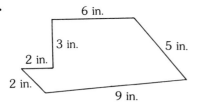
6 in.
3 in.    5 in.
2 in.
2 in.
9 in.

Find the perimeter of each polygon, using the formula.  11.2

**9.**

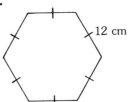
12 cm

**10.**

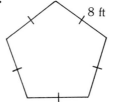
8 ft

**11.**

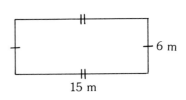
6 m
15 m

Find the circumference of each circle. Use 3.14 for $\pi$.

11.3

**12.**
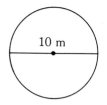
10 m

**13.**

25 ft

**14.**
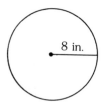
8 in.

How many square units are in each rectangle?

11.4

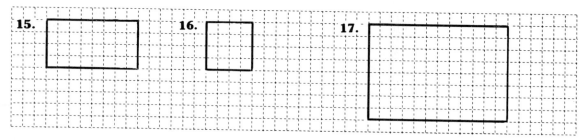

**15.**  **16.**  **17.**

Find the area of each polygon.

11.5

**18.**
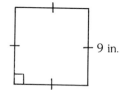
9 in.

**19.**
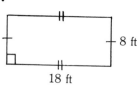
8 ft
18 ft

**20.**
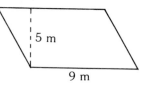
5 m
9 m

**21.**
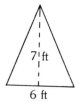
7 ft
6 ft

**22.**
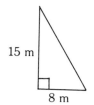
15 m
8 m

**23.**
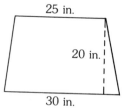
25 in.
20 in.
30 in.

11.6

Find the area of each circle.

11.7

**24.** Use 3.14 for $\pi$.

12 m

**25.** Use 3.14 for $\pi$.

9 in.

**26.** Use $\frac{22}{7}$ for $\pi$.

10 ft

**336**

In each figure, how many faces are there? How many edges?

11.8

**27.**

**28.**

**29.**

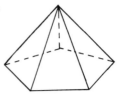

Find the number of cubes needed to fill each rectangular solid.

11.9

**30.**

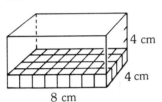

4 cm

4 cm

8 cm

**31.**

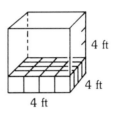

4 ft

4 ft

4 ft

**32.**

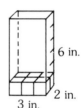

6 in.

2 in.

3 in.

Find the volume of each solid figure. Use 3.14 for π.

11.10, 11.11

**33.**

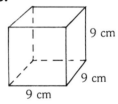

9 cm

9 cm

9 cm

**34.**

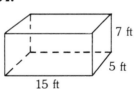

7 ft

5 ft

15 ft

**35.**

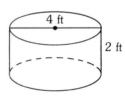

4 ft

2 ft

Find the surface area of each right prism.

11.12

**36.**

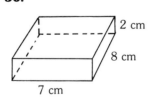

2 cm

8 cm

7 cm

**37.**

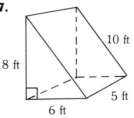

8 ft

10 ft

5 ft

6 ft

**38.**

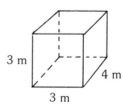

3 m

3 m

4 m

**39.** A watering tank for cattle is shaped like a cylinder. It is 4 feet high and has a diameter of 10 feet. How many cubic feet of water will the tank hold? Use 3.14 for π.

11.13

CHAPTER REVIEW

Choose the best answer.

**1.** (Perimeter, Area) means "the distance around a polygon."

**2.** A cube has (6, 8) faces.

**3.** Area is measured in (square, cubic) units.

**4.** Volume is measured in (square, cubic) units.

Use the square to find the following:

**5.** perimeter

**6.** area

10 cm

Use the circle to find the following:

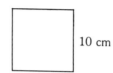

**7.** circumference (Use $\frac{22}{7}$ for $\pi$.)

14 in.

**8.** area (Use $\frac{22}{7}$ for $\pi$.)

Use the right rectangular prism to find the following:

**9.** volume

**10.** surface area

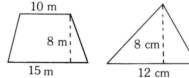

2 m

4 m

6 m

Find the area of the following:

**11.** the trapezoid at the right

**12.** the triangle at the right

10 m

8 m

15 m

8 cm

12 cm

**13.** Find the volume of the cheese wheel (a cylinder) at the right. Use 3.14 for $\pi$.

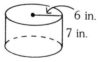

6 in.

7 in.

Solve.

**14.** An airport radar covers a circular region that has a radius of 50 miles. What is the area of this region? Use 3.14 for $\pi$.

**15.** Lynn built a box to hold wooden cubes that are 1 $cm^3$ in size. If the box is 15 cm long, 12 cm wide, and 10 cm high, how many cubes will it hold?

**1.** Use the bar graph to name the largest zoo.

Size of Selected U.S. Zoos

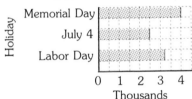

Zoo

Brookfield
Milwaukee
St. Louis
Lincoln Park

0   40  80 120 160 200
Number of acres

**2.** Use the line graph to find the sales in May.

Sales of Camping Equipment

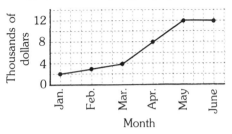

Month

**3.** Which graph is misleading, Graph A or Graph B?

Graph A:
Zoo Attendance

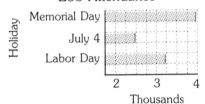

Graph B:
Zoo Attendance

**4.** Use the picture graph to find the value of each 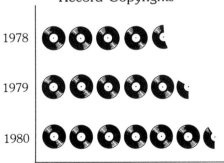 on the graph.

Record Copyrights

1978

1979

1980

Key:   Each ⊙ stands for 2000 records.

**5.** Use the circle graph to find how many cents of every dollar go for packaging frozen pizza.

Your Frozen Pizza Dollar

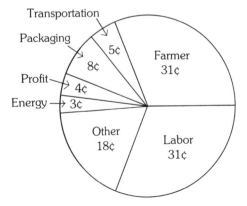

Transportation
Packaging
Profit
Energy

5¢
8¢
4¢
3¢

Farmer
31¢

Other
18¢

Labor
31¢

**339**

**6.** In the schematic of the flashlight, what touches the reflector collar to complete the circuit?

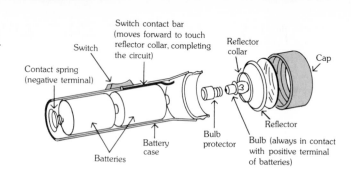

**7.** Make a bar graph for this table.

Points Scored by Starting
Players in Championship Game

| Player | Points |
|---|---|
| Huber | 18 |
| Erhardt | 15 |
| Scanlon | 26 |
| Kraeger | 16 |
| Rothkopf | 13 |

**8.** Make a line graph for this table.

| Daily High Temperature | |
|---|---|
| Day | Temperature (°C) |
| Sunday | 5° |
| Monday | 9° |
| Tuesday | 15° |
| Wednesday | 14° |
| Thursday | 12° |
| Friday | 16° |
| Saturday | 10° |

**9.** Make a circle graph for this table.

| Energy Use | |
|---|---|
| Use | Percent |
| Residential | 16% |
| Industrial | 27% |
| Transportation | 24% |
| Electricity generation | 33% |

Ed Hoppe Photography

The Consumer Information Center in Pueblo, Colorado, publishes the Consumer Information Catalog. This catalog lists booklets from almost 30 federal agencies and helps the agencies share useful consumer information.

The catalog provides titles and descriptions of booklets on several topics, such as automobiles, food, gardening, health, housing, money management, travel, and hobbies. Some titles of booklets that were available in a recent catalog follow.

*Cost of Owning and Operating Automobiles and Vans*

*The Car Book*

*Consumer's Guide to Food Labels*

*Clearing the Air: A Guide to Quitting Smoking*

*The Common Cold*

*Home-Buying Veteran*

You can obtain a copy of the catalog at your public library or by writing to   Consumer Information Center
          Pueblo, CO   81009

Information from these booklets often appears in graphs like the following:

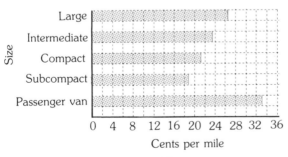

Cost of Owning and Operating
Vehicles in Suburbs

Source:   U.S. Department of Transportation

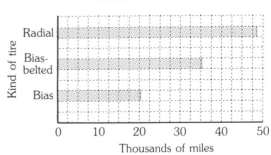

Mileage for Most Frequent
Kinds of Tires

Source:   U.S. Department of Transportation

It is important for today's consumer to understand graphs. This chapter provides a good foundation.

L. LaRue/FPG

***Bar graphs*** are used to *compare amounts*. The bar graph below compares the numbers of endangered species of various kinds of animals.

**The title tells you what the graph is about.**

**There is a bar for each kind of animal.**

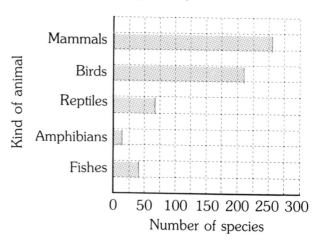

**On a bar graph, the number scale should begin with 0. On the number scale above, each unit stands for 25 species, but only every other unit is numbered.**

To understand a bar graph, first read the title and the labels of the scale and the bars. Then compare the lengths of the bars.

## EXERCISES

Use the graph at the right to answer the following:

1. What is the title of the graph?

2. How many years are listed on the graph?

3. What does each unit on the number scale stand for?

4. What does the length of each bar stand for?

5. What does the red section of each bar stand for?

6. What does the gray section of each bar stand for?

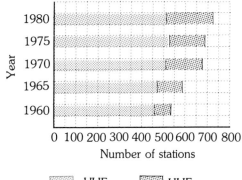

Number of TV Broadcasting Stations

Use the graph at the right to answer the following:

7. What is the title of the graph?

8. Which fruit has the smallest number of calories?

9. Which two fruits have the most calories?

10. How many calories does a whole cantaloupe have?

11. How many calories does a whole grapefruit have?

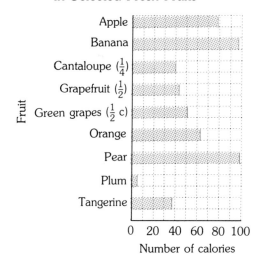

Number of Calories
in Selected Fresh Fruits

EXTRA PRACTICE page 507, set 99

343

A **line graph** is often used to show *change* over a period of time. Since 1965, the number of visits to national parks has, in general, been increasing. In 1965 there were 37 million visits, and in 1982 there were 64 million visits.

Dr. E.R. Degginger

**Title**

**The vertical number scale shows the number of visits in millions.**

**This means that there is a break in the number scale between 0 and 34.**

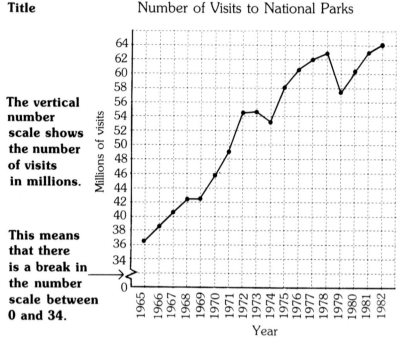

Number of Visits to National Parks

Millions of visits

Year

**The horizontal scale shows the years from 1965 to 1982.**

To understand a line graph, first read the title and the labels on the scales. Then read the graph from left to right.

# EXERCISES

Use the graph above to answer each of the following:

1. For which year does the graph show the greatest number of visits? Estimate the number of visits to the nearest million.

2. Which years showed a decrease in the number of visits when compared with the previous year?

3. Describe the trend from 1965 to 1973.

Use the line graph at the right to answer each of the following:

**4.** How many years are listed on the graph?

**5.** How many years showed an increase in the number of manufacturers?

**6.** What year showed the greatest increase?

**7.** How many years showed a decrease in the number of manufacturers?

**8.** Estimate the number of manufacturers in each year.

Number of Manufacturers of
Solar Heating Equipment

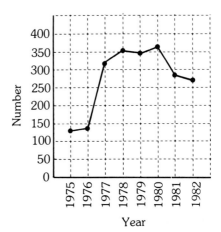

Sometimes line graphs do not include information for *every* year. When some years are skipped, the graph is less accurate. But often the general trend still shows.

Use the line graph at the right to answer each of the following:

**9.** How many years are listed on the graph?

**10.** Why is there a break in the number scale below 4.6?

**11.** How many years showed an increase in the hours of TV viewing?

**12.** How many years showed a decrease in the hours of TV viewing?

Average Viewing of TV per Day

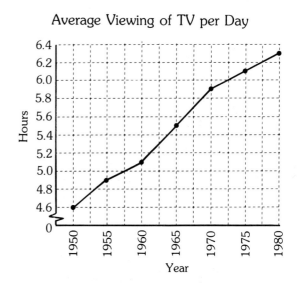

*EXTRA PRACTICE page 508, set 100*

**345**

## 12.3 MISUSING BAR AND LINE GRAPHS

Bar graphs are used to compare information. When reading a bar graph, the reader compares the lengths of the bars.

## EXERCISES

Use Graph A at the right to answer each of the following:

1. How many times longer is the bar for Our Brand than the bar for Brand X?

2. How many times longer is the bar for Our Brand than the bar for Brand Y?

3. What are the sales of Brand X?

4. What are the sales of Brand Y?

5. What are the sales of Our Brand?

Graph A:

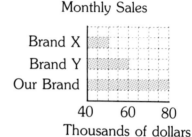

Monthly Sales

Use Graph B at the right to answer each of the following:

6. What are the sales of Brand X?

7. What are the sales of Brand Y?

8. What are the sales of Our Brand?

Graph B:

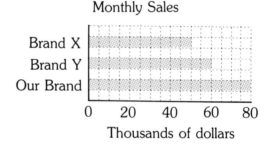

Monthly Sales

Use both Graph A and Graph B to answer each of the following:

9. Do both graphs show the same dollar amount of sales for each company?

10. Which graph is misleading? Why?

Line graphs are sometimes used to show trends. The way information is put on a graph can change the appearance of a trend.

Graph C:

Subscriptions, 1980–1985
VIDEO TODAY

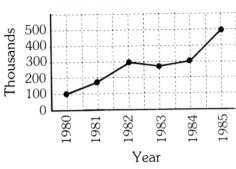

Graph D:

Subscriptions, 1980–1985
VIDEO TODAY

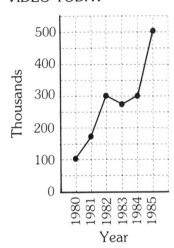

**11.** Use Graph C above to estimate the number of subscriptions for each year.

**12.** Use Graph D above to estimate the number of subscriptions for each year.

**13.** Do both Graph C and Graph D give the same information?

**14.** Which graph makes it look as if the number of subscriptions has increased faster?

**15.** Which graph makes it look as if the number of subscriptions has increased more?

*SKILLS REVIEW*

Add.

**16.**  84
       + 79

**17.**  48
       + 87

**18.**  7.6
       + 3.85

**19.**  70.49
       +  8.08

**20.**  306
       +  84.7

Subtract.

**21.**  2064
       − 1283

**22.**  3500
       − 1782

**23.**  57.3
       − 18.78

**24.**  80
       − 47.3

**25.**  105.7
       −   16

Ben Weddle/Picture Group

A ***picture graph*** is a special kind of bar graph. Picture graphs are frequently used in newspapers and magazines and can be more fun to read. Often the picture used in the graph is related to the topic of the graph.

**Title**

**There is a row of ⌐’s for each state.**

**Often a *key* takes the place of the number scale.**

Production of Peanuts

| State | |
|---|---|
| Alabama | ⌐ ⌐ ⌐ |
| Florida | ⌐ ⌐ |
| Georgia | ⌐ ⌐ ⌐ ⌐ ⌐ ⌐ ⌐ ⌐ ⌐ ⌐ |
| North Carolina | ⌐ ⌐ ⌐ |
| Oklahoma | ⌐ ⌐ |
| Texas | ⌐ ⌐ ⌐ |
| Virginia | ⌐ ⌐ |

Key: Each ⌐ stands for 100 million pounds of peanuts.

# EXERCISES

Use the picture graph above to answer each of the following:

**1.** What does each ⌐ stand for?

**2.** How many states are listed on the graph?

**3.** Estimate the amount of peanuts produced in each state.

Use the picture graph at the right to answer each of the following:

**4.** What does each 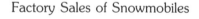 stand for?

**5.** How many years are listed on the graph?

**6.** Estimate the number of snowmobiles sold in the most recent year.

**7.** Estimate the number of snowmobiles sold in 1970.

Factory Sales of Snowmobiles

Key: Each 🛷 stands for 25,000 snowmobiles.

Use the picture graph at the right to answer each of the following:

**8.** What does each 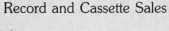 stand for?

**9.** How many years are listed on the graph?

**10.** Estimate the value of the coins in circulation for each year.

Value of Coins in Circulation

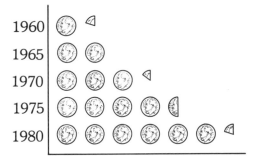

Key: Each 🪙 stands for 2 million dollars.

*EXTRA PRACTICE page 508, set 101*

## CHECKPOINT

**1.** Using the bar graph, estimate the number of miles of coastline on each coast.

**2.** For which year does the line graph show the greatest amount of sales?

**3.** If the number scale on a bar graph does not begin with 0, do the lengths of the bars give a true comparison of amounts?

**4.** What often takes the place of the number scale on a picture graph?

Miles of U.S. Coastline

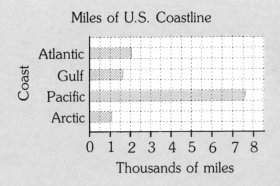

Record and Cassette Sales

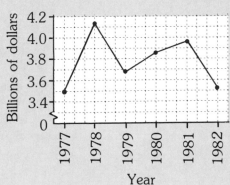

# CIRCLE GRAPHS AND 100% BAR GRAPHS

Brent Jones

*Circle graphs* are used to *compare parts of a whole*. Often a circle graph is labeled in percents, with the whole circle standing for 100%.

Number of Persons in U.S. Households

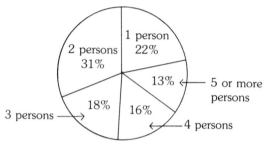

**Example 1:** Use the graph to find what percent of all households consist of only 1 person.

22% of all households consist of only 1 person.

**Example 2:** If there are 80 million U.S. households, how many consist of only 1 person?

**22% of 80   $0.22 \times 80 = 17.6$**

So 17.6 million U.S. households consist of only 1 person.

Sometimes a circle graph is not labeled with percents, but the whole circle still stands for 100%.

Internal Revenue Collections (cents per dollar)

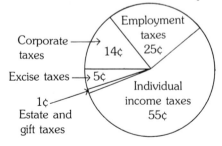

**Example 3:** How many cents out of every dollar come from individual taxpayers?

55¢ out of every dollar come from individual taxpayers.

# EXERCISES

Use the circle graphs on page 350 for exercises 1–8. If there are 80 million U.S. households, how many consist of the following numbers of persons?

**1.** 2 persons     **2.** 3 persons     **3.** 4 persons     **4.** 5 or more persons

How many cents out of every dollar of Internal Revenue collections come from each kind of tax?

**5.** corporate taxes     **6.** employment taxes     **7.** excise taxes     **8.** estate and gift taxes

***100% bar graphs*** are similar to circle graphs. The whole bar stands for 100%.

Use the 100% bar graphs below to answer the following: If there were 957,000 houses built, how many houses had

**9.** 1 story

**10.** 2 or more stories

**11.** a garage

**12.** a carport

Number of Stories in New Houses

Parking Facilities in New Houses

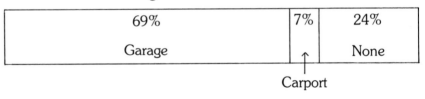

EXTRA PRACTICE page 509, set 102

## MATH NOTE

Find examples of bar graphs, line graphs, picture graphs, and circle graphs in newspapers and magazines. Try to find graphs that look interesting and give information about a topic that interests you. Bring them to class for a bulletin-board display.

A **schematic** is a diagram that shows how the parts of a system fit together. The following schematics of an upright vacuum cleaner show the entire handle and the switch-plate area of the handle.

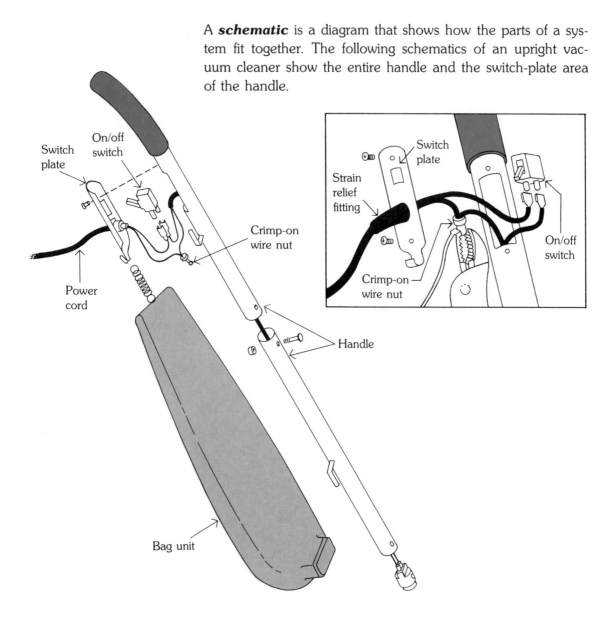

## EXERCISES

1. How many wires does the on/off switch plug into?

2. How many screws hold the switch plate in place?

3. Describe how to replace the on/off switch in the handle.

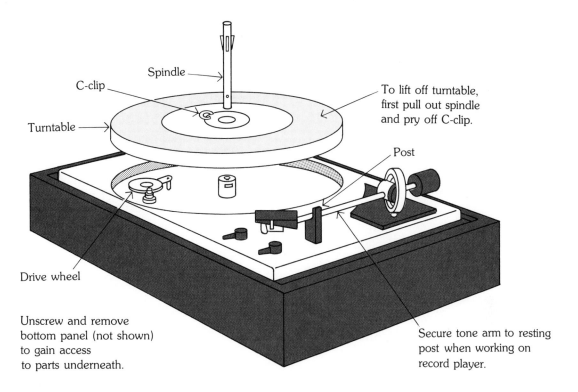

Spindle

C-clip

Turntable

To lift off turntable, first pull out spindle and pry off C-clip.

Post

Drive wheel

Unscrew and remove bottom panel (not shown) to gain access to parts underneath.

Secure tone arm to resting post when working on record player.

Use the schematic above to answer the following:

**4.** What should you do with the tone arm when working on a record player?

**5.** What two things should you do to lift off the turntable of a record player?

**6.** What controls the movement of the turntable?

Use the schematic at the right to answer the following:

**7.** How many screws hold the trim ring in place?

Headlight Replacement

**8.** How many screws hold the retaining ring in place?

**9.** How many screws aim the headlight?

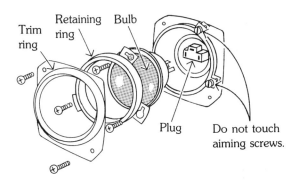

Retaining    Bulb
Trim    ring
ring

Plug          Do not touch
              aiming screws.

EXTRA PRACTICE page 509, set 103

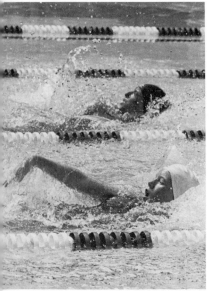

Everett C. Johnson/Photri

The number of calories used per hour by a person varies according to the activity. The table below shows the numbers of calories used per hour by a 150-pound person.

Calories Used per Hour by a 150-Pound Person

| Activity | Calories per hour |
|---|---|
| Sleeping | 80 |
| Swimming ($\frac{1}{4}$ mi/h) | 300 |
| Cycling (13 mi/h) | 660 |
| Driving a car | 120 |
| Walking ($2\frac{1}{2}$ mi/h) | 210 |
| Mowing a lawn (power mower) | 250 |
| Playing table tennis | 360 |
| Running (10 mi/h) | 900 |
| Skiing (10 mi/h) | 600 |

The information in the table can be compared more easily by making a bar graph.

**Use the title of the table as the title of the graph.**

**Label the vertical scale with the various activities. Allow for space between the bars.**

**Label the horizontal scale with a range from 0 to 900 calories per hour.**

Calories Used per Hour by a 150-Pound Person

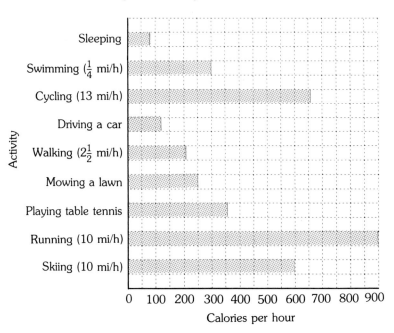

# EXERCISES

Make a bar graph for each table.

**1.** Number of Visitors to Selected National Parks

| National park | Millions of visitors |
| --- | --- |
| Glacier | 1.5 |
| Grand Canyon | 2.5 |
| Grand Teton | 3.5 |
| Great Smoky Mountains | 11.9 |
| Rocky Mountain | 2.6 |
| Yellowstone | 2.0 |
| Yosemite | 2.6 |

**2.** Threatened Species

| Kind of animal | Number of species |
| --- | --- |
| Mammals | 24 |
| Birds | 3 |
| Reptiles | 12 |
| Amphibians | 3 |
| Fishes | 12 |

*EXTRA PRACTICE page 510, set 104*

---

## CALCULATOR NOTE

Some printing calculators (calculators that print the calculation and the result of the calculation on a paper tape) may have a graph printout key [G] . When [G] is pressed after any whole number from 2 to 100 is entered, a bar graph printout of that number results.

|  | ENTER | PRINTOUT |
| --- | --- | --- |
| **Example 1:** | 10 [G] | 10 ▦ |
| **Example 2:** | 30 [G] | 30 ▦ ▦ ▦ |

What would the PRINTOUT be for each of the following?

**1.** 20 [G]     **2.** 40 [G]     **3.** 90 [G]

BUG CATCHER
Flying nocturnal insects,
a good source of protein,
are attracted by the
ultraviolet light and blown
either into a collection bag or
into the water providing a
low cost fish food.

John D. Cunningham

The table below shows the number of patents issued for inventions in each year from 1975 to 1982.

Patents Issued for Inventions

| Year | Thousands |
|------|-----------|
| 1975 | 72 |
| 1976 | 70 |
| 1977 | 65 |
| 1978 | 66 |
| 1979 | 49 |
| 1980 | 62 |
| 1981 | 66 |
| 1982 | 58 |

You can make a line graph of the information in the table.

**Use the title of the table
as the title of the graph.**

**Since the numbers in the
table range from 49,000
to 72,000, label the vertical scale with numbers
from 45 to 75.**

**Show that there is a →
break in the vertical
scale between 0 and 45.**

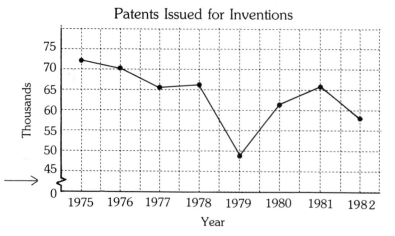

**Label the horiontal scale with
each year from 1975 to 1982.**

356

# EXERCISES

Make a line graph for each table.

**1.** Licenses Issued for CB
(citizens band) Radios

| Year | Millions |
|------|----------|
| 1975 | 1.7 |
| 1976 | 5.8 |
| 1977 | 4.7 |
| 1978 | 2.3 |
| 1979 | 1.1 |
| 1980 | 0.6 |
| 1981 | 0.5 |
| 1982 | 0.4 |

**2.** Average Number of Radios
per U.S. Households

| Year | Number |
|------|--------|
| 1950 | 2.1 |
| 1955 | 2.4 |
| 1960 | 3.7 |
| 1965 | 4.1 |
| 1970 | 5.1 |
| 1975 | 5.6 |
| 1980 | 5.5 |

**3.** Percent of Households With TV Sets

| Year | Percent |
|------|---------|
| 1950 | 9 |
| 1955 | 65 |
| 1960 | 87 |
| 1965 | 93 |
| 1970 | 95 |
| 1975 | 97 |
| 1980 | 98 |

*EXTRA PRACTICE page 510, set 105*

**MAKING CIRCLE GRAPHS**

Frank Siteman/Taurus

Make a circle graph of the information in the table below.

Dogs Registered by Groups

| Group | Percent |
|---|---|
| Sporting | 26% |
| Hound | 10% |
| Working | 28% |
| Terrier | 7% |
| Toy | 12% |
| Nonsporting | 17% |

Compute the measure of each central angle by using the fact that a circle contains 360°. (A **central angle** of a circle has its vertex at the center of the circle.)

**26% of 360 → 0.26 × 360 = 93.6° ≈ 94°**     Remember that ≈
**10% of 360 → 0.10 × 360 = 36°**     means *is approxi-*
**28% of 360 → 0.28 × 360 = 100.8° ≈ 101°**     *mately equal to.*
 **7% of 360 → 0.07 × 360 = 25.2° ≈ 25°**
**12% of 360 → 0.12 × 360 = 43.2° ≈ 43°**
**17% of 360 → 0.17 × 360 = 61.2° ≈ 61°**

Use a protractor to draw the central angles. Label the parts of the circle and give the graph a title.

Dogs Registered by Groups

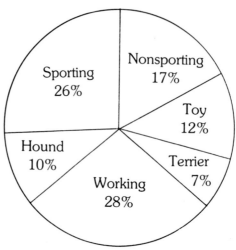

## EXERCISES

Make a circle graph for each table.

**1.**
### Number of Stations That Can Be Received by U.S. Homes With TVs

| Number of stations | Percent of homes |
|---|---|
| 1–4 | 8% |
| 5–7 | 27% |
| 8–10 | 33% |
| 11 or more | 32% |

**2.** Occupational Groups of Employed Persons

| Group | Percent |
|---|---|
| White-collar | 53% |
| Blue-collar | 31% |
| Service | 13% |
| Farm | 3% |

EXTRA PRACTICE page 510, set 106

## SKILLS REVIEW

Multiply.

**3.**
$$\begin{array}{r} 47 \\ \times 28 \\ \hline \end{array}$$

**4.**
$$\begin{array}{r} 608 \\ \times 12 \\ \hline \end{array}$$

**5.**
$$\begin{array}{r} 3.8 \\ \times 4.6 \\ \hline \end{array}$$

**6.**
$$\begin{array}{r} 2.08 \\ \times 0.7 \\ \hline \end{array}$$

**7.**
$$\begin{array}{r} 36.5 \\ \times 0.82 \\ \hline \end{array}$$

**8.**
$$\begin{array}{r} 3.19 \\ \times 0.05 \\ \hline \end{array}$$

**9.**
$$\begin{array}{r} 0.36 \\ \times 8 \\ \hline \end{array}$$

**10.**
$$\begin{array}{r} 4.25 \\ \times 24 \\ \hline \end{array}$$

**11.**
$$\begin{array}{r} 6.09 \\ \times 0.51 \\ \hline \end{array}$$

**12.**
$$\begin{array}{r} 7.7 \\ \times 0.56 \\ \hline \end{array}$$

Divide.

**13.** $22\overline{)2035}$  **14.** $36\overline{)9504}$  **15.** $8.06 \div 100$  **16.** $29\overline{)88.45}$  **17.** $0.7\overline{)16.709}$

1. Floorboards that are 4 in. wide are to be placed side by side to cover a hallway floor that is 5 ft wide. How many boards are needed?

2. Bob drives $1\frac{3}{4}$ hours each day, commuting to and from work. How many hours does he spend commuting in a 5-day workweek?

3. Molding is to be installed around the ceiling in a square room $16\frac{1}{2}$ feet on each side. How many feet of molding are needed?

4. A health insurance company will pay 80% of a $1500 hospital bill. How much will the company pay?

**5.** It takes $1\frac{1}{4}$ yards of tissue paper to make one kite. How many kites can be made with 5 yards of tissue paper?

**6.** How many pieces of wood, each $1\frac{1}{3}$ feet long, can be cut from a board 8 feet long?

**7.** In a student-council election, one candidate received 232 votes out of 400 ballots. What percent of the votes did the candidate get?

**8.** A $35 video game is on sale at a 30% discount. The sales tax is 6%. Find the total cost of the game.

**9.** A garment bag is on sale at a 20% discount. If the regular price is $55 and the sales tax is 4%, find the total cost.

**10.** The fee for traveler's checks is $3 for $300 in checks. What percent of the amount of the checks is the fee?

The Dreyer family spent $18,000 on their household budget last year. Use the Family Spending circle graph to find the yearly amount for each item.

**11.** housing and utilities

**12.** food

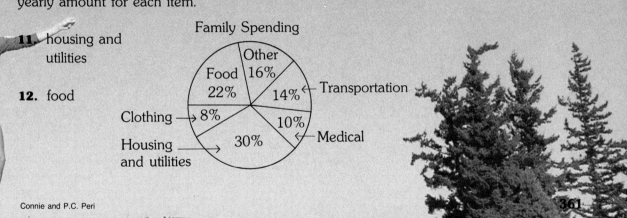

Family Spending

Other 16%
Food 22%
Transportation 14%
Clothing 8%
Medical 10%
Housing and utilities 30%

Market-research workers try to determine the wants and needs of consumers. The researchers gather information by telephone and mail surveys, as well as by interviews with people. Most market researchers are employed by manufacturers, advertisers, and independent research companies.

Mary Elenz Tranter

Sometimes researchers use graphs to display the information they gather. Hair Performance Company is putting a new shampoo on the market. A researcher made these graphs of the results of a survey.

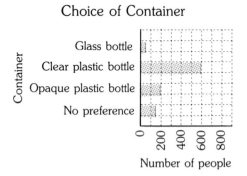

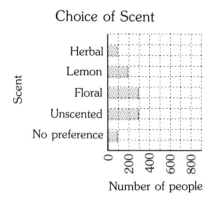

**1.** Which kind of container do you think the company should use?

**2.** Which scent(s) do you think the company should use?

Use the bar graph at the right to answer the following:

**1.** How many years are listed on the graph?

**2.** What does each unit on the number scale stand for?

**3.** What does the length of each bar stand for?

Voter Participation in Presidential Elections

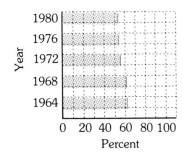

12.1

Use the line graph at the right to answer the following:

**4.** What is the title of the graph?

**5.** How many years are listed on the graph?

**6.** Why is there a break in the vertical scale below 60?

**7.** Describe the trend shown on the graph.

Percent of U.S. Households with Telephone Service

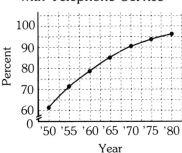

12.2

Use the graphs below to answer the following:

**8.** Do both graphs give the same information?

**9.** Which graph is misleading? Why?

Graph A:

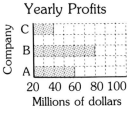

Graph B:

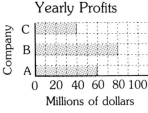

**10.** On a picture graph, what often takes the place of the number scale?

12.3

12.4

Use the circle graph at the right to answer the following:

12.5

**Federal Budget Expenses (cents per dollar)**

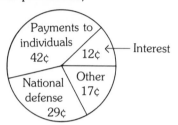

**11.** How many cents out of every dollar are used to pay interest?

**12.** How many cents out of every dollar go for national defense?

Use the schematic at the right to answer the following:

12.6

**13.** What keeps the ventilator in place?

**14.** Where is the cleaning needle?

**15.** Where is the oiling hole located?

**16.** Make a bar graph for this table.

12.7

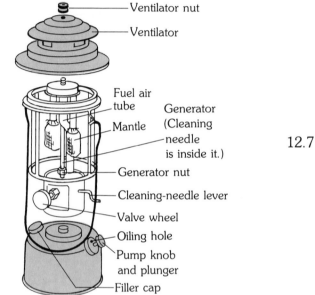

### National Park System

| Type of park | Number |
|---|---|
| National | 48 |
| National historical | 25 |
| National military | 10 |
| National battlefield | 3 |

**17.** Make a line graph for this table.

**18.** Make a circle graph for this table.

12.8, 12.9

Winning Times in the New York Marathon

| Year | Time (hours: minutes) |
|---|---|
| 1977 | 2:11 |
| 1978 | 2:12 |
| 1979 | 2:11 |
| 1980 | 2:09 |
| 1981 | 2:08 |
| 1982 | 2:09 |

### Federal Budget

| Source of income | Percent |
|---|---|
| Individual income taxes | 35% |
| Borrowing | 22% |
| Social Security taxes | 29% |
| Excise taxes | 5% |
| Corporate income taxes | 6% |
| Other | 3% |

**1.** Use the bar graph to list the ways students get to school.

Methods of Transportation to School

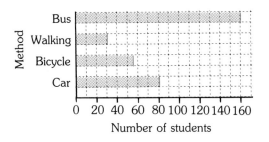

**2.** Use the line graph to find the year in which the greatest number of tornadoes occurred.

Tornadoes Occurring Each Year

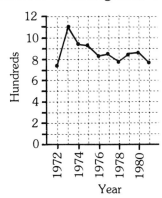

**3.** Which graph is misleading, Graph A or Graph B?

Graph A:

Yearly Sales

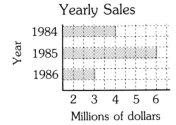

Graph B:

Yearly Sales

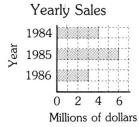

**4.** Use the picture graph to find the value of each 🚗 on the graph.

Communities With the Busiest Intersections in Cook County, Illinois

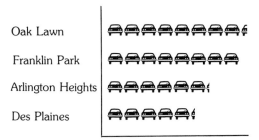

Key: Each 🚗 represents 10,000 cars daily.

**5.** Use the circle graph to name the source of energy from which the most electricity is produced.

Sources of Energy Used to Produce Electricity

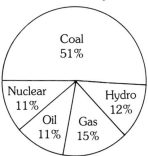

**6.** How many chimney retainers are shown in the schematic of the oil lamp?

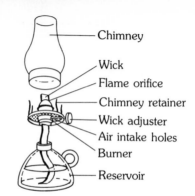

- Chimney
- Wick
- Flame orifice
- Chimney retainer
- Wick adjuster
- Air intake holes
- Burner
- Reservoir

**7.** Make a bar graph for this table.

Favorite Pizza Toppings of 60 People

| Topping | Number |
|---|---|
| Sausage | 20 |
| Extra cheese | 15 |
| Green peppers | 5 |
| Mushrooms | 15 |
| Pepperoni | 5 |

**8.** Make a line graph for this table.

U.S. Households With Cable TV

| Year | Millions |
|---|---|
| 1965 | 1.3 |
| 1968 | 2.8 |
| 1971 | 5.3 |
| 1974 | 8.7 |
| 1977 | 11.9 |
| 1980 | 15.5 |

**9.** Make a circle graph for this table.

Age of Cars in Use in the United States in a Recent Year

| Age | Percent |
|---|---|
| Under 3 years | 26% |
| 3–5 years | 24% |
| 6–8 years | 24% |
| 9–11 years | 14% |
| 12 years and over | 12% |

1. Make a stem-and-leaf display. Use one-digit stems.

   83, 92, 74, 80, 97, 78, 64, 83, 93, 87, 63, 61

2. Make a frequency table for the following pets of students:

   dog, cat, dog, parakeet, hamster, dog, cat, cat, dog, parakeet, dog

3. Use the intervals 10–12, 13–15, and 16–18 to make a frequency table for the following data:

   11, 15, 16, 11, 10, 12, 17, 17, 17, 18, 12, 14, 16, 17, 17

Use the following data in exercises 4–7:

4, 7, 6, 8, 10, 13

4. Find the range.

5. Find the mean.

6. Find the median.

7. Find the mode.

Use the frequency table below in exercises 8–11.

| Number | Frequency |
|--------|-----------|
| 3 | 2 |
| 4 | 10 |
| 5 | 4 |
| 6 | 4 |
| total | 20 |

8. Find the range.

9. Find the mean.

10. Find the median.

11. Find the mode.

12. Find the mode for each group. Which group has the smaller mode?

   Group 1:  8, 8, 7, 8, 9, 9, 7, 6, 10, 11, 12
   Group 2:  6, 7, 7, 9, 8, 5, 10, 12, 15

13. Ten students ran once around the track in the following times (in minutes). What was the median time required?

   3, 3, 10, 5, 4, 4, 4, 5, 4, 4

14. The average person uses 7.1 calories per minute while playing tennis. Can you tell how many calories per minute *you* will use while playing tennis?

Kenji Kerins

A health clinic kept a record of the number of pounds each person lost. The weight losses were as follows:

12, 42, 12, 24, 37, 34, 20, 21, 18

Statistics involves collecting, organizing, and studying **data** (numbers or facts).

One way to organize a set of numbers is with a **stem-and-leaf display.**

**Example 1:** Make a stem-and-leaf display for the weight losses above.

The *stems* are the tens digits. Arrange them in increasing order from top to bottom.

| 1 | 2, 2, 8 |
| 2 | 4, 0, 1 |
| 3 | 7, 4 |
| 4 | 2 |

The *leaves* are the ones digits. Write each leaf in the same row as its stem.

Then arrange the leaves so that they are in increasing order from left to right.

| 1 | 2, 2, 8 |
| 2 | 0, 1, 4 |
| 3 | 4, 7 |
| 4 | 2 |

You can have more than one digit for the stems or for the leaves.

**Example 2:** Use one-digit stems.

127, 436, 234, 106, 98, 303, 149, 226, 137, 498

| 0 | 98  → 098, or 98 |
| 1 | 06, 27, 37, 49 |
| 2 | 26, 34 |
| 3 | 03 |
| 4 | 36, 98 |

The stems are the hundreds digits.

**Example 3:** Use two-digit stems.

110, 106, 139, 137, 126, 104, 104, 116, 122, 128

| 10 | 4, 4, 6 |
| 11 | 0, 6 |
| 12 | 2, 6, 8 |
| 13 | 7, 9 |

The stems are the hundreds and the tens digits.

## EXERCISES

For exercises 1–8, use the stem-and-leaf display at the right.

| | |
|---|---|
| 3 | 2, 4, 9 |
| 4 | 3, 6, 6, 8 |
| 5 | 2, 3 |
| 6 | |
| 7 | 0 |

1. Name the stems.

2. Name the leaves for the stem 3.

3. How many numbers have the stem 5?

4. How many numbers have the leaf 3?

5. How many numbers have the stem 6?

6. What is the smallest number?

7. What is the largest number?

8. How many times does the number 46 occur?

Make a stem-and-leaf display. Use one-digit stems.

9. 26, 32, 21, 15, 35, 32, 29, 40, 21, 16

10. 98, 42, 87, 82, 73, 56, 68, 71, 80, 51

11. 11, 26, 15, 9, 32, 15, 23, 21, 13, 12

12. 423, 531, 357, 480, 572, 394, 476, 583, 410, 327

13. 15, 27, 18, 30, 37, 29, 27, 10, 14, 26, 34, 37, 30

14. 126, 394, 472, 271, 110, 169, 497, 503, 475, 143

Make a stem-and-leaf display. Use two-digit stems.

15. 120, 139, 115, 129, 127, 132, 130, 138, 112, 133

16. 226, 221, 204, 200, 218, 207, 209, 225, 216, 211

17. 106, 124, 137, 98, 131, 102, 113, 119, 121, 133, 101, 110, 94, 94

18. 5893, 6021, 5642, 5721, 5924, 5672, 6018, 5735, 5947, 5801, 5978, 5736, 5691, 5824, 6035, 6093

19. 1579, 1392, 1508, 1470, 1436, 1320, 1376, 1509, 1584, 1676, 1659, 1327, 1400, 1602, 1547, 1370

20. 153, 169, 149, 172, 140, 186, 163, 151, 148, 180

21. 760, 754, 759, 778, 772, 757, 761, 763, 750

Brent Jones

Paul and Lisa want to buy a pickup truck. They asked the dealer about the miles per gallon they could expect from several different models. The estimated average miles per gallon for each is listed below.

18, 17, 16, 15, 20, 19, 18, 19, 15, 20, 19, 19, 14, 16, 16

Paul and Lisa need a better way to organize the data so that they can compare them more easily.

**Example 1:** Make a *frequency table* for the numbers above.

Use tally marks to count how many times each number occurs.

In the "box" method for tally marks,

$| = 1$     $\ulcorner = 2$     $\llcorner = 3$     $\square = 4$     $\boxed{/} = 5$

For many people, the box method leads to fewer errors than the familiar fence (卌) method.

| | Miles per gallon | Tally | Frequency |
|---|---|---|---|
| **List the numbers from smallest to largest.** | 14 | $|$ | 1 |
| | 15 | $\ulcorner$ | 2 |
| | 16 | $\llcorner$ | 3 |
| | 17 | $|$ | 1 |
| | 18 | $\ulcorner$ | 2 |
| | 19 | $\square$ | 4 |
| | 20 | $\ulcorner$ | 2 |
| | | total | 15 |

When you are organizing a large set of numbers, you can make a frequency table by using *equal intervals*. This makes the frequency table shorter, and you can study the numbers more easily.

**Example 2:** Use the intervals 0–2, 3–5, 6–8, 9–11,

12–14, 15–17, and 18–20 to make a frequency table for the following data:

0, 2, 9, 7, 6, 11, 7, 8, 10, 9, 10, 11, 7, 9, 10, 15, 12, 16, 13, 16, 17, 19, 19, 17, 6, 2, 20, 19, 20, 17, 6, 4, 5, 3, 17, 4, 7, 4, 5

| Interval | Tally | Frequency |
|----------|-------|-----------|
| 0–2 | | 3 |
| 3–5 | | 6 |
| 6–8 | | 8 |
| 9–11 | | 8 |
| 12–14 | | 2 |
| 15–17 | | 7 |
| 18–20 | | 5 |
| | total | 39 |

## EXERCISES

**1.** Copy the frequency table at the right. Using the names below, complete it.

Meri, Meri, Joseph, Tom, Tom, Leesa, Leesa, Leesa, Joseph, Meri, Meri, Joseph, Meri, Leesa, Tom, Tom, Joseph, Meri

Votes for Class Representative

| Name | Tally | Frequency |
|------|-------|-----------|
| Joseph | | ? |
| Leesa | ? | 4 |
| Meri | | ? |
| Tom | ? | ? |

Make a frequency table for the following:

**2.** *Quiz scores:* 6, 7, 9, 10, 5, 2, 4, 6, 7, 8, 7, 8, 8, 9, 10, 7, 3, 5, 9, 9, 9, 8, 9, 7, 5, 10, 3, 2, 4, 6, 7, 8

**3.** *Gold medals won by countries in the Summer Olympics:* 2, 1, 1, 2, 5, 8, 8, 8, 2, 2, 3, 6, 47, 1, 0, 0, 7, 1, 0, 8, 0, 0, 0, 0, 0, 3, 6, 1, 3, 2, 0, 80, 0, 0, 2, 1

**4.** Use the intervals 50–59, 60–69, 70–79, 80–89, and 90–99 to make a frequency table for the following data:

97, 58, 76, 94, 83, 82, 71, 64, 75, 69, 87, 91, 83, 74, 73, 66, 80, 72, 76, 87, 52, 84, 73, 77, 89, 62, 82, 85, 72, 79

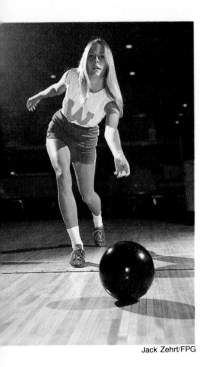

Jack Zehrt/FPG

The secretary of a bowling league recorded the following scores for the first game:

137, 180, 114, 162, 111, 125, 117, 142, 213, 121, 128, 157, 96, 115, 95, 110, 167, 159, 121, 176, 94, 109

The difference between the largest and the smallest number in a set of numbers is called the **range.** The range tells how much spread there is in the set.

**Example 1:** Find the range for the bowling scores.

Look through the set of numbers to find the largest score and the smallest score.

**largest score** ⟶ **213** ⟵
**smallest score** ⟶ **− 94** ⟵ ⎤ **Subtract.**
**119**

The range is 119.

It is easier to find the range of numbers that are in a frequency table.

**Example 2:** Find the range of heights.

|  | Heights (inches) | Frequency |
|---|---|---|
| **smallest height** ⟶ | 59 | 1 |
|  | 60 | 2 |
|  | 61 | 3 |
|  | 63 | 4 |
|  | 64 | 6 |
|  | 65 | 6 |
| **largest height** ⟶ | 66 | 1 |
|  | total | 23 |

**66**
**−59**
**7**

The range is 7 inches.

## EXERCISES

Find the range for each set of numbers.

**1.** *Quiz scores:* 12, 16, 13, 15, 15, 18, 20, 9, 11, 17

**2.** *Test scores:* 93, 42, 86, 53, 72, 84, 67, 79, 82, 75

**3.** *Weights:* 104, 115, 98, 100, 87, 120, 150, 116, 107, 118

**4.** *Miles driven to and from work:* 8, 20, 5, 6, 12, 2, 4

Find the range for each frequency table.

**5.** 

| Most home runs in one season | Frequency |
|---|---|
| 49 | 8 |
| 50 | 1 |
| 51 | 3 |
| 52 | 3 |
| 54 | 4 |
| 56 | 1 |
| 58 | 2 |
| 59 | 1 |
| 60 | 1 |
| 61 | 1 |
| total | 25 |

**6.** 

| Record times for 100-meter run (seconds) | Frequency |
|---|---|
| 11.0 | 2 |
| 11.07 | 1 |
| 11.08 | 1 |
| 11.4 | 1 |
| 11.5 | 3 |
| 11.6 | 1 |
| 11.9 | 2 |
| 12.2 | 1 |
| total | 12 |

EXTRA PRACTICE page 511, set 107

## SKILLS REVIEW

Complete the table.

| | Decimal | Fraction | Percent |
|---|---|---|---|
| **7.** | 0.35 | ___ | ___ |
| **8.** | ___ | $\frac{3}{8}$ | ___ |
| **9.** | ___ | ___ | 25% |

**Chris took 5 tests and received scores of 72, 83, 70, 85, and 90. What is Chris's average, or _mean_, test score?**

To find the mean of a set of numbers:

1. Find the sum.

2. Divide the sum by how many numbers there are.

**Example 1:** Find the mean of 72, 83, 70, 85, and 90.

Step 1: **Find the sum.**

$$\underbrace{72 + 83 + 70 + 85 + 90}_{\textbf{5 numbers}} = 400$$

Step 2: **Divide.**

$$\frac{400}{5} = 80 \longleftarrow \text{mean}$$

Chris's mean test score is 80.

**Example 2:** Find the mean of 104, 123, 116, 137, 151, and 127.

Round the mean to the nearest tenth.

$$\left.\begin{array}{r} 104 \\ 123 \\ 116 \\ 137 \\ 151 \\ +127 \\ \hline 758 \end{array}\right\} \textbf{6 scores} \qquad \begin{array}{r} 126.33 \cdots \\ \hline 6\overline{)758.00} \end{array}$$

So the mean is 126.3.

374

# EXERCISES

Find the mean for each set of numbers.

**1.** 86, 74, 78, 82    **2.** 104, 121, 115, 129    **3.** 5, 6, 9, 3, 7    **4.** 24, 18, 20, 15, 18, 19

**5.** 30, 24, 3, 50, 51, 42, 37, 45, 83, 52, 36, 27

**6.** 116, 120, 104, 92, 135, 141, 126, 131, 97

**7.** 432, 561, 392, 486, 289, 572, 503, 460, 501, 397, 476, 544

**8.** *Hours per week different people listen to the radio:* 20, 18, 24, 30, 10, 22, 25, 30, 22, 12

**9.** *Number of records owned by different people:* 20, 53, 41, 12, 38

**10.** *Price of one pound of hamburger:* $1.09, $1.39, $1.19, $1.89, $1.69

**11.** *Monthly electric bills:* $86.52, $83.18, $51.35, $43.81, $41.36, $32.23, $14.36, $12.07, $38.14, $46.91, $52.53, $78.46

In exercises 12–16, round the mean to the nearest tenth.

**12.** 15, 23, 72, 46, 91, 85      **13.** 33, 30, 24, 20, 16, 25

**14.** 30, 25, 20, 40, 35, 35      **15.** 110, 112, 111, 131, 107, 105

**16.** 3.4, 6.1, 3.5, 2.9, 5.3, 7.8, 4.9, 3.5, 8.1, 2.7, 5.3, 7.6, 8.7, 9.3, 2.5, 3.6, 8.1, 5.2, 9.1, 7.3

## SKILLS REVIEW

Find each answer.

**17.** 315 is what percent of 630?      **18.** What number is 27% of 200?

**19.** 80 is 40% of what number?      **20.** What number is 80% of 12,000?

**21.** 35 is 70% of what number?      **22.** 30 is what percent of 6?

Jack Corn/Corn's Photo Service

**Sam and Louise Martin want to buy a cabin. The prices of five cabins they are interested in are $32,900; $42,000; $32,500; $39,900; and $48,500. What is the median price?**

The *median* is the middle number when the numbers are arranged from smallest to largest.

**Example 1:** Find the median of the cabin prices.

$32,500
$32,900 } 2 numbers

$39,900 ⟵ middle number

$42,000
$48,500 } 2 numbers

The median price is $39,900.

When there are 2 middle numbers, the median is found by:

1. Adding the 2 middle numbers.

2. Dividing the sum by 2.

**Example 2:** Find the median: 36, 74, 83, 69, 97, 78, 75, 85

36  69  74   75  78   83  85  97

3 numbers   2 middle   3 numbers
            numbers

Step 1:  $75 + 78 = 153$

Step 2:  $\dfrac{153}{2} = 76.5$  **median**

## EXERCISES

Find the median for each set.

**1.** 3, 4, 7

**2.** 13, 14, 19, 23, 26

**3.** 93, 72, 69, 85, 87, 75, 79

**4.** 19, 17, 15, 18, 19, 17, 16

**5.** *Heights (inches):* 59, 71, 63, 60, 59, 68, 64

**6.** *Yearly income:* $15,000; $91,000; $16,500; $30,000; $24,000; $36,000; $15,000; $12,000; $12,500

**7.** 2, 3, 5, 9

**8.** 14, 23, 25, 28, 30, 41

**9.** 75, 82, 93, 69, 84, 78, 79, 75, 85

**10.** 4.5, 6.3, 4.9, 4.5, 5.8, 5.3, 4.3, 6.4

**11.** *Shoe sizes:* 7, $6\frac{1}{2}$, 8, $7\frac{1}{2}$, $6\frac{1}{2}$, 6, $8\frac{1}{2}$, 8

**12.** *Scores for a contest:* 8.8, 8.7, 8.3, 8.9, 8.2, 8.9, 8.5, 8.9, 8.4, 8.2

**13.** Find the median of the following scores: 82, 86, 75, 79, 99. Replace 75 with 52. Now find the median of the scores. Did you get the same median both times?

**14.** Find the median of the following scores: 8, 10, 10, 12, 3, 9, 8. Then leave off the largest and smallest scores. Now find the median of the scores. Did you get the same median both times?

EXTRA PRACTICE page 511, set 108

---

## CHECKPOINT

Use the following data for the exercises:
32, 35, 71, 45, 65, 57, 58, 76, 76, 45, 43, 64, 64, 64, 60

**1.** Make a stem-and-leaf display. Use one-digit stems.

**2.** Make a frequency table.

**3.** Find the range.

**4.** Find the mean.

**5.** Find the median.

**THE MEAN AND THE MEDIAN FROM A FREQUENCY TABLE**

**Mrs. Parker made a frequency table showing the number of book reports turned in by each student during one month. What is the mean number of book reports? What is the median?**

| Number of book reports | Frequency |
|:---:|:---:|
| 1 | 3 |
| 2 | 11 |
| 3 | 10 |
| 4 | 4 |
| 5 | 2 |
| total | 30 |

**Example 1:** Find the mean, using the frequency table above.

| Number | Frequency | Multiply each number by its frequency. |
|:---:|:---:|:---:|
| 1 | 3 | $1 \times 3 = 3$ |
| 2 | 11 | $2 \times 11 = 22$ |
| 3 | 10 | $3 \times 10 = 30$ |
| 4 | 4 | $4 \times 4 = 16$ |
| 5 | 2 | $5 \times 2 = 10$ |
| total | 30 | $81 \longleftarrow$ **sum** |

**Divide the sum by the total number of students.** $\quad 30\overline{)81.0}^{\,2.7}$

The mean number of book reports is 2.7.

**Example 2:** Find the median, using the frequency table.

| Number | Frequency | |
|:---:|:---:|:---|
| 1 | 3 | $\left.\begin{array}{c} \\ \end{array}\right\}$ **14 numbers** |
| 2 | 11 | |
| **median** $\longrightarrow$ 3 | 10 **2** | **There are 2 middle numbers.** $\quad 3+3=6 \quad \frac{6}{2}=3$ |
| 4 | 4 **8** | $\left.\begin{array}{c} \\ \end{array}\right\}$ **14 numbers** |
| 5 | 2 | |
| total | 30 | |

The median number of book reports is 3.

## EXERCISES

Find the mean and the median for each of the frequency tables.

**1.**

| Number | Frequency |
|--------|-----------|
| 3 | 1 |
| 5 | 4 |
| 6 | 4 |
| 8 | 4 |
| 9 | 3 |
| 10 | 2 |
| total | 18 |

**2.**

| Number | Frequency |
|--------|-----------|
| 50 | 2 |
| 60 | 2 |
| 70 | 3 |
| 80 | 1 |
| 90 | 4 |
| 100 | 3 |
| total | 15 |

**3.**

| Number | Frequency |
|--------|-----------|
| 5 | 1 |
| 10 | 4 |
| 12 | 3 |
| 15 | 1 |
| 20 | 3 |
| total | 12 |

**4.**

| Number | Frequency |
|--------|-----------|
| 3 | 2 |
| 4 | 2 |
| 7 | 2 |
| 8 | 1 |
| 9 | 2 |
| total | 9 |

## CALCULATOR NOTE

If your calculator has a memory key, you can use it to help you find the mean for a frequency table.

| Number | Frequency | ENTER | DISPLAY | ENTER | In its memory, the calculator does this: |
|--------|-----------|-------|---------|-------|------------------------------------------|
| 23 | 3 | 23 ⊗ 3 ⊜ | 69 | M+ | ← stores 69 |
| 41 | 5 | 41 ⊗ 5 ⊜ | 205 | M+ | ← adds 205 to 69 |
| 67 | 2 | 67 ⊗ 2 ⊜ | 134 | M+ | ← adds 134 to 274 |
| total | 10 | RM ÷ 10 ⊜ | 40.8 | | |

→ RM ÷ 10 = recalls the sum of 408

Check the answers to the 4 exercises above.

**379**

Connie and P.C. Peri

**A physical-education teacher recorded the number of chin-ups each student was able to complete on the first try:**

**5, 3, 9, 1, 8, 3, 3, 0, 3, 3, 2, 6, 0, 8, 9, 1, 3, 3, 3, 3, 3, 3**

**What is the mode of the number of chin-ups?**

The number that occurs the most often is called the **mode.**

**Example 1:** Find the mode of the numbers above.

| Digit | Frequency | |
|---|---|---|
| 0 | 2 | |
| 1 | 2 | |
| 2 | 1 | |
| mode ⟶ 3 | 11 | ⟵ **the highest frequency,** |
| 5 | 1 | **so the mode is 3** |
| 6 | 1 | |
| 8 | 2 | |
| 9 | 2 | |
| total | 22 | |

The mode is 3 chin-ups.

There can be more than one mode for a set of data.

**Example 2:** 2, 2, 2, 3, 4, 7, 8, 8, 8, 9

2 and 8 each occur three times. The other numbers occur only once. 2 and 8 are the modes.

In some cases, a set of data will not have a mode.

**Example 3:** 4, 7, 9, 15

No number occurs more often than the others. There is no mode.

The mode can be used to describe data that are not numbers.

**Example 4:**

| Favorite color | Frequency |
|---|---|
| red | 10 |
| blue | 15 |
| yellow | 10 |
| brown | 2 |
| green | 6 |
| total | 43 |

15 ←———— **The mode is "blue". More people preferred blue than any other color.**

## EXERCISES

Find the mode or modes for each of the following. If there is no mode, say so.

**1.** 5, 5, 7, 7, 7, 15, 18, 18, 18, 18, 20, 26, 26, 30, 30, 30, 40

**2.** 35, 42, 77, 88, 91, 91, 91, 94, 97, 97, 102, 105, 110, 110, 125

**3.** 4.3, 2.7, 5.1, 4.3, 2.7, 6.1, 3.8, 8.6, 4.3, 6.1, 2.7, 6.4

**4.** 2, 5, 7, 3, 2, 7, 3, 5, 6, 10, 8, 10, 8, 6, 12, 12

**5.** 3, $6\frac{1}{2}$, $4\frac{1}{4}$, 5, 9, $2\frac{3}{4}$, 3, $8\frac{1}{3}$, $7\frac{1}{5}$, 3, $8\frac{1}{3}$, $4\frac{1}{4}$, 5

**6.** 114, 108, 125, 142, 138, 120, 116, 124, 139, 162, 157, 189

**7.** 0.2, 0.8, 0.8, 0.7, 0.6, 0.3, 0.2, 0.6, 0.4, 0.9, 0.9, 0.4

**8.** Physical fitness activities done on a regular basis

| | Frequency |
|---|---|
| Bowling | 13 |
| Playing football | 4 |
| Playing basketball | 7 |
| Jogging | 11 |
| Doing exercises | 14 |
| Walking | 22 |
| Swimming | 17 |
| total | 88 |

**9.** Survey of plans of high-school seniors

| | Frequency |
|---|---|
| College | 50 |
| Work | 26 |
| Trade school | 9 |
| Armed services | 3 |
| Apprenticeship | 3 |
| total | 91 |

EXTRA PRACTICE page 512, set 109

Carson Baldwin Jr./FPG

An airline wanted to know how the passengers felt about the quality of service during a flight. Each passenger was asked to rate the service as 5—superior; 4—excellent; 3—good; 2—fair; or 1—poor. The results are listed below.

5, 2, 4, 3, 2, 4, 5, 4, 4, 3, 5, 4, 5, 4, 1, 5, 4,
5, 4, 4, 4, 4, 4, 5, 4, 3, 4, 3, 4, 3, 3, 5, 5, 4,
5, 4, 4, 5, 4, 5, 3, 4, 5, 4, 4, 4, 4, 4, 4, 5, 4

The airline can use statistics to make sense of all the data collected.

**Example:** Make a frequency table for the data above.

| Rating | Frequency |
|--------|-----------|
| 1 | 1 |
| 2 | 2 |
| 3 | 7 |
| 4 | 27 |
| 5 | 14 |
| total | 51 |

The frequency table can help the airline interpret the passengers' reactions more easily.

The mode is 4. Most people felt that the service was excellent. The median is 4.

The mean is 4.

The mean, the median, and the mode are not always the same number. But any one of them can be used to represent an entire set of data.

The airline could interpret from the data that the "typical" passenger felt that the service was excellent.

## EXERCISES

Two classes took a math test with the following results:

Class 1:  85, 96, 53, 27, 83, 75, 72, 76, 64, 65, 87, 81, 59, 67, 70, 74, 78, 83, 79, 91, 74, 82, 65, 66, 79

Class 2:  98, 52, 87, 76, 51, 80, 72, 79, 64, 65, 81, 72, 73, 69, 77, 62, 71, 65, 58, 65, 80, 72, 86, 94, 89

**1.** Find the mean score for Class 1 and for Class 2.

**2.** If the mean is used to represent each class, which class did better on the test?

**3.** Find the median score for Class 1 and for Class 2.

**4.** If the median is used to represent each class, which class did better on the test?

**5.** Which class had the smaller range of test scores?

Richard made a list of the prices he had paid for his records. He then turned the list into the following frequency table:

| Price | Frequency |
|-------|-----------|
| $24.99 | 1 |
| 10.99 | 2 |
| 9.99 | 1 |
| 8.99 | 7 |
| 6.99 | 10 |
| 5.99 | 4 |
| total | 25 |

**6.** Find the mean price of the records Richard bought.

**7.** Find the median price.

**8.** What is the mode?

E. Lettau/FPG

**The yearly salaries of 7 employees are as follows: $120,000; $18,000; $16,500; $16,000; $15,500; $12,000; $12,000. Find the mean salary and the median salary. Which gives a better idea of the salary most of these employees earn?**

To find the mean, add the salaries and divide by 7.

**120,000**
**18,000**
**16,500**
**16,000**
**15,500**
**12,000**
**12,000**
**210,000**

$$30{,}000$$
$$7\overline{)210{,}000}$$

The mean is $30,000.

To find the median, list the salaries in order.

**12,000**
**12,000**
**15,500**
**16,000** ⟵ **middle salary**
**16,500**
**18,000**
**120,000**

The median is $16,000.

As you can see, the median gives you a better idea of the salary earned by these employees.

Keep in mind that

a. to find the mean, you add all the numbers, no matter how large or small, then divide the total by the number of data.

b. the median is not affected by a very large or very small number and the median is the middle number when the data are arranged from smallest to largest.

In many situations, the mean is preferred to the median. Sports statistics often are means. Very good and very bad performances must be included when you compare players or teams.

For example

a. A person's bowling average is the mean of the scores of all of the games bowled.

b. In football, the mean is used when the average yardage per carry is figured.

# EXERCISES

1. The prices of 5 houses for sale in Willow Creek are $23,000; $80,000; $90,000; $75,000; and $77,000. Find the mean selling price and the median selling price. Which seems more typical of the selling prices?

2. Dennis took 5 tests during the semester and scored 90, 83, 75, 86, and 80. What is his mean test score?

3. The selling prices for 6 new cars are $8729, $7999, $6423, $9109, $8247, and $12,431. What is the mean price? What is the median price? Find the difference between the mean and the median.

4. Five basketball players have the following heights (in inches): 72, 74, 75, 71, and 84. What is the mean height? How many heights are less than the mean? How many are greater?

5. Six families have the following incomes: $12,200; $16,900; $77,280; $36,400; $60,430; and $145,000. What is the median income? How many incomes are less than the median? How many are greater?

6. A football team gained the following numbers of yards in the 4 quarters: 62, 80, 93, and 76. What was the average number of yards gained per quarter?

7. Mittens sell for $2.00, $1.75, $1.50, and $1.25, according to size. The frequency table shows the number sold at each price. For mittens of which price should the largest order be placed?

| Price | Frequency |
|-------|-----------|
| $2.00 | 8 |
| 1.75 | 21 |
| 1.50 | 35 |
| 1.25 | 9 |
| total | 73 |

8. The lake has a mean depth of 4 feet. If you swim here, why might you like to know the range of depths?

EXTRA PRACTICE page 512, set 110

| MORE PROBLEM SOLVING |

James M. Mejuto/FPG

**The manager of a shoe store kept a record of the sizes of women's shoes sold. Would the mean, the median, or the mode be the best help in deciding which size to order to fit the "average" customer?**

| Shoe size | Frequency |
|---|---|
| 5 | 1 |
| $5\frac{1}{2}$ | 2 |
| 6 | 10 |
| $6\frac{1}{2}$ | 4 |
| 7 | 4 |
| $7\frac{1}{2}$ | 4 |
| 8 | 5 |
| total | 30 |

In this case, the *mode* best describes the shoe size of the "average" customer. The manager needs to know the shoe size sold to the most customers.

The mean *could* be a size not even made, such as $6\frac{2}{3}$ for this set of data.

The median doesn't necessarily help the manager, either. The median for this set of data is $6\frac{1}{2}$. The median tells us only that 15 customers bought shoes of size $6\frac{1}{2}$ or smaller and that 15 bought shoes of size $6\frac{1}{2}$ or larger. The median does not tell us the most popular size.

Remember: The mode can describe data that are not numbers.

## EXERCISES

**1.** Arlene scored the following numbers of points in 6 basketball games: 12, 13, 13, 9, 8, and 5. What is her mean number of points per game?

**2.** A salesclerk sold the following dress sizes: 9, 11, 13, 15, 7, 7, 10, 12, 10, 10, 8, 10, 16, 10, 8, 7, 10, 11. What is the mode of the dress sizes?

**3.** Thomas studied for the following numbers of minutes on five nights: 35, 20, 45, 10, 105. What is the median number of minutes that Thomas studied?

**4.** A family drove the following distances on a 4-day trip: 231 mi, 157 mi, 250 mi, 186 mi. What was the mean number of miles driven per day?

Use the table for exercises 5–8.

| Name | Height (in.) | Weight (lb) |
|---|---|---|
| Antonelli | 64 | 121 |
| Greene | 73 | 183 |
| Robins | 67 | 146 |
| Wojcik | 68 | 139 |
| Kruse | 67 | 132 |
| Mills | 64 | 140 |
| Esposito | 59 | 98 |
| Yee | 63 | 130 |
| Zimmer | 60 | 108 |

**5.** Find the mean height. Find the median height. By how much do they differ?

**6.** Find the mean weight. How many people weigh more than the mean? How many weigh less than the mean?

**7.** Find the median weight. How many people weigh more than the median? How many weigh less?

**8.** What is the mode for the heights? For the weights?

**9.** Five students scored the following on a test: 98, 83, 80, 74, 72. What is the mean test score? What is the median?

**10.** The 5 students from exercise 9 scored the following on a second test: 96, 94, 89, 87, 60. What is the mean test score? What is the median?

Frank A. Cezus/FPG

The salaries of 7 employees are given below, along with the mean, the median, and the mode.

$120,000; $18,000; $16,500; $16,000; $15,500; $12,000; $12,000

mean = $30,000        median = $16,000        mode = $12,000

When you see the word *average,* it can stand for the mean, the median, or the mode. Sometimes one average can influence you more than another average would. Unless the kind of average is specified, the writer could be using any one of them.

**Example 1:**   Which average salary might the employer use to attract employees?

The employer might use the mean. It is the largest average and could attract more people to apply for the job.

**Example 2:**   Which average salary might the union use in trying to get raises for the employees?

The union might use the mode. It is the smallest average and could suggest a bigger raise is needed.

Statistics are sometimes given as ratios. These ratios can be misleading.

**Example 3:**   "9 out of 10 of our customers are satisfied" is a statistic. When you read a statistic like this one, you should ask yourself some questions.

a. Were *all* the customers asked?

b. *What* were the customers asked about? A product? The salesclerk? The location of the store?

c. What is meant by "satisfied"? Could a customer who bought a bad product or got poor service still be satisfied— say, by a refund?

## EXERCISES

The average precipitation for April in Miami is 3.6 inches.

**1.** Do you think that the precipitation for each April is exactly 3.6 inches?

4 out of 5 people we asked said they preferred our brand to Brand X.

**2.** Do you know which people were asked?

**3.** Does their preferring one brand to another tell you if they actually *like* the brand?

**4.** Does the statistic tell you if *you* will prefer the brand?

Our medicine works up to 12 hours.

**5.** Can you tell how long the medicine will work for you?

**6.** Do you know how long the medicine usually works for people?

---

## MATH NOTE

When you set out to ask people a question, you soon find out it is impossible to ask *everyone*. Instead, you pick a **sample** and ask only those who are in the sample.

Sometimes the sample you pick may give you results that are not true for the whole group. It is very important to choose a **random sample,** one in which *every* person has the same chance of being selected for questioning.

Discuss with your classmates why each of these may not be a random sample.

**1.** A person asked only those who lived within 3 blocks of the school.

**2.** A person knocked on doors only from 9 A.M. to 11 A.M., Monday through Friday, to ask the question.

Harold M. Lambert/Lambert Studios

**1.** Beatrice wants a record costing $8.95. She has $3.47. How much more does she need?

**2.** Marty practices his guitar 45 minutes every day. How many minutes does he practice in 5 days?

**3.** A sewing pattern calls for $24\frac{1}{2}$ inches of $\frac{1}{4}$-inch-wide elastic for a waistline and $18\frac{1}{4}$ inches of $\frac{1}{4}$-inch-wide elastic for a neckline. How much elastic is needed?

**4.** How many boards $2\frac{1}{2}$ inches wide will it take to cover a space 280 inches wide?

**5.** A salesperson is paid a 6% commission. If the salesperson earned $300 in commissions last week, what were last week's sales?

**6.** What is the volume of a can having a 3-inch diameter and a 6-inch height? Use 3.14 for $\pi$.

**7.** Tyrone bowled three games, scoring 150, 152, and 176. What was his total for the three games?

**8.** Mr. Edmunds earns $14,400 a year. What is his average monthly salary?

**9.** Tom weighs $124\frac{1}{2}$ pounds. Last month, he weighed $121\frac{3}{4}$ pounds. How much weight did he gain?

**10.** A sales job pays an 8% commission. What amount of sales would be needed to earn $300 in commissions?

**11.** You need 1.5 meters of material to make one drapery panel. How much material do you need to make 4 panels?

**12.** Fran saves $35 every month. How much does she save in a year?

**13.** Anne drove 288 miles in 6 hours. What was the average number of miles per hour for the trip?

**14.** The radius is $\frac{1}{2}$ the diameter. What is the radius of a pipe if its diameter is $4\frac{3}{4}$ inches?

**15.** The number of cars in a parking lot varies daily. For 10 days, the totals were as follows: 63, 72, 58, 69, 75, 80, 50, 74, 78, 60. What was the mean number of cars for those 10 days?

**16.** What is the area of a rectangular plot of land measuring 12 yards by 15 yards?

**17.** Terese made 2 out of 5 of her attempted free throws. If she attempted 15 free throws, how many did she make?

**18.** Duane bought 3 pairs of socks at $1.19 a pair. How much did the socks cost?

**19.** A map was drawn to the scale 1 inch to 25 miles. What distance is represented by $3\frac{1}{2}$ inches on the map?

**20.** Lydia paid $42 to camp at a site for 7 days. What was she charged per day?

Jacqueline Durand

A meteorologist can work as a weather observer, as a forecaster, or as a researcher. A meteorologist uses instruments such as a thermometer, a barometer, radar, and a computer to study weather conditions, to make predictions, and to give warnings of severe weather.

Here is a chart that lists the normal temperature and precipitation during each month for four cities.

The temperature (T) is in degrees Fahrenheit. The precipitation (P) is in inches.

L.L.T. Rhodes/Taurus

| | | Ja | F | Mr | Ap | My | Je | Jl | Au | S | O | N | D |
|---|---|---|---|---|---|---|---|---|---|---|---|---|---|
| Atlanta | T | 42 | 45 | 51 | 61 | 69 | 76 | 78 | 78 | 72 | 62 | 51 | 44 |
| | P | 4.3 | 4.4 | 5.8 | 4.6 | 3.7 | 3.7 | 4.9 | 3.5 | 3.2 | 2.5 | 3.4 | 4.2 |
| Denver | T | 30 | 33 | 37 | 48 | 57 | 66 | 73 | 72 | 63 | 52 | 39 | 33 |
| | P | 0.6 | 0.7 | 1.2 | 1.9 | 2.6 | 1.9 | 1.8 | 1.3 | 1.1 | 1.1 | 0.8 | 0.4 |
| Pittsburgh | T | 28 | 29 | 38 | 50 | 60 | 69 | 72 | 70 | 64 | 53 | 41 | 31 |
| | P | 2.8 | 2.4 | 3.6 | 3.4 | 3.6 | 3.5 | 3.8 | 3.2 | 2.5 | 2.5 | 2.5 | 2.5 |
| Seattle | T | 38 | 42 | 44 | 49 | 55 | 60 | 65 | 64 | 60 | 52 | 45 | 41 |
| | P | 5.8 | 4.2 | 3.6 | 2.5 | 1.7 | 1.5 | 0.7 | 1.1 | 2.0 | 3.9 | 5.9 | 5.9 |

1. What is the mean of the monthly normal temperatures for Atlanta?

2. What is the mean of the monthly normal temperatures for Denver?

3. What is the median monthly precipitation for Pittsburgh?

4. What is the median monthly precipitation for Seattle?

5. Which city has the coldest monthly normal temperature for December?

6. Which city has the widest range of monthly normal temperatures?

7. What is the median of the monthly normal temperatures for Seattle?

# CHAPTER REVIEW

Choose the best answer to complete each.

Words to choose from: *range, median, frequency table, mode, mean*

**1.** A _____ is a way to organize a set of data.                              13.2

**2.** The difference between the largest number and the smallest number in a         13.3
set is called the _____.

**3.** The _____ is found by adding all of the numbers and then dividing        13.4
by how many numbers there are.

**4.** The _____ is the middle number when all of the numbers are ar-           13.5
ranged from smallest to largest.

**5.** The _____ is the number or the item that occurs the most often.          13.7

**6.** Make a stem-and-leaf display for the following numbers. Use one-digit          13.1
stems.

26, 18, 15, 34, 25, 23, 18, 36, 32, 20,
17, 15, 29, 26, 31, 34, 28, 25, 37, 10

**7.** Make a stem-and-leaf display for the following numbers. Use two-digit
stems.

364, 359, 351, 364, 369, 378, 370, 352,
380, 384, 356, 367, 362, 381, 356, 367

Make a frequency table for each set of numbers.                                      13.2

**8.** 15, 18, 19, 16, 15, 17, 17, 16,
19, 20, 15, 19, 18, 15, 17

**9.** $\frac{3}{4}$, $1\frac{1}{2}$, $\frac{5}{8}$, $\frac{3}{4}$, $1\frac{1}{4}$, $\frac{5}{8}$, $1\frac{1}{4}$, $1\frac{1}{4}$, $1\frac{1}{4}$, $1\frac{1}{2}$, $\frac{5}{8}$,

$\frac{3}{4}$, $\frac{3}{4}$, $1\frac{1}{2}$, $\frac{3}{4}$, $\frac{5}{8}$, $\frac{3}{8}$, $1\frac{1}{4}$, $\frac{5}{8}$, $\frac{7}{8}$, $1\frac{1}{4}$, $1\frac{1}{4}$

Use the following data in exercises 10–13:
37, 96, 52, 87, 83, 75, 74, 79, 83, 83

**10.** Find the range.                                                                13.3

**11.** Find the mean.                                          13.4

**12.** Find the median.                                        13.5

**13.** Find the mode.                                          13.7


Use the following data in exercises 14–17:
1.2, 1.1, 1.3, 1.2, 0.9, 1.5, 0.3, 1.3

**14.** Find the range.                                         13.3

**15.** Find the mean.                                          13.4

**16.** Find the median.                                        13.5

**17.** Find the mode.                                          13.7


Use the frequency table below in exercises 18–21.

| Number | Frequency |
| --- | --- |
| 12 | 3 |
| 13 | 4 |
| 14 | 2 |
| 15 | 5 |
| 16 | 1 |
| total | 15 |

**18.** Find the range.                                         13.3

**19.** Find the mean.                                          13.6

**20.** Find the median.

**21.** Find the mode.                                          13.7


Use the frequency table below in exercises 22–25.

| Number | Frequency |
| --- | --- |
| 10 | 2 |
| 20 | 1 |
| 30 | 2 |
| 40 | 5 |
| total | 10 |

**22.** Find the range.                                         13.3

**23.** Find the mean.                                          13.6

**24.** Find the median.

**25.** Find the mode.                                          13.7

**26.** Use the intervals 4–7, 8–11, 12–15, and 16–19 to make a frequency table for the following data:

7, 6, 13, 17, 19, 8, 14, 12, 6, 5, 4,
4, 15, 13, 12, 4, 9, 18, 11, 19, 10

13.2

**27.** Use the intervals 101–110, 111–120, 121–130, and 131–140 to make a frequency table for the following data:

102, 106, 123, 115, 138, 136, 116, 109,
121, 137, 119, 126, 113, 128, 104, 135

**28.** Find the mean of each group. Which group has the greater mean?

Group 1:   4, 7, 10, 8, 5, 8, 7, 9, 6, 6, 5, 7, 8, 7, 8

Group 2:   10, 5, 3, 5, 8, 7, 8, 7, 4, 10, 10, 10

13.8

**29.** What is the mode for the following car colors?

white, tan, blue, red, tan, white, white, yellow, white, blue, blue, gray, white, blue, blue, blue, gray, yellow, red, blue

13.7

**30.** Find the median test score for each group. Based on the median, which group did better?

Group 1:   89, 57, 78, 96, 45, 65, 78, 72, 80, 91, 73, 77, 84, 89, 72,
64, 69, 68, 91, 49, 58, 60, 63, 58, 86, 75, 79, 72, 61, 64,
73, 80

Group 2:   78, 43, 75, 67, 87, 85, 92, 74, 83, 90, 59, 68, 70, 82, 53,
86, 79, 69, 63, 78, 75, 73, 72, 81, 60, 42

13.8

**31.** What is the mean rainfall (in mm)? What is the median? Find the difference between the mean and the median.

0.1, 0.1, 0.2, 0.3, 1.2, 0.2, 0.2, 0.1

13.10

**32.** Find the mean and the median for the following set of data. Which seems to be more typical of all of the data?

37, 223, 215, 223, 218, 211, 215, 214, 216, 123

13.9

Tests show that this product works longer than others.

13.11

**33.** Can you tell how long the other products work?

**34.** Do you know if the products were tested in exactly the same way?

1. Make a stem-and-leaf display. Use two-digit stems.

   763, 752, 740, 741, 765, 758, 742, 763, 768, 752

2. Make a frequency table for the following data:

   15, 14, 15, 16, 15, 14, 16, 15, 15, 15, 15, 14, 15, 16, 16, 15

3. Use the intervals 81–110, 111–140, 141–170, and 171–200 to make a frequency table for the following data:

   84, 143, 182, 196, 97, 156, 194, 187, 92,
   109, 163, 152, 115, 97, 132, 187, 199, 186

Use the following data in exercises 4–7:

15, 27, 14, 39, 23, 27, 30

4. Find the range.

5. Find the mean.

6. Find the median.

7. Find the mode.

Use the frequency table below in exercises 8–11.

| Number | Frequency |
|--------|-----------|
| 10 | 2 |
| 20 | 2 |
| 30 | 5 |
| 40 | 1 |
| total | 10 |

8. Find the range.

9. Find the mean.

10. Find the median.

11. Find the mode.

12. Find the median score for each group. Which group has the greater median?

    Group 1:  84, 72, 73, 69, 52, 47, 95, 98, 62, 75, 78

    Group 2:  16, 83, 91, 100, 50, 87, 89, 75, 82, 85

13. What is the median neck size? What is the mode?

    $15, 15\frac{1}{2}, 14\frac{1}{2}, 15, 16, 16\frac{1}{2}, 15,$

    $15\frac{1}{2}, 15\frac{1}{2}, 15\frac{1}{2}, 15$

14. An advertisement said "We asked people to test our product in their homes. They preferred it 4 to 1 over their own." Do you know how the people were chosen? Do you know how each tested the product? Do you know if *you* will prefer it?

Find each probability. Without looking, you pick a card.

**1.** picking a red card

**2.** picking an even number

**3.** picking a blue card

**4.** picking the number 13

**5.** picking a number less than 11

**6.** picking either a 5 or a 6

**7.** picking either a blue card or a red card

**8.** The probability of drawing a blue marble from a bag is $\frac{5}{8}$. What is the probability of drawing a marble that is not blue?

**9.** The spinner is spun twice. What is the probability of the pointer's stopping on 3 the first time and 6 the second time?

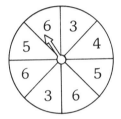

**Assume the pointer cannot stop on a line between two regions.**

**10.** Without looking, you pick a card from the deck above, put the card back, and pick again. What is the probability that both cards will be red?

**11.** Without looking, you pick a card from the deck above and then, without replacing the first card, you pick another card. What is the probability that both cards will be blue?

Use the table below to find each experimental probability as a percent. The table shows the results of picking a marble from a bag 40 times.

**12.** picking a blue marble

**13.** picking a red marble

| Outcome | Number |
|---------|--------|
| green | 25 |
| red | 5 |
| blue | 10 |
| total | 40 |

**397**

## WRITING PROBABILITIES

Ed Hoppe Photography

**Only one of the keys will open the lock. If you pick a key without looking, what is the *probability* that it will open the lock?**

There are six possible **outcomes.** Only one outcome is a *favorable outcome.* You can use the following rule to find the probability (p), sometimes called **mathematical probability:**

$$p = \frac{\text{number of favorable outcomes}}{\text{total number of outcomes}}$$

**Example 1:**

p (key opens the lock) = $\frac{1}{6}$ ⟵ only 1 key will open lock
⟵ total number of keys

The probability that the key will open the lock is $\frac{1}{6}$. (There is 1 chance out of 6 that the key picked will open the lock.)

**Example 2:** Without looking, you pick one of the six keys above. What is the probability of picking a red key?

p (red key) = $\frac{4}{6}$ ⟵ 4 red keys
⟵ total number of keys

= $\frac{2}{3}$    Reduce to lowest terms.

The probability of picking a red key is $\frac{2}{3}$. (There are 2 chances out of every 3 that the key picked will be red.)

# EXERCISES

Find each probability.

A die is rolled.

**1.** p (3)

**2.** p (6)

**3.** p (even number)

**4.** p (number less than 4)

A coin is tossed.

**5.** p (heads)

**6.** p (tails)

Without looking, you pick a disk.

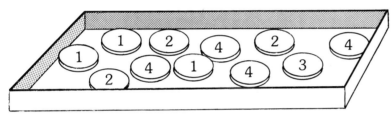

**7.** p (3)

**8.** p (2)

**9.** p (1)

**10.** p (4)

A card is picked from a standard deck of 52 playing cards.

Hearts     Clubs     Diamonds     Spades

**11.** p (king)

**12.** p (red card)

**13.** p (diamond)

**14.** p (black card)

**15.** p (8)

**16.** p (club)

**17.** p (10 of hearts)

**18.** p (red jack)

**19.** p (black ace)

**20.** p (4 of spades)

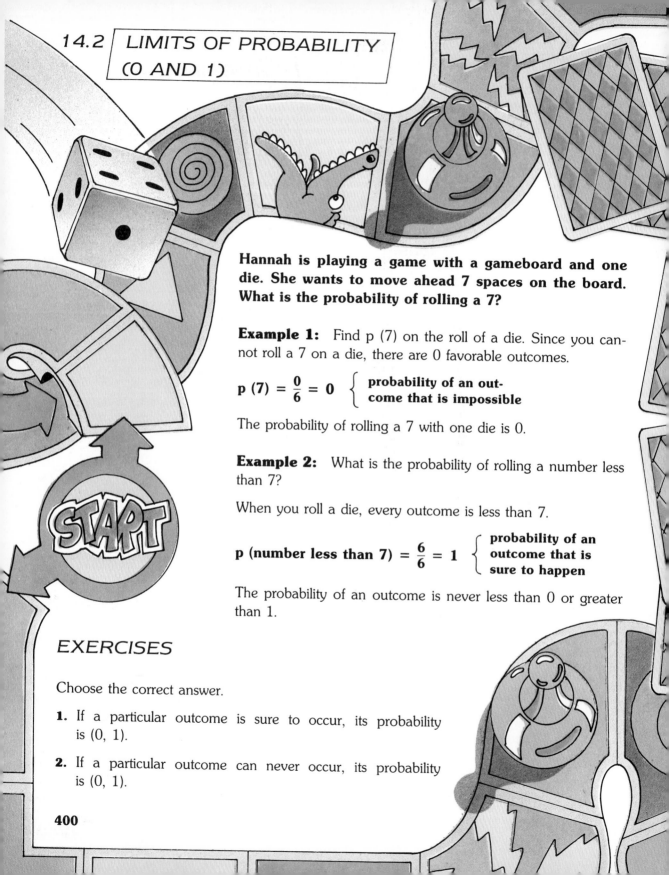

## 14.2 | LIMITS OF PROBABILITY (0 AND 1)

**Hannah is playing a game with a gameboard and one die. She wants to move ahead 7 spaces on the board. What is the probability of rolling a 7?**

**Example 1:** Find p (7) on the roll of a die. Since you cannot roll a 7 on a die, there are 0 favorable outcomes.

$$p \ (7) = \frac{0}{6} = 0 \ \left\{ \begin{array}{l} \textbf{probability of an out-} \\ \textbf{come that is impossible} \end{array} \right.$$

The probability of rolling a 7 with one die is 0.

**Example 2:** What is the probability of rolling a number less than 7?

When you roll a die, every outcome is less than 7.

$$p \ (\textbf{number less than 7}) = \frac{6}{6} = 1 \ \left\{ \begin{array}{l} \textbf{probability of an} \\ \textbf{outcome that is} \\ \textbf{sure to happen} \end{array} \right.$$

The probability of an outcome is never less than 0 or greater than 1.

## EXERCISES

Choose the correct answer.

**1.** If a particular outcome is sure to occur, its probability is (0, 1).

**2.** If a particular outcome can never occur, its probability is (0, 1).

Find each probability.

Without looking, you pick a card.

| 6 | 10 | 10 |
|---|----|----|
| 8 | 4  | 2  |

**3.** p (green)    **4.** p (blue)

**5.** p (number less than 12)

The spinner is spun. Assume the pointer cannot stop on a line between two regions.

**6.** p (green)    **7.** p (yellow)

**8.** p (A)    **9.** p (not A)

**10.** A "fixed" coin has two heads (no tails). What is p (heads)? What is p (tails)?

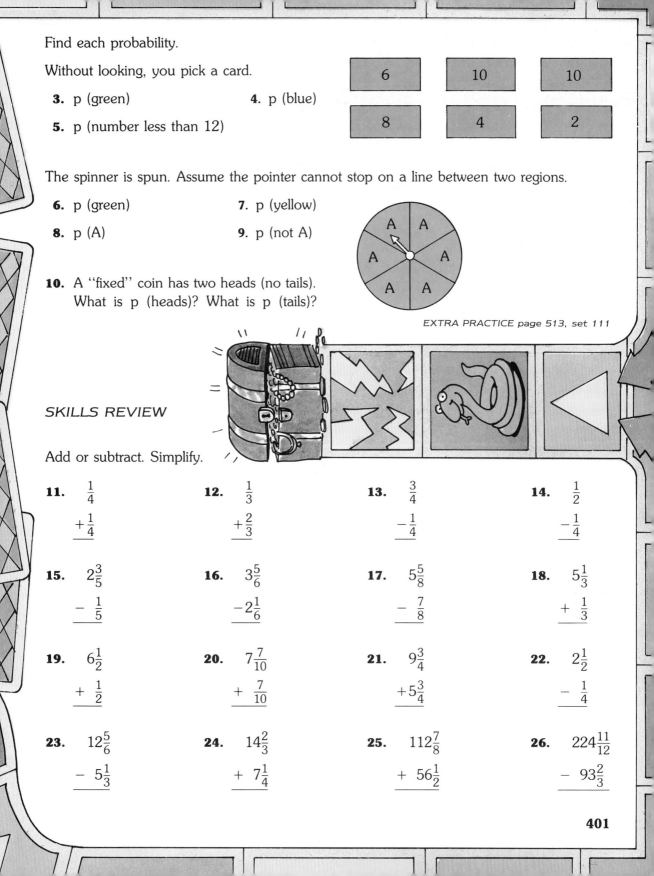

EXTRA PRACTICE page 513, set 111

*SKILLS REVIEW*

Add or subtract. Simplify.

**11.**    $\dfrac{1}{4}$
       $+\dfrac{1}{4}$

**12.**    $\dfrac{1}{3}$
       $+\dfrac{2}{3}$

**13.**    $\dfrac{3}{4}$
       $-\dfrac{1}{4}$

**14.**    $\dfrac{1}{2}$
       $-\dfrac{1}{4}$

**15.**    $2\dfrac{3}{5}$
       $-\ \dfrac{1}{5}$

**16.**    $3\dfrac{5}{6}$
       $-2\dfrac{1}{6}$

**17.**    $5\dfrac{5}{8}$
       $-\ \dfrac{7}{8}$

**18.**    $5\dfrac{1}{3}$
       $+\ \dfrac{1}{3}$

**19.**    $6\dfrac{1}{2}$
       $+\ \dfrac{1}{2}$

**20.**    $7\dfrac{7}{10}$
       $+\ \dfrac{7}{10}$

**21.**    $9\dfrac{3}{4}$
       $+5\dfrac{3}{4}$

**22.**    $2\dfrac{1}{2}$
       $-\ \dfrac{1}{4}$

**23.**    $12\dfrac{5}{6}$
       $-\ 5\dfrac{1}{3}$

**24.**    $14\dfrac{2}{3}$
       $+\ 7\dfrac{1}{4}$

**25.**    $112\dfrac{7}{8}$
       $+\ 56\dfrac{1}{2}$

**26.**    $224\dfrac{11}{12}$
       $-\ 93\dfrac{2}{3}$

**401**

What is the probability that the pointer will stop on either 3 or 6? Since the pointer can stop on only one region at a time, both outcomes could not occur at the same time. You can find the probability by adding.

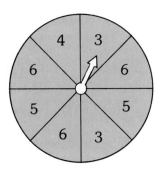

**For spinners, we will always assume the pointer cannot stop on a line between two regions.**

**Example 1:** $p\ (3\ or\ 6) = p\ (3) + p\ (6)$
$$= \frac{2}{8} + \frac{3}{8}$$
$$= \frac{5}{8}$$

The probability that the pointer will stop on either 3 or 6 is $\frac{5}{8}$.

**Example 2:** A die is rolled. Find p (1, 3, or 5)

$p\ (1,\ 3,\ or\ 5) = p\ (1) + p\ (3) + p\ (5)$
$$= \frac{1}{6} + \frac{1}{6} + \frac{1}{6}$$
$$= \frac{3}{6}$$
$$= \frac{1}{2}$$

# EXERCISES

Find each probability.

A die is rolled.

**1.** p (1 or 3)  **2.** p (6 or odd number)  **3.** p (2, 4, or 5)

Without looking, you pick a disk.

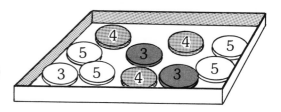

**4.** p (3 or gray)  **5.** p (white or red)

**6.** p (3, 5, or gray)  **7.** p (5, gray, or red)

The spinner is spun.

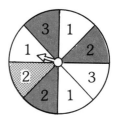

**8.** p (red or gray)  **9.** p (white or gray)

**10.** p (red or 1)  **11.** p (gray or 3)

A card is drawn from a standard deck of 52 playing cards.

**12.** p (king or queen)  **13.** p (club or heart)

**14.** p (8, 9, or 10)  **15.** p (2, 7, or jack)

Outcomes A and B on a spinner cannot occur at the same time. Find p (A or B) if

**16.** p (A) = $\frac{2}{4}$; p (B) = $\frac{1}{4}$  **17.** p (A) = $\frac{5}{8}$; p (B) = $\frac{3}{8}$

**18.** p (A) = $\frac{1}{6}$; p (B) = $\frac{1}{3}$  **19.** p (A) = $\frac{2}{5}$; p (B) = $\frac{1}{10}$

*EXTRA PRACTICE page 513, set 112*

---

## MATH NOTE

Probabilities are sometimes expressed as "odds."

**odds for** = $\dfrac{\text{number of favorable outcomes}}{\text{number of outcomes that are not favorable}}$

**Example:** What are the odds for rolling a 2 on the roll of a die?

**odds for** = $\dfrac{1}{5}$ ⟵ **number of favorable outcomes**
⟵ **number of unfavorable outcomes**

What are the odds for drawing an ace from a standard deck of cards?
How do you think the odds against an outcome should be determined?

COMPLEMENTARY PROBABILITIES

A card is drawn from a standard deck of 52 playing cards.

Ed Hoppe Photography

**p (heart)** $= \dfrac{13}{52} = \dfrac{1}{4}$

**p (not a heart)** $= \dfrac{39}{52} = \dfrac{3}{4}$

**p (heart) + p (not a heart)** $= \dfrac{1}{4} + \dfrac{3}{4} = 1$

p (*drawing a heart*) and p (*not drawing a heart*) are called **complementary probabilities.** If you know one probability, you can find the complementary probability by subtracting from 1.

**Example:** The probability of drawing a blue marble from a bag is $\frac{2}{3}$. What is the probability of drawing a marble that is not blue?

**p (not blue) = 1 − p (blue)**
$$= 1 - \frac{2}{3}$$
$$= \frac{1}{3}$$

The probability of drawing a marble that is not blue is $\frac{1}{3}$.

## EXERCISES

Find each probability.

A die is rolled.

**1.** p (2)  **2.** p (not a 2)  **3.** p (not a 6)

**4.** p (even number)  **5.** p (not an even number)

A card is drawn from a standard deck of 52 playing cards.

**6.** p (not a club)  **7.** p (not a heart)  **8.** p (not a red card)

Find the complementary probability of each given probability.

**9.** p (A) $= \frac{1}{5}$  **10.** p (B) $= \frac{3}{5}$  **11.** p (C) $= \frac{5}{8}$

**12.** p (D) $= \frac{4}{9}$  **13.** p (E) $= \frac{3}{7}$  **14.** p (F) $= \frac{7}{10}$

---

## CHECKPOINT

Without looking, you pick a card. Find each probability.

 1    4    5    3     2    2    5     2

**1.** p (2)  **2.** p (3)  **3.** p (odd number)

**4.** p (blue)  **5.** p (number less than 7)

**6.** p (green)  **7.** p (blue or green)

**8.** p (6)  **9.** p (2 or 4)  **10.** p (1, 2, or yellow)

**11.** The probability of drawing a jack from a standard deck of 52 playing cards is $\frac{1}{13}$. What is the probability of not drawing a jack?

**405**

**Suppose you are going to toss two coins, a penny and a dime. What is the probability of getting heads on both the penny and the dime?**

By showing all the possible results, you can see that p (both heads) $= \frac{1}{4}$.

Ed Hoppe Photography

You know p (heads on penny) $= \frac{1}{2}$ and p (heads on dime) $= \frac{1}{2}$. Since $\frac{1}{4} = \frac{1}{2} \times \frac{1}{2}$, you can write

**p (both heads) = p (heads on penny) × p (heads on dime)**

When two outcomes do not depend on each other, you can multiply the probabilities of the outcomes to find the probability that *both* will occur.

**Example:** A die is rolled and a coin is tossed. What is p (4 and heads)?

$$\textbf{p (4 and heads) = p (4) × p (heads)}$$
$$= \frac{1}{6} \times \frac{1}{2}$$
$$= \frac{1}{12}$$

# EXERCISES

Find each probability.

A penny and a dime are tossed.

**1.** p (heads on penny and tails on dime)

A coin is tossed and a die is rolled.

**2.** p (heads and 5)

**3.** p (tails and 3)

**4.** p (heads and even number)

**5.** p (tails and a number less than 3)

A red die and a white die are rolled.

**6.** p (red 5 and white 6)

**7.** p (red 4 and white odd number)

**8.** p (red odd number and white 6)

**9.** p (red prime number and white even number)

Find p (A and B) if A and B do not depend on each other and if

**10.** p $(A) = \frac{1}{3}$ and p $(B) = \frac{1}{3}$

**11.** p $(A) = \frac{5}{8}$ and p $(B) = \frac{1}{4}$

**12.** p $(A) = \frac{1}{2}$ and p $(B) = \frac{5}{6}$

**13.** p $(A) = \frac{3}{4}$ and p $(B) = \frac{2}{5}$

EXTRA PRACTICE page 513, set 113

## SKILLS REVIEW

Multiply or divide. Simplify.

**14.** $\frac{1}{2} \times \frac{1}{4}$

**15.** $\frac{2}{3} \times \frac{3}{4}$

**16.** $\frac{7}{8} \div \frac{1}{2}$

**17.** $\frac{5}{6} \div \frac{3}{10}$

**18.** $2\frac{1}{4} \times \frac{2}{3}$

**19.** $5 \times \frac{5}{8}$

**20.** $3\frac{1}{2} \div \frac{1}{4}$

**21.** $6 \div \frac{2}{3}$

**22.** $5\frac{1}{5} \times 3\frac{1}{3}$

**23.** $6\frac{1}{2} \times 2\frac{3}{4}$

**24.** $4\frac{7}{8} \div 1\frac{1}{2}$

**25.** $9\frac{1}{4} \div 2\frac{1}{4}$

If you pick a card from a standard deck, put the card back, and then pick another card, what is the probability that both cards will be hearts?

Mary Elenz Tranter

**Example 1:**

p (both cards are hearts) = p (first card is a heart) × p (second card is a heart)

$$= \frac{1}{4} \times \frac{1}{4}$$

$$= \frac{1}{16}$$

The probability that both cards will be hearts is $\frac{1}{16}$.

If you do not replace the first card, what is the probability that both cards will be hearts?

**Example 2:**

p (first card is a heart) = $\frac{1}{4}$

p (second card is a heart) = $\frac{12}{51}$ ← If the first card is a heart, there are 12 hearts left.
← We did not replace the first card.

p (both cards are hearts) = $\frac{1}{4} \times \frac{12}{51}$

$$= \frac{12}{204}$$

$$= \frac{1}{17}$$

The probability that both cards will be hearts if the first card is not replaced in the deck is $\frac{1}{17}$.

# EXERCISES

Find each probability.

A die is to be rolled twice in a row.

**1.** p (2 and then 4)

**2.** p (3 and then 6)

**3.** p (4 and then an even number)

A coin is tossed twice in a row.

**4.** p (heads and then tails)

**5.** p (heads and then heads)

The spinner is spun twice in a row.

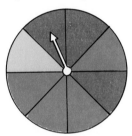

**6.** p (red and then red)

**7.** p (blue and then red)

**8.** p (red and then yellow)

**9.** p (yellow and then red)

You pick a card from a standard deck of 52 playing cards and then pick another card without replacing the first card.

**10.** p (both cards are black)

**11.** p (both cards are diamonds)

**12.** p (both cards are kings)

**13.** p (both cards are 10's)

**14.** p (first card is a jack and second card is a queen)

**15.** p (first card is the king of spades and second card is the 10 of clubs)

**16.** In Monopoly, two dice are rolled for each turn. The probability of rolling "doubles" is $\frac{1}{6}$. If doubles are rolled three times in a row, the player "goes to jail." What is the probability of rolling doubles three times in a row?

*EXTRA PRACTICE page 514, set 114*

# DETERMINING PROBABILITIES FROM DATA

Bill tossed a coin 100 times. The results are in the table below.

| Outcome | Tally | Number |
|---------|-------|--------|
| tails | ▨▨▨ ▨▨▨ ▨▨▨ ◻ | 48 |
| heads | ▨▨▨ ▨▨▨ ▨▨▨ ▨⌐ | 52 |
| | total | 100 |

The table shows that tails came up 48 out of 100 times. So, the **experimental probability (ex p)** of getting tails on the toss of this coin is $\frac{48}{100}$ or $\frac{12}{25}$.

**ex p (tails)** $= \dfrac{48}{100} = 0.48 = 48\%$  $\left\{\begin{array}{l}\textbf{NOTE: Probability can} \\ \textbf{be written as a deci-} \\ \textbf{mal or as a percent.}\end{array}\right.$

The mathematical probability of tossing tails is

**p (tails)** $= \dfrac{1}{2} = 0.5 = 50\%$

Notice that the experimental probability of tossing tails is 48%, while the mathematical probability is 50%. It is normal for experimental probabilities to vary from the mathematical probabilities. But for a large number of trials the two probabilities will be very close.

# EXERCISES

The table shows the results of spinning the spinner below 60 times. Use the table to find each experimental probability as a percent.

| Outcome | Number |
|---------|--------|
| red | 24 |
| gray | 27 |
| white | 9 |
| total | 60 |

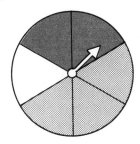

**1.** ex p (red)　　　　**2.** ex p (gray)　　　　**3.** ex p (white)

Toss a die 50 times and record the results. Use the results to find each experimental probability as a percent.

**4.** ex p (3)　　　　**5.** ex p (5)　　　　**6.** ex p (6)

Shuffle a standard deck of 52 playing cards and pick one without looking. Record the suit (hearts, diamonds, clubs, spades), replace the card, and shuffle again. Do 50 trials and use the results to find each experimental probability as a percent.

**7.** ex p (hearts)　　　　　　　**8.** ex p (diamonds)

**9.** ex p (clubs)　　　　　　　**10.** ex p (spades)

---

*MATH NOTE*

Ann tossed a coin 4 times. She got heads each time. By "the law of averages" can she expect to get tails on the next toss? The toss of a coin is not affected by past results. No matter what the result of a previous toss of a fair coin, the probability is always $\frac{1}{2}$ that tails will appear on the next toss.

1. An experimental car traveled 477 miles on 9 gallons of fuel. How many miles to the gallon did the car average?

2. The makers of a dry dog food recommend $1\frac{1}{2}$ cups of dog food per day for every 10 pounds the dog weighs. How much should you feed a 25-pound dog per day?

3. Of 1500 people, 1335 approved of the new city ordinance. What percent of the people approved of the ordinance?

4. A magazine subscription is offered at 12 weekly issues for $19.80. At that rate, what is the cost for 52 weeks?

5. Miller High School had 94% of its 1600 pupils in attendance on Monday. How many pupils were in school on that day?

6. A baseball pitcher gave up 17 earned runs in 51 innings. How many earned runs is that per 9 innings pitched?

7. In Monopoly, there is a deck of 16 "Community Chest" cards. Two of the cards are "collect $200" cards. If you draw a card from a full deck, and then draw another card without replacing the first card, what is the probability that both cards will be "collect $200" cards?

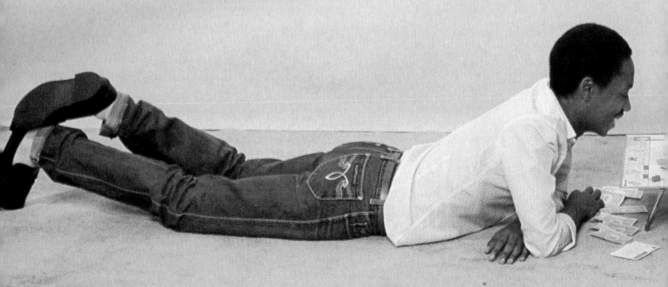

8. A pharmacist has a 2-liter container of cough medicine. How many 200-milliliter bottles can be filled from the container?

9. A test car traveled 900 kilometers on 75 liters of gas. How many kilometers per liter did the car average?

10. At the start of a trip, the odometer on a car read 9156.7 miles. At the end of the trip, it read 10,004.5 miles. How far did the car travel?

11. Lynn jogs 4 kilometers every day. If she runs around a track that is 800 meters long, how many laps must she run?

12. Steve earns $28 a day. If he worked 21 days last month, how much did he earn?

13. A roast costing $13.68 is sliced into thin slices for sandwiches. If a total of 38 sandwiches are made from the roast, what is the average cost for meat in a sandwich?

14. In Monopoly, there is a deck of 16 "Chance" cards. Two of the cards are "advance to the nearest railroad" cards. When you draw from a full deck, what is the probability of your drawing an "advance to the nearest railroad" card?

A survey shows that the probability a voter will vote for candidate A is $\frac{2}{5}$. If 2500 people vote in the election, how many votes can candidate A expect to receive?

Eric Kroll/Taurus

To predict how many votes candidate A can expect to receive, multiply the number of voters by the probability that a voter will choose candidate A.

**Example:**   $2500 \times \dfrac{2}{5} = 1000$

Candidate A can expect to receive 1000 votes.

1. The probability that a machine will produce a defective part is $\frac{1}{500}$. How many defective parts would you expect in an order of 50,000?

2. The probability of a person's winning a prize in a contest is $\frac{1}{1000}$. If 200,000 people enter the contest, how many can expect to win a prize?

3. How many seedlings can a nursery expect to get out of 750 seeds if the probability that a seed will grow is $\frac{2}{3}$?

Fill in the blank.

**1.** If an outcome is sure to happen, it has a probability of ___.            14.2

**2.** If an outcome is impossible, it has a probability of ___.

**3.** p (blue) and p (not blue) are called _____ probabilities.            14.4

**4.** p (A and B) = p (A) ___ p (B), if A and B do not depend on each            14.3
other.

**5.** p (A or B) = p (A) ___ p (B), if A and B cannot occur at the same time.            14.5

Find each probability.

Without looking, you pick a card.

| 4 | 3 | 6 |
| 3 | 2 | 4 |
| 8 | 3 | 3 |
| 4 | 2 | 3 |

**6.** p (3)      **7.** p (red)            14.1

**8.** p (even number)

**9.** p (number less than 9)            14.2

**10.** p (green)

A die is rolled.

**11.** p (1 or 3)            **12.** p (3 or even number)            **13.** p (2, 3, or 5)            14.3

A card is drawn from a standard deck of 52 playing cards.            14.4

**14.** p (not a club)            **15.** p (not a black card)            **16.** p (not a king)

Find the complementary probability of each given probability.

**17.** p (A) = $\frac{5}{6}$            **18.** p (B) = $\frac{2}{3}$            **19.** p (C) = $\frac{7}{10}$

Find each probability.

A red die and a white die are rolled.                                14.5

**20.** p (red 3 and white 6)          **21.** p (red 4 and white 4)

**22.** p (red 5 and white even number)

**23.** p (red odd number and white 3)

The spinner is spun twice in a row.                                  14.6

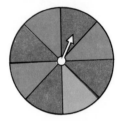

**24.** p (red and then blue)          **25.** p (red and then red)

You pick a disk without looking and then pick another disk without replacing the first disk.

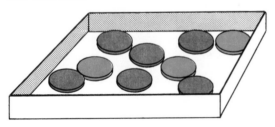

**26.** p (both disks are blue)          **27.** p (both disks are red)

**28.** p (first disk is blue and second disk is red)

Use the tables below to find each experimental probability as a percent.    14.7

| Outcome | Number |
|---------|--------|
| 2 | 21 |
| 3 | 33 |
| 4 | 21 |
| total | 75 |

| Outcome | Number |
|---------|--------|
| blue | 5 |
| green | 40 |
| yellow | 35 |
| red | 20 |
| total | 100 |

**29.** ex p (3)       **30.** ex p (4)       **31.** ex p (blue)       **32.** ex p (green)

Find each probability. A card is picked from a standard deck.

**1.** p (10 of hearts)　　　　　　**2.** p (red card)

**3.** p (jack)　　　　　　　　　　**4.** p (diamond)

The spinner is spun.

**5.** p (blue)　　　**6.** p (odd number)

Without looking, you pick a disk.

**7.** p (1 or red)　　**8.** p (2, blue, or yellow)

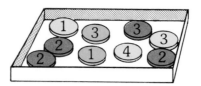

**9.** The probability of drawing a heart from a standard deck of 52 playing cards is $\frac{1}{4}$. What is the probability of not drawing a heart?

Find each probability. A coin is tossed and a die is rolled.

**10.** p (tails and 5)　　　　　　**11.** p (heads and 2)

**12.** p (heads and even number)

You pick a card from a standard deck of 52 playing cards and then pick another card without replacing the first card.

**13.** p (both cards are clubs)　　　**14.** p (both cards are 9's)

**15.** p (first card is a 10 and second card is the jack of hearts)

Use the table below to find each experimental probability as a percent.

**16.** ex p (2)

**17.** ex p (4)

**18.** ex p (6)

| Outcome | Number |
| --- | --- |
| 2 | 50 |
| 4 | 10 |
| 6 | 40 |
| total | 100 |

# CUMULATIVE REVIEW

**1.** ◯ ◯ ◯ △ △

Write a ratio for the number of circles to the number of triangles.

**2.** First express both amounts in the same unit, and then simplify the ratio:

32 in. to 2 ft

**3.** Express the ratio as a rate:

$65 for 5 hours

**4.** Is the following proportion true?

$$\frac{25}{15} = \frac{10}{6}$$

Solve these proportions by using equivalent fractions.

**5.** $\frac{4}{?} = \frac{12}{18}$

**6.** $\frac{5}{2} = \frac{35}{?}$

**7.** $\frac{5}{?} = \frac{25}{15}$

**8.** $\frac{16}{?} = \frac{12}{21}$

Solve these proportions by using cross products.

**9.** $\frac{2}{3} = \frac{?}{18}$

**10.** $\frac{8}{?} = \frac{48}{30}$

**11.** $\frac{?}{14} = \frac{12}{21}$

**12.** $\frac{20}{14} = \frac{50}{?}$

**13.**

Draw a 2:1 enlargement.

**14.**

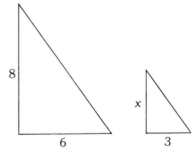

The two triangles are similar. Use a proportion to find x.

Solve.

**15.** A floor plan was drawn to the scale $\frac{1}{4}$ in. to 1 ft. What is the real length represented by $3\frac{1}{4}$ in. on the drawing?

**16.** A family drove 90 miles in 2 hours. At that rate, how long will it take them to drive 450 miles?

Change each percent to a fraction in lowest terms.

**17.** 34%

**18.** 15%

**19.** 19%

**20.** 85%

Change each percent to a decimal.

**21.** 56%    **22.** 134%    **23.** $\frac{1}{4}$%    **24.** $25\frac{3}{4}$%

Change to a percent.

**25.** 0.42    **26.** 0.7    **27.** $\frac{17}{20}$    **28.** $\frac{19}{50}$

Find each number.

**29.** 16% of 300    **30.** 20% of 45    **31.** 3% of 2000    **32.** $\frac{1}{2}$% of 600

Solve.

**33.** 8 is what percent of 32?

**34.** 81 is what percent of 450?

**35.** 20 is 40% of what number?

**36.** 495 is 55% of what number?

**37.** Tim scored 80% on a test. If there were 50 questions, how many did he answer correctly?

**38.** Myra bought a sweater priced at $24.50. Find the total cost, if there is a 6% sales tax.

**39.** The original price of a coat was $80. The coat is on sale at a 15% discount. What is the sale price?

**40.** What is the commission on sales of $3600 if the commission rate is 8%?

For each segment below, find the length in millimeters. Then rewrite the same length, using centimeters.

**41.** _____    **42.** _____

Draw line segments with the following measurements:

**43.** 18 mm    **44.** 2.3 cm

Choose the most reasonable measurement.

**45.** width of a textbook
18 cm    0.8 m    28 mm

**46.** distance a car can travel using 1 liter of gas
3 m    0.08 km    8 km

**47.** capacity of a carton of milk
20 mL    2 L    2 kL

**48.** weight of the contents of a can of mushrooms
113 g    20 g    35 kg

Copy and complete.

**49.** 150 mm = ___ cm

**50.** 2.3 km = ___ m

**51.** 4.76 m = ___ mm

**52.** 2400 g = ___ kg

**53.** 6.28 kg = ___ g

**54.** 23 000 mg = ___ g

**55.** 6.9 g = ___ mg

**56.** 7.2 L = ___ mL

**57.** 450 mL = ___ L

What is the most reasonable temperature for each of the following?

**58.** a glass of juice

3°C   30°C   80°C

**59.** a rainy day

⁻5°C   15°C   ⁻2°C

Solve.

**60.** Charlene lives 1500 m from school. How many kilometers is this?

**61.** Troy weighs 63 kilograms. Gordon weighs 62 900 grams. Who weighs more? How much more?

**62.**

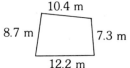

10.4 m

8.7 m        7.3 m

12.2 m

Find the perimeter of the polygon.

**63.**

5 yd

Find the circumference of the circle. Use 3.14 for π.

**64.** What is the perimeter of a regular octagon if the length of one side is 4 inches?

Find the area of each figure.

**65.**

4 m

**66.**

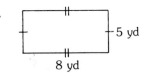

5 yd

8 yd

**67.**

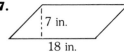

7 in.

18 in.

**68.**

14 ft

16 ft

**69.**

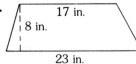

17 in.

8 in.

23 in.

**70.**

20 cm

Use 3.14 for π.

Find the volume.

**71.**

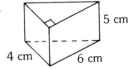

5 cm

4 cm        6 cm

**72.**

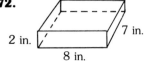

7 in.

2 in.

8 in.

**73.**

7 ft

12 ft

Use $\frac{22}{7}$ for π.

Find the surface area.

**74.**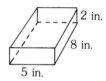

2 in.

8 in.

5 in.

**75.**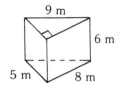

9 m

6 m

5 m    8 m

Solve.

**76.** A pan used in making a loaf of bread measures $9\frac{1}{4}$ inches by $6\frac{1}{4}$ inches by $2\frac{3}{4}$ inches. What is the volume of the pan?

**77.** Annual Fresh Fish Products in the U.S.

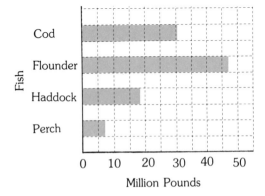

For which type of fish was production the greatest?

**78.** Amounts Spent for TV Advertising by Different Types of Companies

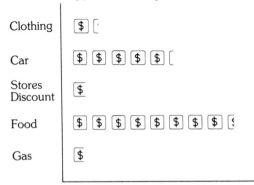

Key: Each $ = 100 million dollars

What does each $ stand for?

**79.** Draw a line graph for the table.

Cars With Factory-Installed Air-conditioning

| Year | Number ($\times 100,000$) |
|------|------|
| 1975 | 49 |
| 1976 | 63 |
| 1977 | 77 |
| 1978 | 75 |
| 1979 | 73 |
| 1980 | 54 |

**80.** Make a circle graph for the following table.

| Size of farms (in acres) in the U.S. | Percent |
|------|------|
| 1–49 | 6% |
| 50–99 | 8% |
| 100–179 | 12% |
| 180–499 | 24% |
| 500 or more | 50% |

Use the following data in exercises 81–86: 24, 37, 25, 24, 24, 24, 25, 42, 42, 43, 24, 25, 37, 37, 36, 24, 42, 43, 42, 43

**81.** Make a stem-and-leaf display. Use one-digit stems.

**82.** Make a frequency table.

**83.** Find the range.

**84.** Find the mean.

**85.** Find the median.

**86.** Find the mode.

Use the frequency table below in exercises 87–90.

| Number | Frequency |
|--------|-----------|
| 8 | 1 |
| 10 | 8 |
| 15 | 4 |
| 20 | 3 |
| total | 16 |

**87.** Find the range.

**88.** Find the mean.

**89.** Find the median.

**90.** Find the mode.

Without looking, you pick a card. Find the probability of each of the following:

**91.** picking the number 1

**92.** picking an odd number

**93.** picking the number 7

| 1 | 1 | 2 | 3 |

| 4 | 4 | 5 | 6 |

**94.** The spinner is spun twice. What is the probability of the pointer's stopping on A the first time and B the second time?

**95.** The probability of drawing a red marble is $\frac{9}{16}$. What is the probability of drawing a marble that is not red?

**96.** Without looking, you pick a card from a standard deck and then without replacing the first card, you pick another card. What is the probability that both cards will be 2's?

**1.** Is 9 a factor of 62?

**2.** Is 7 a factor of 21?

Choose the correct answer.

**3.** 9 is a (prime, composite) number.

**4.** 13 is a (prime, composite) number.

**5.** In a computer, information is stored in the (memory unit, arithmetic unit).

**6.** In BASIC, $17 \times 24$ is written (17/24, 17*24).

**7.** A computer program is called (hardware, software).

Write each number as the product of prime factors.

**8.** 8          **9.** 15          **10.** 24          **11.** 30

**12.** Find the greatest common factor (GCF) of 18 and 27.

Write in lowest terms.

**13.** $\frac{6}{9}$

**14.** $\frac{10}{12}$

**15.** Find the least common multiple (LCM) of 4 and 15.

Find the least common denominator of each pair of fractions.

**16.** $\frac{1}{2}$, $\frac{1}{10}$

**17.** $\frac{1}{4}$, $\frac{2}{3}$

**18.** Give one example of how a computer is used.

Solve, if possible. Identify and list unnecessary information.

**19.** Cartons 12 inches tall are stacked next to cartons 18 inches tall. What is the shortest height at which the stacks will be the same height?

**20.** Jane drove 340 miles in two days. She still has 280 miles to go. How far did she drive the first day?

Scott Loy/Photo Network

**Linda won 20 ribbons for horseback riding. She wants to display them so that there are the same number of ribbons in each row. She found she could display the ribbons in the following ways:**

**1 row of 20 ribbons**

**2 rows of 10 ribbons**

**4 rows of 5 ribbons**

**5 rows of 4 ribbons**

**10 rows of 2 ribbons**

**20 rows of 1 ribbon**

The numbers 1, 2, 4, 5, 10, and 20 are all *factors* of 20. When a number such as 20 is divided by one of its factors, the remainder is 0.

**Example 1:** List all the factors of 20.

$$20 = 1 \times 20$$
$$20 = 2 \times 10$$
$$20 = 4 \times 5$$

} **These three products give all the factors of 20.**

**Example 2:** Is 5 a factor of 15?

**15 ÷ 5 = 3 R0**

So 5 is a factor of 15

**Example 3:** Is 3 a factor of 8?

**8 ÷ 3 = 2 R2**

So 3 is not a factor of 8

## EXERCISES

1. Is 2 a factor of 6?

2. Is 3 a factor of 18?

3. Is 6 a factor of 15?

4. Is 8 a factor of 24?

5. Is 10 a factor of 30?

6. Is 12 a factor of 20?

List all the factors of each number.

7. 4

8. 5

9. 9

10. 8

11. 15

12. 16

13. 13

14. 17

15. 22

16. 25

17. 26

18. 34

19. 35

20. 38

21. 40

22. 50

23. 68

24. 75

25. 121

26. 126

For each fraction, find all the factors of its numerator and of its denominator.

**Example:** $\dfrac{12}{16}$  factors of 12:  1, 2, 3, 4, 6, 12

factors of 16:  1, 2, 4, 8, 16

27. $\dfrac{2}{4}$

28. $\dfrac{4}{6}$

29. $\dfrac{6}{8}$

30. $\dfrac{6}{9}$

31. $\dfrac{4}{12}$

32. $\dfrac{5}{10}$

33. $\dfrac{8}{16}$

34. $\dfrac{10}{25}$

*EXTRA PRACTICE page 514, set 115*

## 15.2 PRIME NUMBERS

P. Wechsler/FPG

Can 17 flags be arranged in more than one row having the same number of flags in each row? The only factors of 17 are 1 and 17. So the flags cannot be arranged in more than one row. A number like 17 is called a **prime number.**

**Any whole number greater than 1 that has only 1 and itself as factors is a** *prime number.*

**Any whole number greater than 1 that is not a prime number is a** *composite number.*

The first five prime numbers are 2, 3, 5, 7, and 11.

The first five composite numbers are 4, 6, 8, 9, and 10.

## EXERCISES

**1.** Find the prime numbers less than 100 as follows:

a. Make a list of the whole numbers from 2 through 100.

b. Circle 2 and cross out every second number after 2.

c. Circle 3 and cross out every third number after 3.

d. Circle 5 and cross out every fifth number after 5.

e. Circle 7 and cross out every seventh number after 7.

◄ Some numbers will be crossed out more than once.

The numbers you circled and the remaining numbers that have not been crossed out are the prime numbers less than 100.

Is each number prime or composite?

| | | | | |
|---|---|---|---|---|
| **2.** 12 | **3.** 13 | **4.** 14 | **5.** 15 | **6.** 16 |
| **7.** 17 | **8.** 18 | **9.** 19 | **10.** 20 | **11.** 21 |
| **12.** 22 | **13.** 23 | **14.** 30 | **15.** 42 | **16.** 51 |
| **17.** 57 | **18.** 63 | **19.** 78 | **20.** 89 | **21.** 99 |

**PRIME FACTORS**

A composite number can be written as the product of prime factors by using a *factor tree.*

**Example:**

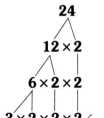

24
12 × 2
6 × 2 × 2
3 × 2 × 2 × 2 ← Each factor is a → 2 × 2 × 2 × 3
prime number.

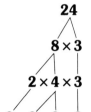

24
8 × 3
2 × 4 × 3
2 × 2 × 2 × 3

## EXERCISES

Complete each factor tree.

**1.**

20
10 × 2
_ × _ × _

**2.**

8
4 × 2
_ × _ × _

**3.**

12
4 × 3
_ × _ × _

**4.**

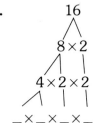

16
8 × 2
4 × 2 × 2
_ × _ × _ × _

**5.**

48
4 × 12
2 × 2 × 4 × 3
_ × _ × _ × _ × _

**6.**

60
6 × 10
_ × _ × _ × _

Write each composite number as the product of prime factors.

**7.** 18  **8.** 22  **9.** 28  **10.** 30

**11.** 34  **12.** 36  **13.** 45  **14.** 55

**15.** 63  **16.** 84  **17.** 100  **18.** 144

EXTRA PRACTICE page 514, set 116

Ed Hoppe Photography

**A packaging firm wants to cut a 36-cm-wide roll of cellophane and a 60-cm-wide roll of aluminum foil into strips of the same width, without any waste. What is the greatest width of the strips that can be cut?**

**Example 1:** Find the *greatest common factor (GCF)* of 36 and 60.

Write the prime factors of each number.

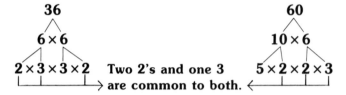

List the common prime factors.

**2, 2, and 3**

Find the product of the common factors.

$2 \times 2 \times 3 = 12 \longleftarrow$ **GCF**

The greatest width of the strips that can be cut is 12 centimeters. The greatest common factor can be used to write fractions in lowest terms and to simplify fractions when multiplying or dividing.

**Example 2:** Write $\frac{27}{36}$ in lowest terms.

The GCF of 27 and 36 is 9.

$$\frac{27}{36} = \frac{27 \div 9}{36 \div 9} = \frac{3}{4}$$

As a shortcut, we often write $\dfrac{\overset{3}{\cancel{27}}}{\underset{4}{\cancel{36}}}$

**Example 3:** Find $\frac{8}{9} \times \frac{3}{10}$.

The GCF of 3 and 9 is 3.
The GCF of 8 and 10 is 2.

$$\frac{8}{9} \times \frac{3}{10} = \frac{\overset{4}{\cancel{8}}}{\underset{3}{\cancel{9}}} \times \frac{\overset{1}{\cancel{3}}}{\underset{5}{\cancel{10}}}$$

$$= \frac{4}{15}$$

**Example 4:** Find $\frac{4}{5} \div \frac{7}{10}$.

$$\frac{4}{5} \div \frac{7}{10} = \frac{4}{5} \times \frac{10}{7}$$

$$= \frac{4}{\underset{1}{\cancel{5}}} \times \frac{\overset{2}{\cancel{10}}}{7}$$

$$= \frac{8}{7} = 1\frac{1}{7}$$

# EXERCISES

Find the greatest common factor (GCF) of each pair of numbers.

**1.** 3 and 6  **2.** 4 and 10  **3.** 6 and 8  **4.** 6 and 12

**5.** 6 and 10  **6.** 8 and 12  **7.** 9 and 12  **8.** 6 and 15

**9.** 8 and 16  **10.** 10 and 24  **11.** 12 and 24  **12.** 30 and 48

Use the GCF of the numerator and of the denominator to write each fraction in lowest terms.

**13.** $\frac{6}{10}$  **14.** $\frac{10}{15}$  **15.** $\frac{8}{12}$  **16.** $\frac{4}{16}$

**17.** $\frac{18}{24}$  **18.** $\frac{12}{20}$  **19.** $\frac{3}{24}$  **20.** $\frac{14}{28}$

Use the GCF to simplify the exercises before multiplying or dividing. Then find each answer.

**21.** $\frac{9}{10} \times \frac{5}{12}$  **22.** $\frac{2}{3} \times \frac{1}{2}$  **23.** $\frac{5}{8} \div \frac{7}{8}$  **24.** $\frac{1}{2} \div \frac{1}{6}$

**25.** $\frac{4}{9} \div \frac{2}{3}$  **26.** $\frac{5}{6} \times \frac{3}{5}$  **27.** $\frac{5}{6} \times \frac{9}{20}$  **28.** $\frac{8}{15} \div \frac{4}{9}$

**29.** $\frac{3}{16} \div \frac{3}{4}$  **30.** $\frac{18}{25} \times \frac{5}{6}$  **31.** $\frac{7}{12} \div \frac{3}{8}$  **32.** $\frac{1}{2} \times \frac{4}{1}$

EXTRA PRACTICE page 515, set 117

## SKILLS REVIEW

Reduce to lowest terms.

**33.** $\frac{6}{8}$  **34.** $\frac{8}{12}$  **35.** $\frac{10}{25}$  **36.** $\frac{50}{100}$

Express as a mixed number. Simplify.

**37.** $\frac{21}{7}$  **38.** $\frac{32}{9}$  **39.** $\frac{26}{6}$  **40.** $\frac{50}{15}$

**41.** $\frac{44}{8}$  **42.** $\frac{68}{10}$  **43.** $\frac{51}{12}$  **44.** $\frac{70}{20}$

Brent Jones

**Mr. Clark wants to buy paper cups and paper plates for a birthday party. Paper cups come in packages of 12 and paper plates come in packages of 8. What is the least number of packages of each he would have to buy to have the same number of cups and plates?**

**Example 1:** Find the **least common multiple (LCM)** of 8 and 12.

Write the prime factors of each number.

| 8 | 12 |
|---|---|
| $\wedge$ | $\wedge$ |
| **2 × 4** | **2 × 6** |
| **2 × 2 × 2** | **2 × 2 × 3** |

Notice that these two factors have already occurred as factors of 8.

First, list all the prime factors of 8. Then list the prime factors of 12 that do not occur as factors of 8.

**2, 2, 2, 3**

Multiply the factors.

**2 × 2 × 2 × 3 = 24** ⟵ **LCM**

He would have to buy 3 packages of plates ($8 \times 3 = 24$) and 2 packages of cups ($12 \times 2 = 24$).

When you add or subtract fractions, the least common multiple of the denominators is the **least common denominator** for the fractions.

**Example 2:** Add $\frac{1}{2} + \frac{3}{5}$.

The LCM of 2 and 5 is 10.

$$\frac{1}{2} + \frac{3}{5} = \frac{5}{10} + \frac{6}{10}$$
$$= \frac{11}{10} = 1\frac{1}{10}$$

**Example 3:** Subtract $\frac{11}{12} - \frac{3}{4}$.

The LCM of 12 and 4 is 12.

$$\frac{11}{12} - \frac{3}{4} = \frac{11}{12} - \frac{9}{12}$$
$$= \frac{2}{12} = \frac{1}{6}$$

## EXERCISES

Find the least common multiple (LCM) of each pair of numbers.

**1.** 4 and 6      **2.** 6 and 9      **3.** 4 and 5      **4.** 8 and 10

**5.** 5 and 10 **6.** 9 and 12 **7.** 9 and 15 **8.** 6 and 15

**9.** 12 and 18 **10.** 15 and 20 **11.** 12 and 16 **12.** 24 and 36

Find the least common multiple of the denominators of each pair of fractions.

**13.** $\frac{2}{5}, \frac{1}{10}$ **14.** $\frac{1}{6}, \frac{2}{3}$ **15.** $\frac{7}{12}, \frac{1}{3}$ **16.** $\frac{3}{8}, \frac{1}{4}$

**17.** $\frac{9}{10}, \frac{1}{4}$ **18.** $\frac{5}{8}, \frac{1}{2}$ **19.** $\frac{1}{2}, \frac{1}{6}$ **20.** $\frac{3}{20}, \frac{7}{10}$

Use the LCM to find a common denominator before adding or subtracting. Then find each answer.

**21.** $\frac{5}{8} + \frac{1}{4}$ **22.** $\frac{3}{10} + \frac{2}{5}$ **23.** $\frac{9}{10} - \frac{2}{5}$ **24.** $\frac{3}{8} + \frac{1}{4}$

**25.** $\frac{5}{6} - \frac{5}{8}$ **26.** $\frac{1}{2} + \frac{1}{3}$ **27.** $\frac{5}{6} - \frac{3}{4}$ **28.** $\frac{11}{12} + \frac{1}{8}$

**29.** $\frac{2}{5} - \frac{1}{6}$ **30.** $\frac{4}{15} + \frac{3}{4}$ **31.** $\frac{4}{5} - \frac{3}{4}$ **32.** $\frac{5}{12} + \frac{3}{8}$

*EXTRA PRACTICE page 515, set 118*

## CHECKPOINT

List all the factors of each number.

**1.** 12 **2.** 25 **3.** 30 **4.** 100

Is each number prime or composite?

**5.** 3 **6.** 8 **7.** 9

Write each composite number as the product of prime factors.

**8.** 36 **9.** 54

Find the greatest common factor of each pair of numbers.

**10.** 6 and 12 **11.** 12 and 16

Find the least common multiple of each pair of numbers.

**12.** 10 and 24 **13.** 6 and 15

Find each result.

**14.** $\frac{5}{9} \times \frac{6}{15}$ **15.** $\frac{2}{3} \div \frac{4}{5}$ **16.** $\frac{2}{3} - \frac{1}{4}$ **17.** $\frac{3}{5} + \frac{7}{10}$

Kent Whitehead/Photo Network

**A company runs an advertisement for their product every 8 hours on one radio station and every 6 hours on another radio station. The first time the commercial is run, it is played at the same time on both stations. How long will it take before both stations run the commercial at the same time again?**

**Read:**  *Given:*  1st station every 8 hours;

2nd station every 6 hours

*To find:*  When will the commercial be played again at the same time?

**Plan:**  Find the LCM of 6 and 8.

**Compute:**

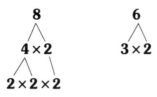

$$2 \times 2 \times 2 \times 3 = 24 \longleftarrow \text{LCM}$$

**Answer:**  It will take 24 hours before the commercial is played again at the same time on both stations.

**Check:**

| every 6 hours | 6 | 12 | 18 | 24 |
|---|---|---|---|---|
| every 8 hours | 8 | 16 | 24 | ✔ |

# EXERCISES

**1.**

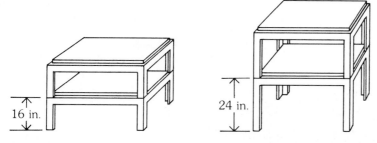

16 in.

24 in.

What is the shortest height at which the stacks will be the same height?

**2.** One piece of material is 36 inches wide and another piece of material is 45 inches wide. Both pieces of material are to be cut into strips of the same width without wasting any material. What is the greatest width of the strips that can be cut?

**3.** How many different ways can 20 fishing lures be packaged if each package must contain the same number of lures?

**4.** Can 31 pictures be arranged in more than one row with the same number of pictures in each row?

**5.** In a bottling plant every fourth bottle is checked for full content and every sixth bottle is checked for a good seal. If the same bottle is checked for both seal and content, how many more bottles must pass through the inspection line before another bottle is checked for both seal and content?

**6.** Leslie has to set up 24 chairs on the left side of the lecture hall and 30 chairs on the right side of the hall. There has to be the same number of rows on each side. How many rows will each side have? How many chairs will be in each row on the left side? How many chairs will be in each row on the right side?

*EXTRA PRACTICE page 515, set 119*

L. Druskis/Taurus

Just as we use a hammer to increase our strength when hitting a nail, we use a computer to increase our speed when organizing information and performing arithmetic calculations. A computer can best be understood by looking at its parts. A computer is made up of five parts called **hardware.**

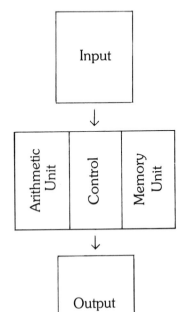

**The Input Device**   Just as you need to know the facts of a problem, so does the computer. These facts can be entered into the computer on a *keyboard* that looks like a typewriter keyboard. (Cassette recorders and disk drives are other types of input devices.)

**The Memory Unit**   When solving a problem, you either remember the facts or write them down for later use. The computer also has a memory, where it stores facts and information about how to work a problem.

**The Arithmetic Unit**   The computer's arithmetic unit is comparable to the paper where you work the problem. This is where the computer adds, subtracts, multiplies, and divides.

**The Output Device**   Once the computer has found the answer to the problem, it can show the result on a screen that looks like a television screen. (The computer could also display the results by using a printer, or it could record the results by using a cassette recorder or disk drive.)

**The Control Unit** The computer's control unit controls the input device, the memory unit, the arithmetic unit, and the output device. Together, the arithmetic unit and the control unit are often called the Central Processing Unit (CPU).

## EXERCISES

Choose the correct answer.

1. The (memory unit, arithmetic unit) adds, subtracts, multiplies, and divides.

2. Information can be entered into a computer on a (printer, keyboard).

3. Information is stored in the (memory unit, control unit).

4. The (input device, output device) displays the answer to a problem.

5. The input device is controlled by the (memory unit, control unit).

6. Bring to class pictures and articles about computers and make a bulletin-board display.

7. Read a book about computers and discuss the book with the class. (There are many science-fiction books as well as factual books on computers. A librarian can help you find these books).

## SKILLS REVIEW

Find each result.

8. $\dfrac{1}{5} + \dfrac{2}{5}$

9. $\dfrac{1}{4} + \dfrac{3}{4}$

10. $\dfrac{1}{2} + \dfrac{1}{3}$

11. $\dfrac{2}{3} + \dfrac{3}{4}$

12. $\dfrac{3}{4} - \dfrac{1}{4}$

13. $\dfrac{7}{8} - \dfrac{3}{8}$

14. $\dfrac{1}{2} - \dfrac{1}{3}$

15. $\dfrac{7}{10} - \dfrac{3}{5}$

16. $\dfrac{5}{8} + \dfrac{5}{12}$

17. $\dfrac{9}{10} - \dfrac{4}{15}$

18. $\dfrac{13}{20} + \dfrac{3}{5}$

19. $\dfrac{2}{5} - \dfrac{9}{25}$

```
READY
>LIST
10 FOR A = 1 TO 12
20 PRINT A;
30 NEXT A
40 PRINT "COMPUTING IS FUN"
50 END
>RUN
  1 2 3 4 5 6 7 8 9 10 11 12
COMPUTING IS FUN
READY
>
```

A **computer program** is a set of instructions written in a computer language that tells the computer what to do. BASIC (**B**eginner's **A**ll-purpose **S**ymbolic **I**nstruction **C**ode) is an easy and useful programming language.

In BASIC $*$ is used instead of $\times$ to indicate multiplication and / is used instead of $\div$ to indicate division.

| Math | BASIC |
|------|-------|
| $4+6$ | 4+6 |
| $18-7$ | 18−7 |
| $45 \div 5$ | 45/5 |
| $10 \times 9$ | 10*9 |

A computer does only what it is instructed to do by a computer program. A computer program is called **software.** A program is a set of numbered statements that the computer follows in numbered order. In a computer program, words like PRINT, LET, and END are used to tell the computer what to do.

BASIC
computer language

**Example 1:**

| Program | Output | |
|---------|--------|--|
| 10 LET C = 5 + 6 | | |
| 20 PRINT "5 PLUS 6 EQUALS" | 5 PLUS 6 EQUALS | The computer will print whatever appears between quotes. |
| 30 PRINT C | 11 | The value of C. |

Kenji Kerins

**Example 2:**

| Program | Output |
|---|---|
| 10 PRINT "HELLO AND GOODBYE" | HELLO AND GOODBYE |
| 20 PRINT "20 − 13 =" | 20 − 13 = |
| 30 PRINT 20 − 13 | 7 |

## EXERCISES

Complete the table.

| | Math | BASIC |
|---|---|---|
| **1.** | $16 + 12$ | ___ |
| **2.** | $105 − 32$ | ___ |
| **3.** | $6 \times 8$ | ___ |
| **4.** | $40 \div 10$ | ___ |
| **5.** | $4 \times 12 − 6$ | ___ |
| **6.** | $30 \div 5 + 7$ | ___ |

Give the output.

**7.**  10 PRINT "I AM"
    20 PRINT "A COMPUTER"

**8.**  10 PRINT "9 + 3"
    20 PRINT "NINE PLUS THREE"
    30 PRINT "9 PLUS 3"
    40 PRINT 9 + 3

**9.**  10 LET C = 12
    20 PRINT "C"
    30 PRINT C
    40 PRINT C∗C
    50 PRINT C/4

**10.**  10 LET A = 10
    20 LET B = 6
    30 LET C = A∗B
    40 PRINT A
    50 PRINT "TIMES"
    60 PRINT B
    70 PRINT "EQUALS"
    80 PRINT C

*EXTRA PRACTICE page 516, set 120*

Al Stephenson/Corn's Photo Service

Computers affect our daily lives. Here is just a short list of things a computer can do.

Business—compute a payroll, print checks, bill customers, keep track of inventory

Medicine—monitor vital signs, provide diagnosis based on test results, store medical histories for instant retrieval

Education—provide classroom instruction, keep records

Recreation—generate computer art, compute sports statistics, operate video games

Computers are not always used in the public's best interest. Unless access to information in a computer is controlled, the information obtained may violate a person's right to privacy. Also, computers have been used illegally to transfer money from one bank account to another.

## EXERCISES

1. Bring to class items that are produced or used by a computer—for example, a receipt from an automatic teller.

2. List ways, other than those mentioned above, that computers are used.

3. Go to a local business or an agency such as a fire department and find out how computers are used in its work.

L. Druskis/Taurus

The use of computers has opened up a whole new range of jobs. Some of these jobs, like data entry clerk or maintenance engineer, require vocational training. A data entry clerk types information into the computer. A maintenance engineer keeps the computers in working order. Other positions, such as systems analyst and computer programmer, require a college degree. A computer programmer uses a computer language like BASIC to write instructions for the computer. A systems analyst works with the programmer to make sure that the best and most efficient program results.

French/FPG

1. Look in the jobs section of your newspaper and cut out advertisements for data entry clerks, maintenance engineers, programmers, and systems analysts. Use these advertisements to make a bulletin-board display.

2. Discuss the qualifications for the jobs displayed on the bulletin board.

3. Write your state employment agency to obtain information on computer job opportunities.

**439**

PROBLEMS WITH TOO MUCH
OR TOO LITTLE INFORMATION

Some problems contain extra information that is not needed to solve the problem.

**Example 1:** Rafael wants to make a 20% down payment on a new car. The car gets 31 miles to the gallon and costs $8980. How much will the down payment be?

**Read:** *Given:* down payment—20%;

cost—$8980;

miles per gallon—31 **not needed**

*To find:* amount of down payment

**Plan:** Find 20% of 8980.

**Compute:**

$$\frac{?}{8980} = \frac{20}{100}$$

$? \times 100 = 8980 \times 20$   **Find the cross products.**

$? \times 100 = 179{,}600$   **What number times 100 equals 179,600?**

$179{,}600 \div 100 = 1796$   **To find out, divide 179,600 by 100.**

**So, ? = 1796**

**Answer:** The down payment will be $1796.

**Check:** You can use an alternate method to check the result.

Find 20% of 8980.

$0.2 \times 8980 = ?$

$1796 = ?$ ✔

Sometimes you are not given enough information to solve the problem.

**Example 2:** Rafael made a 20% down payment on a new car. How much did the car cost?

   **Read:**    *Given:*  down payment—20%

               *To find:*  cost of the car

You need more information before you can solve this problem. You need to know the amount of the down payment.

## EXERCISES

Solve, if possible. Identify and list unnecessary information.

1. A carpenter has one board $6\frac{3}{4}$ feet long and another 6 feet long. How many $1\frac{1}{2}$-foot boards can be cut from the 6-foot board?

2. A stereo that regularly sells for $375 is on sale. How much less do you have to pay if you buy the stereo during the sale?

3. In November, 7.2 inches of snow fell. In December, 14 inches of snow fell, and in January 16.4 inches of snow fell. How much snow fell in December and January?

4. A radio station plays 30 songs in 2 hours. The station runs 12 commercials each hour. At that rate, how many commercials are played during the afternoon shift?

5. Mark bought a pair of boots at a discount store. The boots cost $54 before they were discounted. How much did Mark pay for the boots?

6. A family traveled 486 miles on vacation. Their car has a 15-gallon tank and the car used 18 gallons of gasoline to make the trip. How many miles per gallon did the car average?

7. Sue earns $5.60 an hour. If she worked 92 hours last month, how much did she earn?

8. A 16-ounce box of cereal provides 12 servings and costs $1.08. What is the cost per serving?

Choose the correct answer.

**1.** 6 is a factor of (3, 12).

15.1

**2.** (17, 24) is a prime number.

15.2

**3.** (3, 6) is a composite number.

**4.** 3 is the (LCM, GCF) of 6 and 15.

15.4

**5.** 12 is the (LCM, GCF) of 3 and 4.

15.5

Is each number prime or composite?

15.2

**6.** 8　　　　　**7.** 5　　　　　**8.** 31　　　　　**9.** 16

Write each number as the product of prime factors.

15.3

**10.** 20　　　　**11.** 15　　　　**12.** 9　　　　**13.** 24

Find the greatest common factor of each pair of numbers.

15.4

**14.** 12 and 9　　　　　　　　**15.** 8 and 15

Write each fraction in lowest terms.

**16.** $\frac{6}{8}$　　　　**17.** $\frac{12}{15}$　　　　**18.** $\frac{16}{20}$

Find each result.

**19.** $\frac{3}{4} \times \frac{2}{3}$　　　**20.** $\frac{5}{6} \div \frac{3}{10}$　　　**21.** $\frac{1}{3} \times \frac{6}{9}$　　　**22.** $\frac{7}{10} \div \frac{5}{8}$

Find the least common multiple of each pair of numbers.

15.5

**23.** 4 and 6　　　　　　　**24.** 10 and 15

Find each result. 15.5

**25.** $\frac{3}{4} + \frac{1}{2}$  **26.** $\frac{2}{3} - \frac{1}{6}$  **27.** $\frac{5}{12} + \frac{1}{4}$  **28.** $\frac{7}{10} - \frac{2}{5}$

Solve. 15.6

**29.** What is the least number of players from which teams of 4 and teams of 6 can be made?

**30.** Both a 36-cm-wide sheet of tin and a 48-cm-wide sheet of tin are to be cut into strips of equal width without wasting any tin. What is the greatest width of the strips that can be cut?

Match each term with the best description. 15.7

**31.** Input Device ___    a. adds

**32.** Arithmetic Unit ___    b. control unit and arithmetic unit

**33.** Memory ___    c. screen

**34.** CPU ___    d. keyboard

**35.** Output Device ___    e. stores information

Write in BASIC 15.8

**36.** $16 \div 8$    **37.** $4 \times 12$    **38.** $24 \times 2 - 5$

Give the output.

**39.** 1Ø PRINT "24 TIMES 6 IS"
20 LET A = 24*6
3Ø PRINT A

**40.** 1Ø PRINT "I AM A COMPUTER"
2Ø PRINT "5*8 ="
3Ø PRINT 5*8

**41.** Give one example of how a computer is used. 15.9

Solve, if possible. Identify and list unnecessary information. 15.10

**42.** Glen worked for 2 days. He earns $3.50 an hour. How much did he earn?

**43.** Clare saved $4 a week for 35 weeks to buy a new bike. The bike costs $190. How much money has she saved?

List all the factors of each number.

**1.** 12           **2.** 30

Is each number prime or composite?

**3.** 6      **4.** 15      **5.** 23      **6.** 32

Write each number as the product of prime factors.

**7.** 30      **8.** 32      **9.** 60

**10.** Find the greatest common factor (GCF) of 12 and 16.

**11.** Find the least common multiple (LCM) of 8 and 12.

Find each result.

**12.** $\frac{2}{3} + \frac{3}{4}$      **13.** $\frac{1}{2} - \frac{1}{6}$      **14.** $\frac{7}{12} + \frac{1}{3}$      **15.** $\frac{9}{10} - \frac{2}{5}$

**16.** $\frac{7}{8} \times \frac{4}{14}$      **17.** $\frac{8}{9} \div \frac{12}{15}$      **18.** $\frac{1}{4} \times \frac{8}{9}$      **19.** $\frac{5}{8} \div \frac{7}{10}$

**20.** List the five parts that make up a computer's hardware.

**21.** Give the output for the program.

```
10 LET A=3*7
20 PRINT "3*7 EQUALS"
30 PRINT A
```

**22.** Give one way in which a business might use a computer.

Solve, if possible. Identify and list unnecessary information.

**23.** It takes 4 minutes for Clare to run one lap of the track. Matt can run one lap in 5 minutes. They both leave the starting point at the same time and keep running around the track. What is the least number of minutes before they arrive at the starting point together again?

**24.** A new car costs $6495 plus $389.70 in taxes. The buyer plans to put $1500 down. What is the total cost for the new car?

**444**

**1.** Find the value of $10 - 2 \times 4$.

**2.** Find the value of $n \times 2 \div 6$ if $n = 9$.

**3.** Find the value of $12 - a \div b$ if $a = 6$ and $b = 3$.

**4.** Write the opposite of $^-4\frac{1}{2}$.

Solve each equation.

**5.** $n + 6 = 10$    **6.** $x - 3 = 7$    **7.** $4x = 20$    **8.** $\frac{n}{3} = 6$

Replace each ● with $<$ or $>$.

**9.** $^-4 ● ^+2$    **10.** $0 ● ^-1$    **11.** $^-4 ● ^-5$    **12.** $^-3 ● ^+4$

Use a number line to find the sums.

**13.** $^+3 + ^+1$    **14.** $^-4 + ^+2$    **15.** $^+1 + ^-3$    **16.** $^-2 + 0$

Add.

**17.** $^+4 + ^+5$    **18.** $^-6 + ^-3$    **19.** $^+7 + ^-4$    **20.** $^-8 + ^+3$

**21.** Name the coordinates of $A$ in the graph below.

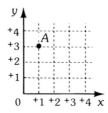

**22.** Complete the table for the equation.

$y = x + ^+1$

| $x$ | $x + ^+1$ | Ordered pairs |
|---|---|---|
| $^+1$ | $^+1 + ^+1 = ^+2$ | $(^+1, ^+2)$ |
| $^+2$ | ___ | ___ |
| $^+3$ | ___ | ___ |

Solve.

**23.** After spending $25 for a baseball mitt, Rosa has $18 left. How much money did she have originally?

445

## ORDER OF OPERATIONS

Which do you put on first, your hat or your gloves? It makes no difference, because the result is the same. Which do you put on first, your shoes or your socks? It does make a difference, because the result is not the same.

Here are two mathematical **expressions.**

$$5+6+3 \qquad 5+6\times3$$

Add 5, 6, and 3 in any order, and the sum is 14.

The value of $5+6\times3$ depends on the order in which the operations are done.

$$5+6\times3 \qquad 5+6\times3$$
$$11\times3 \qquad 5+18$$
$$33 \qquad 23$$

To be sure that an expression has only one value, we use the following order of operations:

1. **Multiply and divide from left to right.**
2. **Add and subtract from left to right.**

**Example 1:** $10-6\div2+4$
$$10-3+4$$
$$7+4$$
$$11$$

**Example 2:** $8+1-3\times2$
$$8+1-6$$
$$9-6$$
$$3$$

To change the order of operations, you can use parentheses. Operations indicated inside a pair of parentheses are always done first.

**Example 3:** $6\times(2+9)-4$
$$6\times11-4$$
$$66-4$$
$$62$$

**Example 4:** $35-(8+2)\times3$
$$35-10\times3$$
$$35-30$$
$$5$$

## EXERCISES

Which operation would you do first?

**1.** $6+9-12$

**2.** $9-4+2$

**3.** $5\times4-8$

**4.** $3+6\times4$

**5.** $7+14\div2$

**6.** $18\div6-3$

**7.** $5\times(3+2)$

**8.** $(9-8)\times5$

**9.** $(7+3)\times6$

**10.** $12\div6+4-1$

**11.** $9\times3-5+2$

**12.** $4\times(3-2)+6$

Find each value.

**13.** $6+5-7$

**14.** $9-3+7$

**15.** $8+3\times5$

**16.** $2\times8-9$

**17.** $6+8\div2$

**18.** $10\div2-3$

**19.** $4\times5+6$

**20.** $12-3\times4$

**21.** $9\div3+4$

**22.** $8-12\div3$

**23.** $6+9-7$

**24.** $5-3+2$

**25.** $8+6+4$

**26.** $3+5+6$

**27.** $9-(4+4)$

**28.** $5+6-7$

**29.** $10-(10-3)$

**30.** $12-7-4$

**31.** $9-2\times3$

**32.** $6\div3+8$

**33.** $2+3\times5$

**34.** $20\div4-3$

**35.** $4\times(7+3)-6$

**36.** $12-6\div3+1$

**37.** $(6\times5)\div(10-4)$

**38.** $(15\div3)\times(8-3)$

**39.** $(9\times2)\div(18\div3)$

Insert ( ) so that each phrase has the given value.

| | Phrase | Value | | Phrase | Value |
|---|---|---|---|---|---|
| **40.** | $6\times4+2$ | 36 | **41.** | $16-3+5$ | 8 |
| **42.** | $5\times2+8$ | 50 | **43.** | $4+5\times2+8$ | 26 |
| **44.** | $15-10\div5\times6$ | 6 | **45.** | $6\times8-8+1$ | 1 |

**447**

Charles Feil/FPG

Joe earns $75 a week, plus tips. The tips vary from week to week. Since the tips vary, we can use a **variable,** such as x, to stand for the total amount of the tips. Joe's weekly salary, then, is

**75 + x.**

**Example 1:** Find the value of $75 + x$ if $x = 25$.

**75 + x**
**75 + 25**   **Replace x with 25.**
**100**

If the *same variable* is used more than once in an expression, replace it with the same number each time.

**Example 2:** Find the value of $(15 - y) \times y$ if $y = 10$.

**(15 − y) × y**
**(15 − 10) × 10**   **Replace both y's with 10.**
**5 × 10**
**50**

Sometimes, an expression will contain *different variables,* which can be replaced with the same number or with different numbers.

**Example 3:** Find the value of $x + 5 - y$ if $x = 3$ and $y = 4$.

**x + 5 − y**
**3 + 5 − 4**   **Replace x with 3 and y with 4.**
**8 − 4**
**4**

Find the value of $x + 5 - y$ if $x = 8$ and $y = 8$.

**x + 5 − y**
**8 + 5 − 8**   **Replace x and y with 8.**
**13 − 8**
**5**

# EXERCISES

Find the value of each expression if $y=5$.

**1.** $4+y$      **2.** $y-3$      **3.** $y\times5$      **4.** $30\div y$

**5.** $3\times y-10$      **6.** $50\div(y+y)$      **7.** $3\times y+y$      **8.** $y+4\times y$

Find the value of each expression if $n=8$.

**9.** $n-6$      **10.** $12+n$      **11.** $n\div2$      **12.** $n\times n$

**13.** $n\times3\div12$      **14.** $n-n\div4$      **15.** $5+n+7-9$      **16.** $(n+2)-(n\div2)$

Find the value of each expression if $a=6$ and $b=6$.

**17.** $a+b$      **18.** $a-b$      **19.** $a\times b$      **20.** $a\div b$

**21.** $6+b-a$      **22.** $a-5+b$      **23.** $a-b+6$      **24.** $3+a\times b$

Find the value of each expression if $a=8$ and $b=4$.

**25.** $10-a\div b$      **26.** $b-16\div a$      **27.** $5\times(a+b)$

**28.** $(a-b)\times6$      **29.** $a-(b-2)\times3$      **30.** $7+(10-a)\times b$

**31.** $22-(6-b)\times a$      **32.** $(4+a)\div b$      **33.** $20-b\times a\div2$

**34.** $(12\div b)+(a\div2)$      **35.** $30-b\times b+a$      **36.** $a+2\times b-10$

**37.** $a\times2-b\times3$      **38.** $b\times(a-2)+6$      **39.** $6+3\times b-b$

*EXTRA PRACTICE page 516, set 121*

## SKILLS REVIEW

Compute.

**40.** $738+14+1723+6$      **41.** $7152-3896$      **42.** $93\times86$

**43.** $31\overline{)2294}$      **44.** $674+763+928$      **45.** $6040-5738$

**46.** $193\times47$      **47.** $695\overline{)50040}$      **48.** $785\times492$

# SOLVING ADDITION AND SUBTRACTION EQUATIONS

Brent Jones

**Sheryl wants to buy a $15 school activity pass. She needs $6 more. How much money does she already have?**

To solve this problem, you can use an **equation.** First, let $x$ stand for how much money Sheryl already has.

Think: What number plus 6 equals 15? Write: $x+6=15$

You solve an equation containing a variable when you find a number that makes the equation true.

**To solve an equation, you can subtract the same number from each side or add the same number to each side.**

**Example 1:** Solve $x+6=15$.

$$x+6=15$$

Subtracting 6 from ⟶ $x+6-6=15-6$  Subtract 6 from
$x+6$ leaves $x$. ⟶ $x=9$  each side.

**Check: Replace $x$ with 9 in the original equation.**

$9+6=15$
$15=15$ ✔

Sheryl already has $9.

**Example 2:** Solve $x-5=7$.

$$x-5=7$$

Adding 5 to ⟶ $x-5+5=7+5$  Add 5 to each side.
$x-5$ leaves $x$. ⟶ $x=12$

**Check: Replace $x$ with 12 in the original equation.**

$12-5=7$
$7=7$ ✔

# EXERCISES

What number should be added to or subtracted from each side?

**1.** $x + 9 = 12$

**2.** $a - 5 = 7$

**3.** $n + 4 = 8$

**4.** $b - 3 = 6$

**5.** $m + 10 = 11$

**6.** $p - 6 = 10$

**7.** $a + 7 = 15$

**8.** $y + 12 = 20$

**9.** $l - 9 = 16$

**10.** $c - 7 = 13$

**11.** $17 = z + 6$

**12.** $23 = x - 4$

Solve and check.

**13.** $x + 5 = 10$

**14.** $y - 8 = 6$

**15.** $a + 3 = 7$

**16.** $b - 6 = 2$

**17.** $n + 8 = 9$

**18.** $c + 4 = 6$

**19.** $m - 9 = 13$

**20.** $l - 10 = 15$

**21.** $d + 7 = 21$

**22.** $g - 8 = 19$

**23.** $x - 5 = 23$

**24.** $y + 12 = 15$

**25.** $a - 13 = 36$

**26.** $b + 15 = 40$

**27.** $n + 18 = 28$

**28.** $c - 16 = 25$

**29.** $m + 19 = 42$

**30.** $l + 24 = 41$

**31.** $13 = x - 8$

**32.** $17 = n + 9$

**33.** $20 = y + 14$

**34.** $10 = a - 20$

**35.** $25 = b + 17$

**36.** $16 = l - 16$

EXTRA PRACTICE page 516, set 122

## SKILLS REVIEW

Compute.

**37.** $3.16 + 0.834 + 2.6$

**38.** $5.7 + 9 + 0.64$

**39.** $48.963 - 25.45$

**40.** $6.7 - 0.842$

**41.** $5.63 \times 2.7$

**42.** $0.35 \times 0.02$

**43.** $4.25 \times 100$

**44.** $34.72 \div 8$

**45.** $5.784 \div 0.6$

**46.** $376 \div 0.4$

## 16.4 SOLVING MULTIPLICATION AND DIVISION EQUATIONS

Brent Jones

**Mr. Diego needs 96 baseballs for his high-school team. There are 8 baseballs in a box. How many boxes does he need to buy?**

To solve this problem, you can use an equation. First, let $x$ stand for the number of boxes he needs to buy.

Think:  Eight times what number equals 96?

Write:  $8x = 96$  (**8x means "8 times x."**)

**To solve an equation, you can multiply or divide each side by the same number (but not by 0).**

**Example 1:**  Solve $8x = 96$.

$$8x = 96$$

**Dividing 8x by 8 leaves x.** $\longrightarrow$ $\dfrac{8x}{8} = \dfrac{96}{8}$  **Divide each side by 8.**

$$x = 12$$

**Check:  Replace x with 12 in the original equation.**

$8 \times 12 = 96$

$96 = 96$ ✔

Mr. Diego needs to buy 12 boxes of baseballs.

**Example 2:**  Solve $\frac{x}{3} = 9$.

$$\frac{x}{3} = 9 \quad \tfrac{x}{3} \text{ means "x divided by 3."}$$

**Multiplying $\frac{x}{3}$ by 3 leaves x.** $\longrightarrow$ $\dfrac{x}{3} \times 3 = 9 \times 3$  **Multiply each side by 3.**

$$\longrightarrow x = 27$$

**Check:  Replace x with 27 in the original equation.**

$\dfrac{27}{3} = 9$

$9 = 9$ ✔

452

## EXERCISES

By what number should each side be multiplied or divided?

**1.** $4x = 12$

**2.** $\frac{a}{5} = 10$

**3.** $6n = 0$

**4.** $\frac{m}{3} = 9$

**5.** $5a = 35$

**6.** $3b = 15$

**7.** $\frac{x}{7} = 3$

**8.** $\frac{y}{8} = 16$

**9.** $24 = 8a$

**10.** $36 = 9x$

**11.** $\frac{b}{4} = 4$

**12.** $18 = 2n$

Solve and check.

**13.** $3x = 18$

**14.** $5a = 25$

**15.** $6b = 24$

**16.** $\frac{n}{7} = 2$

**17.** $\frac{y}{6} = 3$

**18.** $\frac{m}{8} = 4$

**19.** $12b = 0$

**20.** $\frac{a}{9} = 1$

**21.** $15x = 15$

**22.** $\frac{n}{3} = 6$

**23.** $10y = 30$

**24.** $9x = 27$

**25.** $\frac{x}{4} = 12$

**26.** $\frac{a}{5} = 15$

**27.** $11z = 77$

**28.** $12y = 36$

**29.** $\frac{b}{10} = 40$

**30.** $20a = 60$

**31.** $54 = 9x$

**32.** $4 = \frac{n}{3}$

**33.** $96 = 8y$

**34.** $5 = \frac{a}{6}$

**35.** $64 = 8z$

**36.** $12 = \frac{b}{6}$

*EXTRA PRACTICE page 517, set 123*

## CHECKPOINT

Find each value.

**1.** $4 + 6 \times 7$

**2.** $3 \times 6 \div 9$

**3.** $4 + 3 \times 2$

**4.** $8 - 6 \div 3$

Find the value of each expression if $x = 6$ and $y = 2$.

**5.** $x - 3$

**6.** $4 + x$

**7.** $7 \times x - y$

**8.** $x \div 2$

Solve each equation.

**9.** $n + 4 = 7$

**10.** $y - 3 = 8$

**11.** $8x = 56$

**12.** $\frac{n}{5} = 12$

H. Armstrong Roberts

**A railroad rack car carries 12 automobiles. How many rack cars are needed to carry 108 automobiles?**

**Read:**   *Given:*   12 automobiles per rack car;
              108 automobiles in all

         *To find:*   number of rack cars needed

**Plan:**   Let $n$ stand for the number of rack cars.

| (number of auto-mobiles per rack car) | times | (number of rack cars) | equals | (total number of automobiles) |
|:---:|:---:|:---:|:---:|:---:|
| 12 | × | $n$ | = | 108 |

**Compute:**   $12n = 108$

              $\dfrac{12n}{12} = \dfrac{108}{12}$

                  $n = 9$

**Answer:**   9 rack cars are needed.

**Check:**   Do 9 rack cars with 12 automobiles on each rack
            car contain a total of 108 automobiles?   ✔

# EXERCISES

Solve each problem by using an equation.

1. Ellie needs $10 to buy a sweater. She already has $6. How much more does she need?

2. After spending $8 on a field trip, Scott had $4 left. How much did he have originally?

3. Mrs. West bought 5 pairs of gloves for a total of $30. If each pair of gloves was priced the same, what was the cost of each pair?

4. A fish stringer has 5 loops, with enough room for 3 fish on each loop. What is the largest number of fish the stringer can hold?

5. The length of a rectangle is 12 feet and its area is 96 square feet. What is its width?

6. Ho made a birdhouse and sold it for $36. This is 4 times what he paid for the materials. What did he pay for the materials?

7. Laura saved $42 to buy a bicycle. If she has to save $65 more, how much does the bicycle cost?

8. A piggyback flatcar holds 2 truck trailers. How many truck trailers will fit on 11 piggyback flatcars?

9. After a sale, an automobile dealer had 15 cars left. The dealer sold 13 cars during the sale. How many cars did the dealer have before the sale?

10. If Brian earned $5 an hour and was paid $85, how many hours did he work?

11. Todd went to a football game with $10. He spent $8.56. How much did he have left after the game?

12. Yolanda weighed 123 pounds in January. By April, she weighed 105 pounds. How many pounds did she lose?

EXTRA PRACTICE page 517, set 124

John Lidington/Taurus

**On one play, a football team gained 5 yards. On the next play, they did the opposite. What is the opposite of a 5-yard gain?**

Opposites are described with words like *gain* and *loss*, *up* and *down*, or *above* and *below*. In mathematics, **positive** and **negative** are the words used to describe opposites.

**Example 1:** a gain of 5 yards

We write:  $^+5$ or 5   **A $^+$ or no sign at all is used to indicate positive numbers.**

We say:  "positive five" or "five"

**Example 2:** a loss of 5 yards

We write:  $^-5$   **A $^-$ is used to indicate negative numbers.**

We say:  "negative five"

The opposite of a 5-yard gain is a 5-yard loss.

The whole numbers 1, 2, 3, 4, · · · together with their opposites $^-1$, $^-2$, $^-3$, $^-4$, · · · are called **integers.** 0 is also an integer, but it is neither positive nor negative.

We can also write opposites for fractions and decimals.

**Example 3:** What is the opposite of $^-(\frac{1}{2})$?

The opposite of $^-(\frac{1}{2})$ is $\frac{1}{2}$ or $^+(\frac{1}{2})$.

**Example 4:** What is the opposite of 1.3?

The opposite of 1.3 is $^-1.3$.

## EXERCISES

Write the following as a positive or a negative number.

**1.** a loss of 35

**2.** 5° below zero

**3.** 10 feet above sea level

**4.** 30 feet below sea level

**5.** a $50 deposit

**6.** 13° above zero

**7.** a gain of 15 points

**8.** a loss of 2.8 pounds

**9.** an increase of $3

**10.** a decrease of $12

**11.** a $7.50 withdrawal

**12.** a gain of 6 pounds

Write the opposite of each integer.

**13.** $^+13$

**14.** $^-6$

**15.** $^-9$

**16.** $^+10$

**17.** $^+8$

**18.** $^-16$

**19.** $^-12$

**20.** $^+20$

**21.** $^-7$

**22.** $^-13$

**23.** $^+23$

**24.** $^-35$

**25.** $^+67$

**26.** $^-94$

**27.** $^-101$

**28.** $^+563$

**29.** $^-819$

**30.** $^+1265$

Write the opposite of each number.

**31.** $^-\left(\frac{5}{8}\right)$

**32.** $^+3.6$

**33.** $^+1\frac{1}{2}$

**34.** $^-10.5$

**35.** $^-5\frac{1}{6}$

**36.** $^+\left(\frac{4}{5}\right)$

**37.** $^-9.16$

**38.** $^-4\frac{1}{3}$

**39.** $^+8.49$

**40.** $^+6\frac{1}{9}$

**41.** $^-\left(\frac{2}{3}\right)$

**42.** $^+\left(\frac{4}{9}\right)$

**43.** $^-16.1$

**44.** $^-23\frac{2}{3}$

**45.** $^+\left(\frac{11}{15}\right)$

---

## CALCULATOR NOTE

Negative numbers are entered in different ways on different calculators.

| ENTER | DISPLAY |
|---|---|
| (−) 3 | ⁻3 or 3⁻ |
| 3 (−) | ⁻3 or 3⁻ |
| 3 +/− | ⁻3 or 3⁻ |

Which does your calculator use?

0 is neither positive nor negative.

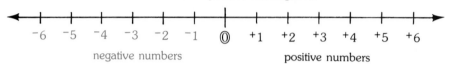

negative numbers                positive numbers

On a number line, the greater of two numbers is farther to the right.

**Example 1:** Compare. Use < or >.

a. $^+1$ and $^+5$

$^+1<^+5$, because $^+5$ is farther to the right than $^+1$.

c. 0 and $^-1$

$0>^-1$, because 0 is farther to the right than $^-1$.

d. $^-1$ and $^-5$

$^-1>^-5$, because $^-1$ is farther to the right than $^-5$.

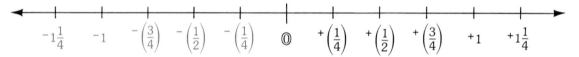

**Example 2:** Compare. Use < or >.

a. $^+\left(\frac{3}{4}\right)$ and $^+1\frac{1}{4}$    $^+\left(\frac{3}{4}\right)<^+1\frac{1}{4}$

b. 0 and $^+\left(\frac{1}{4}\right)$    $0<^+\left(\frac{1}{4}\right)$

d. $^-\left(\frac{1}{4}\right)$ and $^-1$    $^-\left(\frac{1}{4}\right)>^-1$

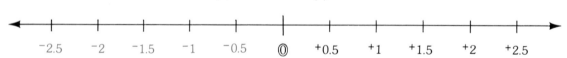

**Example 3:** Compare. Use < or >.

a. $^+0.5$ and $^+2$    $^+0.5<^+2$

c. 0 and $^-2.5$    $0>^-2.5$

d. $^-0.5$ and $^-2$    $^-0.5>^-2$

# EXERCISES

Replace each ⬤ with $<$ or $>$.

1. $^+6$ ⬤ $^+3$      2. $^+5$ ⬤ $^-7$      3. $0$ ⬤ $^+4$      4. $0$ ⬤ $^-1$

5. $^+1$ ⬤ $^+4$      6. $^-8$ ⬤ $^-6$      7. $^-3$ ⬤ $^-5$      8. $^-4$ ⬤ $0$

9. $^+1$ ⬤ $^-1$      10. $^-2$ ⬤ $^+2$      11. $^+1$ ⬤ $^-2$      12. $^-1$ ⬤ $^+2$

13. $^+8$ ⬤ $^+9$      14. $^-8$ ⬤ $^+9$      15. $^+8$ ⬤ $^-9$      16. $^-8$ ⬤ $^-9$

17. $^-3$ ⬤ $0$      18. $0$ ⬤ $^+6$      19. $0$ ⬤ $^-6$      20. $^+6$ ⬤ $^-6$

21. $^-6$ ⬤ $^+6$      22. $^-\left(\frac{1}{2}\right)$ ⬤ $0$      23. $^+\left(\frac{3}{4}\right)$ ⬤ $^+\left(\frac{1}{4}\right)$      24. $^-\left(\frac{3}{4}\right)$ ⬤ $^+\left(\frac{1}{4}\right)$

25. $^-2\frac{1}{2}$ ⬤ $0$      26. $^-1\frac{1}{2}$ ⬤ $^+\left(\frac{1}{2}\right)$      27. $0$ ⬤ $^+2\frac{1}{4}$      28. $^-\left(\frac{1}{2}\right)$ ⬤ $0$

29. $^-1$ ⬤ $^+\left(\frac{1}{4}\right)$      30. $^-\left(\frac{3}{4}\right)$ ⬤ $^+\left(\frac{3}{4}\right)$      31. $^+\left(\frac{1}{4}\right)$ ⬤ $^-2\frac{1}{4}$      32. $^+2$ ⬤ $^-2\frac{1}{2}$

33. $^+0.6$ ⬤ $^-1.5$      34. $^+6.3$ ⬤ $^+6.4$      35. $^+1$ ⬤ $^-0.9$      36. $^+0.9$ ⬤ $^-1$

37. $^-0.8$ ⬤ $0$      38. $0$ ⬤ $^+0.8$      39. $^-0.5$ ⬤ $^+0.5$      40. $^-2.5$ ⬤ $^-2$

41. $^+1$ ⬤ $^+1.5$      42. $^-2$ ⬤ $^+0.5$      43. $^+1.5$ ⬤ $^-1$      44. $0$ ⬤ $^-1.5$

45. $^+1.5$ ⬤ $0$      46. $^+2$ ⬤ $^+0.5$      47. $^-0.5$ ⬤ $^-0.4$      48. $^+0.2$ ⬤ $^+0.7$

Arrange the numbers in order from least to greatest.

49. $^+4, ^-1, ^-3, ^+3, 0, ^-4$      50. $^+3, 0, ^-4, ^-2, ^+8, ^-5$

51. $^-1, ^+1.5, ^+0.5, 0, ^-2.5, ^-2$      52. $^-\left(\frac{1}{4}\right), ^+\left(\frac{1}{2}\right), ^-1, ^-\left(\frac{3}{4}\right), ^+1\frac{1}{4}$

## SKILLS REVIEW

Simplify.

53. $\frac{1}{6}+\frac{3}{4}$      54. $\frac{2}{3}+\frac{5}{6}$      55. $\frac{7}{8}-\frac{1}{4}$

56. $\frac{5}{6}-\frac{1}{3}$      57. $\frac{3}{5}\times\frac{2}{9}$      58. $\frac{2}{3}\times\frac{3}{8}$

59. $\frac{4}{9}\times\frac{3}{16}$      60. $\frac{3}{4}\div\frac{5}{9}$      61. $\frac{4}{9}\div\frac{2}{3}$

**While playing a board game, Barb moved her marker back 3 spaces. On her next turn, she moved her marker forward 2 spaces. How many spaces did she lose on the two moves?**

Use $^-3$ to stand for the number of spaces Barb moved back. Use $^+2$ to stand for the number of spaces Barb moved forward. Use a number line as in Example 4 to show $^-3 + ^+2 = ^-1$. So Barb lost 1 space on the two moves.

**Example 1:**

Find $^+3 + ^+2$.

Step 1: Start at 0 and move 3 units in the positive direction.

Step 2: From $^+3$ move 2 units in the positive direction.

Step 3: The sum is the number at the end of the second move ($^+5$).

**Example 2:**

Find $^-3 + ^-2$.

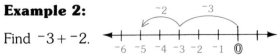

Step 1: Start at 0 and move 3 units in the negative direction.

Step 2: From $^-3$ move 2 units in the negative direction.

Step 3: The sum is the number at the end of the second move ($^-5$).

**Example 3:**

Find $^+3 + ^-2$.

Step 1: Start at 0 and move 3 units in the positive direction.

Step 2: From $^+3$ move 2 units in the negative direction.

Step 3: The sum is the number at the end of the second move ($^+1$).

**Example 4:**

Find $^-3 + ^+2$.

Step 1: Start at 0 and move 3 units in the negative direction.

Step 2: From $^-3$ move 2 units in the positive direction.

Step 3: The sum is the number at the end of the second move ($^-1$).

**Example 5:**

Find $^+3 + ^-3$.

$^+3 + ^-3 = 0$

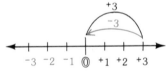

## EXERCISES

Use the number line to find the sums.

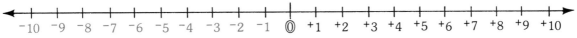

$$-10 \quad -9 \quad -8 \quad -7 \quad -6 \quad -5 \quad -4 \quad -3 \quad -2 \quad -1 \quad \textcircled{0} \quad +1 \quad +2 \quad +3 \quad +4 \quad +5 \quad +6 \quad +7 \quad +8 \quad +9 \quad +10$$

**1.** $^+6 + {}^+1$    **2.** $^-4 + {}^-2$    **3.** $^+7 + {}^-5$    **4.** $^-6 + {}^+3$    **5.** $^+5 + {}^-5$

**6.** $^+2 + {}^+3$    **7.** $^-3 + {}^-6$    **8.** $^-2 + {}^+7$    **9.** $^+3 + {}^-5$    **10.** $^+4 + {}^-4$

**11.** $^-1 + {}^-5$    **12.** $^-7 + {}^+6$    **13.** $^+2 + {}^+2$    **14.** $^+8 + {}^-4$    **15.** $^-8 + {}^+8$

**16.** $^+2 + {}^-8$    **17.** $^-1 + {}^+5$    **18.** $^+3 + {}^+7$    **19.** $^-6 + {}^-1$    **20.** $^-7 + {}^+7$

**21.** $^+5 + {}^+5$    **22.** $^-7 + {}^-3$    **23.** $^+9 + {}^-8$    **24.** $^-3 + {}^+2$    **25.** $^+1 + {}^-1$

**26.** $^+3 + {}^+5$    **27.** $^-4 + {}^-6$    **28.** $^-3 + {}^+8$    **29.** $^-1 + {}^+9$    **30.** $^+2 + {}^-2$

**31.** $^-9 + {}^+3$    **32.** $^+8 + {}^-2$    **33.** $^-6 + {}^-1$    **34.** $^+3 + {}^+3$    **35.** $^+3 + {}^-3$

---

## CALCULATOR NOTE

On page 457, you saw how negative numbers can be entered on some calculators. You can use a calculator to add positive and negative numbers.

**Example:** Add $^-8 + {}^+3$.

| ENTER | DISPLAY |
|-------|---------|
| ⊟ | $0$ |
| **8** | $8$ |
| ⊞ | $8^-$ |
| **3** | $3$ |
| ⊟ | $5^-$ |

Use a calculator to find each sum.

**1.** $^-5 + {}^+3$    **2.** $^+7 + {}^-4$    **3.** $^-6 + {}^-2$    **4.** $^+8 + {}^-8$

## 16.9 | ADDING POSITIVE AND NEGATIVE NUMBERS

You can add positive and negative numbers without using a number line.

**When the numbers have the same sign**

| | both positive | both negative |
|---|---|---|
| | $+3 + {}^+5$ | $^-3 + {}^-5$ |
| Disregard signs and add. | $3 + 5$ | $3 + 5$ |
| Use the sign of the two numbers. | $^+8$ | $^-8$ |

**When the numbers have different signs**

| | negative/positive | positive/negative |
|---|---|---|
| | $^-3 + {}^+5$ | $^+3 + {}^-5$ |
| Disregard signs and subtract. | $5 - 3$ | $5 - 3$ |
| Use the sign of the number that is farther from 0. | $^+2$ | $^-2$ |
| | ($^+5$ is farther from 0 than is $^-3$.) | ($^-5$ is farther from 0 than is $^+3$.) |

## EXERCISES

Is each sum positive, negative, or zero?

**1.** $^+9 + {}^+6$   **2.** $^-3 + {}^-5$   **3.** $^-5 + {}^+3$   **4.** $^+7 + {}^-7$

**5.** $^-6.5 + {}^+3.2$   **6.** $^-\left(\frac{1}{3}\right) + {}^+\left(\frac{1}{3}\right)$   **7.** $^+5.96 + {}^-0.18$   **8.** $^-\left(\frac{5}{6}\right) + {}^+\left(\frac{1}{6}\right)$

Add.

**9.** $^+5 + {}^+3$   **10.** $^-8 + {}^+2$   **11.** $^-9 + {}^-1$   **12.** $^-3 + {}^+10$

**13.** $^-8 + {}^+8$   **14.** $^-8 + {}^-8$   **15.** $^+4 + {}^+6$   **16.** $^+4 + {}^-5$

**17.** $^-3 + {}^-2$   **18.** $^+12 + {}^-4$   **19.** $^+15 + {}^-15$   **20.** $^+6 + {}^+6$

**21.** $^+15 + {}^+3$   **22.** $^-16 + {}^-9$   **23.** $^-28 + {}^+13$   **24.** $^+35 + {}^-10$

**25.** $^+\left(\frac{2}{5}\right) + {}^+\left(\frac{1}{5}\right)$   **26.** $^-\left(\frac{1}{7}\right) + {}^-\left(\frac{5}{7}\right)$   **27.** $^-\left(\frac{7}{9}\right) + {}^+\left(\frac{5}{9}\right)$   **28.** $^+\left(\frac{4}{5}\right) + {}^-\left(\frac{2}{5}\right)$

**29.** $^+6\frac{3}{7} + {}^-3\frac{1}{7}$   **30.** $^-4\frac{2}{9} + {}^-2\frac{5}{9}$   **31.** $^-0.9 + {}^-0.2$   **32.** $^+1.5 + {}^+2.3$

**33.** $^-1.2 + {}^+0.6$   **34.** $^+13.4 + {}^-10.1$   **35.** $^+9.63 + {}^-9.63$   **36.** $^-1.4 + {}^-1.4$

**37.** $^+\left(\frac{1}{3}\right) + {}^+\left(\frac{1}{4}\right)$   **38.** $^-\left(\frac{1}{6}\right) + {}^-\left(\frac{2}{3}\right)$   **39.** $^-\left(\frac{7}{8}\right) + {}^+\left(\frac{1}{4}\right)$   **40.** $^+\left(\frac{7}{9}\right) + {}^-\left(\frac{1}{3}\right)$

*EXTRA PRACTICE page 517, set 125*

Bookkeeping workers keep the records of businesses in an up-to-date and systematic way. They also fill in forms that show all amounts taken in and paid out during certain periods. Bookkeepers often use calculators or computers in their jobs.

Christopher Brown/Picture Group

High-school graduates who have taken business math, bookkeeping, and accounting courses meet the minimum requirements for most bookkeeping jobs.

A bookkeeping worker might have to find the sum below. On page 461, you saw how to add positive and negative numbers on a calculator. Use your calculator to find the sum of the amounts below. The numbers in parentheses are negative.

Account 08265

Monday, January 8, 1985

| | |
|---|---:|
| Received from Tri-State Metals | $2735.56 |
| Received from Urban Mills | 639.68 |
| Paid to Phoenix Steel | (1549.50) |
| Received from Allied Glass | 4719.85 |
| Paid to Boxton Trucking | (357.97) |
| Paid to Airways Delivery | (19.50) |
| Total | |

H. Armstrong Roberts

**A submarine was cruising at a depth of ⁻100 feet. It then changed its depth by ⁺75 feet. What was its depth after the change?**

**Read:**  *Given:*  was cruising at a depth of ⁻100 feet; changed its depth by ⁺75 feet

*To find:*  the depth after the change

**Plan:**  Which operation will be used? Addition.

Find the sum of ⁻100 and ⁺75.

**Compute:**
$$
\begin{array}{r}
^-100 \\
+\ ^+75 \\
\hline
^-25
\end{array}
$$

**Answer:**  The depth after the change was ⁻25 feet.

**Check:**  Will a submarine cruising at ⁻100 feet have a depth of ⁻25 feet after a change of ⁺75 feet? ✔

# EXERCISES

1. The temperature was 4° below zero (⁻4). The temperature dropped 5° (⁻5). What was the temperature after the drop?

2. Juan was on the 10th floor above ground level (⁺10). He went down 9 floors (⁻9). On what floor was he then?

3. The temperature was 5°C (⁺5). It dropped 3°C (⁻3) during the day. What was the temperature after the change?

4. A football team made a 6-yard gain (⁺6). On the next play they made a 10-yard gain (⁺10). How many yards did they make on both plays?

5. A savings account had $100 in it (⁺100). After a $35 withdrawal (⁻35), what was the balance?

6. Lisa's checking account had $15 (⁺15) in it. She wrote a check for $20 (⁻20). What was the balance? (An overdrawn amount is always a negative number.)

7. A football team made a 9-yard gain (⁺9). On the next play they lost 15 yards (⁻15). How many total yards did they make on the two plays?

8. A sky diver jumped from an airplane at 8000 feet (⁺8000). She opened her chute after falling 2500 feet (⁻2500). At what altitude did the sky diver open her chute?

9. An airplane's altitude was ⁺30,000 feet. The pilot changed the altitude by ⁻2000 feet. What was the altitude after the change?

10. The temperature at noon was ⁻1°C. By midnight, the temperature had dropped 3°C (⁻3). What was the temperature at midnight?

11. Angela was on the 38th floor above ground level (⁺38). She went down 16 floors (⁻16). On what floor was she then?

*EXTRA PRACTICE page 518, set 126*

Toni took telephone pledges during a telethon. Her seat assignment was row C, seat 3.

To find her seat, Toni went to row C, then to seat 3 in that row. This may be written (C,3).

An ordered pair of numbers can be graphed by using two perpendicular lines called **axes.** The numbers in an ordered pair are called **coordinates.**

**Example 1:** Graph a point at ($^+2$, $^+3$).

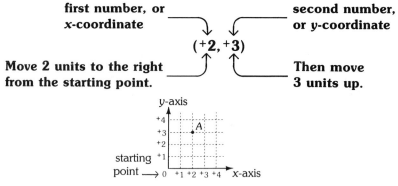

first number, or
x-coordinate

second number,
or y-coordinate

($^+2$, $^+3$)

Move 2 units to the right
from the starting point.

Then move
3 units up.

The axes can be extended to include negative numbers as well as positive numbers.

**Example 2:** Graph points at ($^+3$, $^-2$) and ($^-3$, $^+2$).

Remember, the x-coordinate is always the first number in an ordered pair.

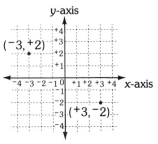

Chuck Pefley

## EXERCISES

Give the ordered pair for each point.

**1.** C          **2.** J          **3.** A          **4.** G

Use with exercises 1–8.

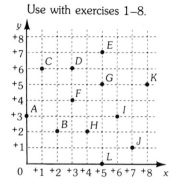

What letter names the point for each ordered pair?

**5.** (+2,+2)     **6.** (+5,0)     **7.** (+6,+3)     **8.** (+3,+6)

Use with exercises 9–20.

Give the letter for each ordered pair.

**9.** (+2,+2)       **10.** (+5,0)       **11.** (+4,−3)

**12.** (0,−2)       **13.** (−4,−5)      **14.** (−4,0)

**15.** (−2,+1)      **16.** (0,+1)       **17.** (+3,+4)

**18.** (+4,−6)      **19.** (−3,+3)      **20.** (−6,+2)

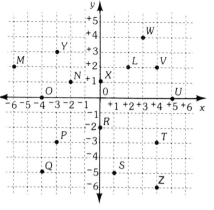

Use with exercises 21–32.

Name the coordinates of each point.

**21.** N          **22.** P          **23.** R

**24.** E          **25.** D          **26.** G

**27.** J          **28.** K          **29.** O

**30.** S          **31.** F          **32.** H

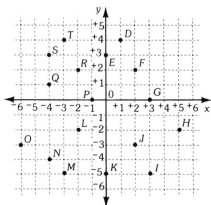

On graph paper draw and label an x-axis and a y-axis. Then graph and label the points below.

**33.** A(+2,+3)      **34.** B(+4,0)      **35.** C(+3,−1)      **36.** D(0,−2)      **37.** E(−4,−2)

**38.** F(−3,0)       **39.** G(−2,+4)     **40.** H(0,+3)       **41.** I(+1,−1)      **42.** J(0,0)

Connie and P.C. Peri

**Rob and John decided to buy a $6 record together. If Rob has no money and John has $6, they have enough to buy the record. If Rob has $1 and John has $5, they also have enough money. What other combinations are possible, not including parts of a dollar?**

Let $x$ stand for Rob's money and $y$ stand for John's money. Each combination can be listed, as in the table below, as long as $x + y = {}^+6$.

| $x$ | 0 | $^+1$ | $^+2$ | $^+3$ | $^+4$ | $^+5$ | $^+6$ |
|---|---|---|---|---|---|---|---|
| $y$ | $^+6$ | $^+5$ | $^+4$ | $^+3$ | $^+2$ | $^+1$ | 0 |

Each solution in the table above is an ordered pair and can be graphed as a point.

Ordered pairs (from the table)

$(0, {}^+6)$
$({}^+1, {}^+5)$
$({}^+2, {}^+4)$
$({}^+3, {}^+3)$
$({}^+4, {}^+2)$
$({}^+5, {}^+1)$
$({}^+6, 0)$

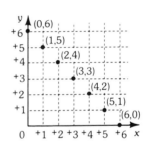

**Example:** Make a table and graph the ordered pairs for $y = x + {}^+3$.

To find the ordered pairs:
1. Choose a value for $x$, such as 0.
2. Replace $x$ with that number in the equation: $y = 0 + {}^+3$.
3. Solve the equation $y = 0 + {}^+3$.   ($y = {}^+3$)
4. Write the ordered pair, placing $x$ first and $y$ second. $(0, {}^+3)$

$y = x + {}^+3$

| $x$ | $x + {}^+3$ | Ordered pairs |
|---|---|---|
| 0 | $0 + {}^+3 = {}^+3$ | $(0, {}^+3)$ |
| $^+1$ | $^+1 + {}^+3 = {}^+4$ | $({}^+1, {}^+4)$ |
| $^+2$ | $^+2 + {}^+3 = {}^+5$ | $({}^+2, {}^+5)$ |
| $^+3$ | $^+3 + {}^+3 = {}^+6$ | $({}^+3, {}^+6)$ |

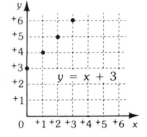

# EXERCISES

Complete the table for each equation. Then draw the graph.

**1.** $y = x + {}^+2$

| $x$ | $x + {}^+2$ | Ordered pairs |
|---|---|---|
| ${}^+1$ | ${}^+1 + {}^+2 = {}^+3$ | $({}^+1, {}^+3)$ |
| ${}^+2$ | ${}^+2 + {}^+2 = \underline{\quad}$ | $({}^+2, \underline{\quad})$ |
| ${}^+3$ | ${}^+3 + \underline{\quad} = \underline{\quad}$ | $({}^+3, \underline{\quad})$ |
| ${}^+4$ | $\underline{\quad} + \underline{\quad} = \underline{\quad}$ | $({}^+4, \underline{\quad})$ |

**2.** $y = x - {}^+1$

| $x$ | $x - {}^+1$ | Ordered pairs |
|---|---|---|
| ${}^+1$ | ${}^+1 - {}^+1 = 0$ | $({}^+1, 0)$ |
| ${}^+2$ | $\underline{\quad}$ | $({}^+2, \underline{\quad})$ |
| ${}^+3$ | $\underline{\quad}$ | $({}^+3, \underline{\quad})$ |
| ${}^+4$ | $\underline{\quad}$ | $({}^+4, \underline{\quad})$ |

**3.** $y = {}^+3x$

| $x$ | ${}^+3x$ | Ordered pairs |
|---|---|---|
| ${}^+1$ | ${}^+3 \times {}^+1 = {}^+3$ | $({}^+1, {}^+3)$ |
| ${}^+2$ | $\underline{\quad}$ | $\underline{\quad}$ |
| ${}^+3$ | $\underline{\quad}$ | $\underline{\quad}$ |
| ${}^+4$ | $\underline{\quad}$ | $\underline{\quad}$ |

**4.** $y = x + {}^+1$

| $x$ | $x + {}^+1$ | Ordered pairs |
|---|---|---|
| ${}^+1$ | ${}^+1 + {}^+1 = {}^+2$ | $({}^+1, {}^+2)$ |
| ${}^+2$ | $\underline{\quad}$ | $\underline{\quad}$ |
| ${}^+3$ | $\underline{\quad}$ | $\underline{\quad}$ |
| ${}^+4$ | $\underline{\quad}$ | $\underline{\quad}$ |

**5.** $y = x - {}^+2$

| $x$ | $x - {}^+2$ | Ordered pairs |
|---|---|---|
| ${}^+2$ | $\underline{\quad}$ | $\underline{\quad}$ |
| ${}^+3$ | $\underline{\quad}$ | $\underline{\quad}$ |
| ${}^+4$ | $\underline{\quad}$ | $\underline{\quad}$ |
| ${}^+5$ | $\underline{\quad}$ | $\underline{\quad}$ |

**6.** $y = x - {}^+3$

| $x$ | $x - {}^+3$ | Ordered pairs |
|---|---|---|
| ${}^+4$ | $\underline{\quad}$ | $\underline{\quad}$ |
| ${}^+5$ | $\underline{\quad}$ | $\underline{\quad}$ |
| ${}^+6$ | $\underline{\quad}$ | $\underline{\quad}$ |
| ${}^+7$ | $\underline{\quad}$ | $\underline{\quad}$ |

Complete each table and draw the graph.

**7.** $y = {}^+2x$

| $x$ | ${}^+1$ | ${}^+2$ | ${}^+3$ | ${}^+4$ |
|---|---|---|---|---|
| $y$ | ${}^+2$ | | | |

**8.** $y = x + {}^+4$

| $x$ | ${}^-1$ | $0$ | ${}^+1$ | ${}^+2$ | ${}^+3$ |
|---|---|---|---|---|---|
| $y$ | | | | | |

**9.** $y = x - {}^+1$

| $x$ | ${}^+2$ | ${}^+3$ | ${}^+4$ | ${}^+5$ |
|---|---|---|---|---|
| $y$ | | | | |

**10.** $y = x + {}^+3$

| $x$ | ${}^-2$ | ${}^-1$ | $0$ | ${}^+1$ | ${}^+2$ |
|---|---|---|---|---|---|
| $y$ | | | | | |

EXTRA PRACTICE page 518, set 127

# CHAPTER REVIEW

Find each value. 16.1

**1.** $8-3+6$

**2.** $2+7-5$

**3.** $3\times6\div2$

**4.** $12\div4\times3$

**5.** $6+3\times4$

**6.** $8-2\times3$

**7.** $4+8\div2$

**8.** $10-(3+5)$

**9.** $(4\times5)\div(6-2)$

Find the value of each expression if $a=9$. 16.2

**10.** $5+a$

**11.** $a-3$

**12.** $6a$

**13.** $a\div3$

**14.** $4a\div3$

**15.** $a+(a-6)$

Find the value of each expression if $n=12$ and $p=4$.

**16.** $n+p$

**17.** $n-p$

**18.** $n\times p$

**19.** $n\div p$

**20.** $n-8+p$

**21.** $n+3+p$

**22.** $n\div(6-p)$

**23.** $(n-p)\div p$

**24.** $(n\times p)\div(n-p)$

Solve each equation.

**25.** $x+4=10$

**26.** $a-9=11$

**27.** $6=m+1$ 16.3

**28.** $10=y-5$

**29.** $7+b=12$

**30.** $x-8=15$

**31.** $\frac{a}{2}=10$

**32.** $7y=21$

**33.** $\frac{n}{3}=9$ 16.4

Write the opposite of each number. 16.6

**34.** $^-13$

**35.** $^+8$

**36.** $^-\left(\frac{5}{6}\right)$

**37.** $^+\left(\frac{3}{4}\right)$

**38.** $^-0.6$

**39.** $^+4\frac{1}{2}$

Replace each ● with < or >.

**40.** $^+3$ ● $^+5$      **41.** $^-4$ ● $^+4$      **42.** $^-3$ ● $^+1$

**43.** $0$ ● $^-1$      **44.** $^-5$ ● $^-2$      **45.** $^+0.5$ ● $^+1.5$

**46.** $^+2.5$ ● $^-1$      **47.** $^+\left(\frac{1}{2}\right)$ ● $-3\frac{1}{2}$      **48.** $^-\left(\frac{1}{2}\right)$ ● $^-1$

Use a number line to find the sums.

16.8

**49.** $^+3 + {}^+1$      **50.** $^+3 + {}^-8$      **51.** $^-4 + {}^-5$

**52.** $^-5 + {}^+7$      **53.** $^+6 + {}^+1$      **54.** $^-7 + {}^+2$

Add.

16.9

**55.** $^-9 + {}^-9$      **56.** $^+3 + {}^+7$      **57.** $^+6 + {}^-6$

**58.** $0 + {}^-6$      **59.** $^+8 + 0$      **60.** $^-9 + {}^+9$

Name the coordinates of each point.

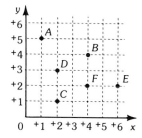

16.11

**61.** $D$      **62.** $A$      **63.** $E$

**64.** $C$      **65.** $B$      **66.** $F$

Complete the table for the equation.

16.12

**67.** $y = x + {}^+4$

| $x$ | $x + {}^+4$ | Ordered pairs |
|---|---|---|
| 0 | $0 + {}^+4 = {}^+4$ | $(0, {}^+4)$ |
| $^+1$ | —— | —— |
| $^+2$ | —— | —— |

**68.** $y = x - {}^+5$

| $x$ | $x - {}^+5$ | Ordered pairs |
|---|---|---|
| $^+6$ | $^+6 - {}^+5 = {}^+1$ | $({}^+6, {}^+1)$ |
| $^+7$ | —— | —— |
| $^+8$ | —— | —— |

Solve.

**69.** If Alan earned $8 an hour and was paid $96, how many hours did he work?

16.5

**70.** A savings account had $250 in it ($^+250$). After a $75 withdrawal ($^-75$), what was the balance?

16.10

CHAPTER REVIEW

**1.** Find the value of $15 - 2 \times 6$.

**2.** Find the value of $x + (x \div 4)$ if $x = 12$.

**3.** Find the value of $20 - (n \times y)$ if $n = 8$ and $y = 2$.

**4.** Write the opposite of $^-\left(\frac{4}{5}\right)$.

Solve each equation.

**5.** $x - 5 = 6$

**6.** $n + 4 = 9$

**7.** $3p = 15$

**8.** $\frac{x}{4} = 12$

Replace each ● with $<$ or $>$.

**9.** $^+3$ ● $^-3$

**10.** $^-2$ ● $^-6$

**11.** $^-8$ ● $0$

**12.** $^-5$ ● $^+1$

Use a number line to find the sums.

**13.** $^-4 + {}^-3$

**14.** $^+6 + {}^-4$

**15.** $^-2 + {}^+5$

**16.** $^-5 + {}^+1$

Add.

**17.** $^-8 + {}^-3$

**18.** $^+4 + {}^+8$

**19.** $^-9 + {}^+5$

**20.** $^+7 + {}^-4$

**21.** Name the coordinates of $Y$ in the graph below.

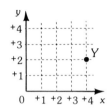

**22.** Complete the table for the equation.

$y = x - {}^+1$

| $x$ | $x - {}^+1$ | Ordered pairs |
|---|---|---|
| $^+1$ | $^+1 - {}^+1 = 0$ | $(^+1, 0)$ |
| $^+2$ | ___ | ___ |
| $^+3$ | ___ | ___ |

Solve.

**23.** A savings account had $230 in it ($^+230$). After a $105 withdrawal ($^-105$), what was the balance?

# EXTRA PRACTICE

Set 1    (Use after page 13.)

Add.

| | | | | | | | | | |
|---|---|---|---|---|---|---|---|---|---|
| **1.** | 85<br>87<br>+124 | **2.** | 64<br>78<br>+155 | **3.** | 268<br>309<br>+875 | **4.** | 190<br>385<br>+727 | **5.** | 403<br>577<br>+647 |
| **6.** | 12,580<br>+ 2,910 | **7.** | 14,403<br>+ 3,599 | **8.** | 34,033<br>+ 4,968 | **9.** | 80,775<br>+29,850 | **10.** | 76,049<br>+37,508 |

**11.** 120 + 65 + 364        **12.** 406 + 790 + 86        **13.** 689 + 420 + 36

Set 2    (Use after page 17.)

Add.

| | | | | | | | | | |
|---|---|---|---|---|---|---|---|---|---|
| **1.** | 2.018<br>+7.64 | **2.** | 8.307<br>+6.9 | **3.** | 20.9<br>+14.87 | **4.** | 59.07<br>+38.694 | **5.** | 94.163<br>+76.08 |

**6.** 12.04 + 6.76        **7.** 40.36 + 9.75        **8.** 7.08 + 29.9

**9.** 56.3 + 107.79        **10.** 90.8 + 318.76        **11.** 125.8 + 91.59

Set 3    (Use after page 19.)

Each of the following problems can be solved by using addition. Write the addition. Solve.

**1.** Donna made 4 plant terrariums. She needs to make 6 more. How many will she make in all?

**2.** Bob planted 48 bulbs for red tulips and 36 bulbs for yellow ones. How many bulbs did he plant in all?

**3.** At the beach, Nora spent $3 to rent a raft, $1.50 for parking, and $2.75 for lunch. How much did she spend in all?

**4.** Nate bought a record album for $8.95 and a magazine for $1.50. The tax was $0.63. How much did he spend in all?

Set 4   (Use after page 21.)

Subtract.

| | | | | | | | | | |
|---|---|---|---|---|---|---|---|---|---|
| **1.** | 605<br>− 283 | **2.** | 704<br>− 343 | **3.** | 430<br>− 276 | **4.** | 620<br>− 364 | **5.** | 1034<br>−  679 |
| **6.** | 6236<br>− 4337 | **7.** | 5625<br>− 1876 | **8.** | 47,316<br>− 18,698 | **9.** | 91,040<br>− 62,387 | **10.** | 24,500<br>−  6,764 |

**11.** 22,058 − 7267          **12.** 43,990 − 7999          **13.** 49,375 − 18,377

Set 5   (Use after page 23.)

Subtract.

| | | | | | | | | | |
|---|---|---|---|---|---|---|---|---|---|
| **1.** | 6.2<br>− 4.41 | **2.** | 4.8<br>− 3.32 | **3.** | 23.77<br>− 18.9 | **4.** | 40.63<br>−  4.9 | **5.** | 28<br>− 19.84 |
| **6.** | 420.5<br>−  64.807 | **7.** | 809.2<br>−  79.372 | **8.** | 717.6<br>−  88.75 | **9.** | 2000<br>−  370.82 | **10.** | 1505<br>−  619.64 |

**11.** 59.01 − 4.851          **12.** 91.59 − 36.96          **13.** 205.3 − 18.53

Set 6   (Use after page 25.)

Each of the following problems can be solved by using subtraction. Write the subtraction. Solve.

**1.** Lori has saved $165 to buy a typewriter. The typewriter costs $250. How much more money does she need?

**2.** 28,550 concert tickets went on sale in the morning. At the end of the day, 2900 tickets had not been sold. How many tickets had been sold?

**3.** Jennifer has filled 37 pages of a photo album. If it has 60 pages in all, how many more pages can she fill?

**4.** 1873 persons entered a 6-mile race. 1698 of them finished the race. How many did not finish the race?

Set 7   (Use after page 27.)

Round to the nearest thousand.

**1.** 16,580        **2.** 9672        **3.** 42,425        **4.** 80,712        **5.** 49,680

Round to the nearest whole number.

**6.** 40.45        **7.** 63.53        **8.** 125.8        **9.** 9.706        **10.** 23.08

Round to the nearest hundredth.

**11.** 3.406        **12.** 41.555        **13.** 6.083        **14.** 9.238        **15.** 63.049

Set 8   (Use after page 29.)

Estimate.

| | 1. | 2. | 3. | 4. | 5. |
|---|---|---|---|---|---|
| | 76 <br> − 43 | 83 <br> + 68 | 71 <br> + 55 | 93 <br> − 28 | 213.5 <br> − 86.3 |
| | 6. | 7. | 8. | 9. | 10. |
| | 859.3 <br> + 248.5 | 7885 <br> + 9159 | 6376 <br> − 3480 | 7354 <br> − 4287 | 6152 <br> + 2864 |

Set 9   (Use after page 31.)

Solve.

**1.** The regular price for a video recorder is $895. During a storewide sale it will sell for $599. By how much will the video recorder be marked down during the sale?

**2.** The lunch check was $4.21. How much change should Nick get from $20?

**3.** Last week Ana earned $12 mowing lawns, $10.50 raking leaves, and $14.75 delivering newspapers. How much money did she earn in all?

**4.** Carlos bought a pocket calculator for $19.95 and batteries for $2.29. The tax was $1.33. How much did he pay in all?

**475**

Set 10    (Use after page 39.)

Multiply.

| | | | | | | | | | |
|---|---|---|---|---|---|---|---|---|---|
| **1.** | 43<br>×2 | **2.** | 32<br>×3 | **3.** | 54<br>×6 | **4.** | 67<br>×5 | **5.** | 85<br>×4 |
| **6.** | 38<br>×4 | **7.** | 49<br>×6 | **8.** | 27<br>×9 | **9.** | 80<br>×7 | **10.** | 70<br>×5 |
| **11.** | 62<br>×9 | **12.** | 76<br>×5 | **13.** | 48<br>×5 | **14.** | 86<br>×3 | **15.** | 94<br>×8 |

Set 11    (Use after page 41.)

Multiply.

| | | | | | | | | | |
|---|---|---|---|---|---|---|---|---|---|
| **1.** | 42<br>×37 | **2.** | 58<br>×43 | **3.** | 28<br>×19 | **4.** | 83<br>×65 | **5.** | 74<br>×76 |
| **6.** | 143<br>×69 | **7.** | 218<br>×73 | **8.** | 356<br>×27 | **9.** | 208<br>×68 | **10.** | 905<br>×83 |
| **11.** | 412<br>×609 | **12.** | 570<br>×421 | **13.** | 607<br>×615 | **14.** | 879<br>×608 | **15.** | 415<br>×924 |

Set 12    (Use after page 43.)

Each of the following problems can be solved by using multiplication. Write the multiplication. Solve.

**1.** David bought 22 baseball tickets at $8 each. How much did he spend?

**2.** Jean planted a rectangular vegetable garden 20 feet long and 14 feet wide. What is the area of the garden?

**3.** The greenhouse has 8 rows of geranium plants. Each row has 45 plants. How many geranium plants are in the greenhouse?

**4.** A box of pencils contains 6 packages. Each package has 12 pencils. What is the total number of pencils in a box?

**476**

Set 13  (Use after page 45.)

Multiply.

**1.** $30 \times 60$  **2.** $80 \times 700$  **3.** $50 \times 80$

**4.** $900 \times 40$  **5.** $60 \times 50$  **6.** $400 \times 70$

Estimate each product.

| **7.** 38 | **8.** 43 | **9.** 287 | **10.** 465 | **11.** 908 |
|---|---|---|---|---|
| $\times 26$ | $\times 59$ | $\times 39$ | $\times 93$ | $\times 64$ |

Set 14  (Use after page 51.)

Multiply.

| **1.** 3.7 | **2.** 4.8 | **3.** 0.39 | **4.** 0.61 | **5.** 2.8 |
|---|---|---|---|---|
| $\times 25$ | $\times 82$ | $\times 2.3$ | $\times 4.3$ | $\times 6.3$ |

| **6.** 7.8 | **7.** 0.79 | **8.** 0.46 | **9.** 7.7 | **10.** 5.8 |
|---|---|---|---|---|
| $\times 3.6$ | $\times 0.09$ | $\times 0.08$ | $\times 0.52$ | $\times 0.69$ |

| **11.** 0.08 | **12.** 0.07 | **13.** 1.8 | **14.** 6.4 | **15.** 0.85 |
|---|---|---|---|---|
| $\times 5.3$ | $\times 7.2$ | $\times 0.45$ | $\times 0.59$ | $\times 0.06$ |

Set 15  (Use after page 53.)

Multiply.

**1.** $5.6 \times 100$  **2.** $0.79 \times 1000$  **3.** $65 \times 100$  **4.** $0.34 \times 100$

**5.** $43 \times 0.01$  **6.** $6.6 \times 0.1$  **7.** $0.75 \times 0.001$  **8.** $8.3 \times 0.01$

**9.** $1.25 \times 100$  **10.** $1.5 \times 0.001$  **11.** $42 \times 0.01$  **12.** $1.9 \times 0.1$

**13.** $73 \times 0.1$  **14.** $8.9 \times 100$  **15.** $6.6 \times 0.01$  **16.** $0.04 \times 1000$

Set 16 (Use after page 57.)

Solve.

1. John bought 6 gallons of paint at $12.95 per gallon. How much did he spend on paint?

2. Round-trip air fare is $239.50 per person. How much is the air fare for 4 people?

3. Postcards sell for $0.15 each. How much would a dozen postcards cost?

4. On vacation, Sally paid $189 for an airline ticket and $83 for car rental. How much did she pay in all?

Set 17 (Use after page 67.)

Divide and check.

1. $8\overline{)77}$    2. $6\overline{)59}$    3. $7\overline{)86}$    4. $9\overline{)62}$    5. $5\overline{)78}$

6. $4\overline{)136}$    7. $8\overline{)196}$    8. $6\overline{)204}$    9. $2\overline{)416}$    10. $8\overline{)840}$

11. $6\overline{)3024}$    12. $9\overline{)1236}$    13. $7\overline{)1628}$    14. $4\overline{)1992}$    15. $5\overline{)1625}$

Set 18 (Use after page 69.)

Divide and check.

1. $42\overline{)299}$    2. $68\overline{)642}$    3. $27\overline{)155}$    4. $36\overline{)288}$    5. $52\overline{)446}$

6. $60\overline{)1925}$    7. $37\overline{)2258}$    8. $53\overline{)4240}$    9. $61\overline{)2750}$    10. $24\overline{)2112}$

11. $26\overline{)5278}$    12. $48\overline{)14788}$    13. $74\overline{)37666}$    14. $41\overline{)13325}$    15. $55\overline{)30525}$

Set 19   (Use after page 71.)

Each of the following problems can be solved by using division. Write the division. Solve.

**1.** An electrician charged $72 for 3 hours labor. What was the charge per hour?

**2.** 48 girls signed up for the overnight bike trip. How many rooms are needed if 4 girls share each room?

**3.** Mrs. Kunya paid $875 for 35 square yards of carpet. How much did she pay per square yard?

**4.** Mr. Barrios earned $19,500 last year. How much did he earn per week? (52 weeks = 1 year)

Set 20   (Use after page 73.)

Divide and check.

**1.** $8\overline{)9.84}$

**2.** $7\overline{)22.75}$

**3.** $9\overline{)18.54}$

**4.** $5\overline{)10.45}$

**5.** $16\overline{)75.2}$

**6.** $29\overline{)185.6}$

**7.** $48\overline{)146.88}$

**8.** $36\overline{)183.24}$

**9.** $52\overline{)1.508}$

**10.** $81\overline{)7.533}$

**11.** $65\overline{)199.55}$

**12.** $77\overline{)37.191}$

Set 21   (Use after page 75.)

Be sure to read the problems below carefully. Make sure you answer the question asked.

**1.** Each package of party favors contains 6 favors. If 50 persons each get 1 favor, how many packages are needed?

**2.** Mari worked 21.5 hours last week. Her pay per hour is $4.50. How much did she earn?

**3.** Jeanette baked a batch of 34 corn muffins. How many pans did she use if each pan holds 12 muffins?

**4.** Ben picked 96 apples. How many apples will be left over if they are packaged in bags of 10 apples each?

*Set 22*   (Use after page 77.)

Divide and check.

**1.** $115\overline{)920}$      **2.** $209\overline{)1045}$      **3.** $186\overline{)1171.8}$      **4.** $250\overline{)2150}$

**5.** $335\overline{)3048.5}$      **6.** $518\overline{)3781.4}$      **7.** $928\overline{)2691.2}$      **8.** $721\overline{)5984.3}$

**9.** $291\overline{)436.5}$      **10.** $144\overline{)792}$      **11.** $354\overline{)2301}$      **12.** $485\overline{)1164}$

**13.** $732\overline{)768.6}$      **14.** $915\overline{)2196}$      **15.** $833\overline{)2249.1}$      **16.** $366\overline{)1281}$

*Set 23*   (Use after page 78.)

Divide.

**1.** $223 \div 1000$      **2.** $19.5 \div 10$      **3.** $1.78 \div 100$

**4.** $19.4 \div 100$      **5.** $8.03 \div 1000$      **6.** $26 \div 1000$

**7.** $4.6 \div 1000$      **8.** $1.8 \div 10$      **9.** $0.06 \div 10$

**10.** $8.5 \div 100$      **11.** $0.48 \div 1000$      **12.** $12.5 \div 100$

**13.** $3.43 \div 10$      **14.** $76 \div 1000$      **15.** $812 \div 1000$

*Set 24*   (Use after page 83.)

Divide and check.

**1.** $0.7\overline{)140}$      **2.** $0.4\overline{)300}$      **3.** $0.08\overline{)20}$      **4.** $0.06\overline{)30}$

**5.** $0.25\overline{)45}$      **6.** $0.39\overline{)468}$      **7.** $4.1\overline{)2173}$      **8.** $5.2\overline{)1924}$

**9.** $0.36\overline{)216}$      **10.** $0.84\overline{)2688}$      **11.** $0.96\overline{)4224}$      **12.** $0.71\overline{)3976}$

**13.** $1.15\overline{)1035}$      **14.** $2.12\overline{)1696}$      **15.** $0.306\overline{)153}$      **16.** $0.121\overline{)1089}$

Set 25   (Use after page 85.)

Divide and check.

**1.** 0.5)64.5          **2.** 0.9)185.4          **3.** 0.08)16.96          **4.** 0.06)18.42

**5.** 0.32)47.36        **6.** 0.28)88.2          **7.** 3.9)47.97           **8.** 4.8)196.8

**9.** 6.5)38.35         **10.** 1.09)4.687        **11.** 0.225)0.018        **12.** 1.79)0.0537


Set 26   (Use after page 87.)

Divide. Round the quotient to the nearest whole number.

**1.** 0.5)44.8          **2.** 7.6)40.3           **3.** 0.16)132.7          **4.** 0.35)26.29

Divide. Round the quotient to the nearest hundredth.

**5.** 80)164.9          **6.** 61)298.2           **7.** 0.09)0.376          **8.** 1.7)8.55


Set 27   (Use after page 89.)

Solve.

**1.** Sue paid $632 for auto insurance for one year. What was the average cost of the insurance per month (to the nearest dollar)?

**2.** A 5-lb bag of potatoes costs $0.89. What is the cost per pound to the nearest cent?

**3.** A package of meat weighs 2.58 pounds and is marked $5.55. What is the cost per pound to the nearest cent?

**4.** Each month, Luis has $21.25 deducted from his pay to buy insurance. How much is deducted in 12 months?

Find a fraction equivalent to the given fraction by multiplying the numerator and the denominator by the number in red.

**1.** $\frac{3}{8}$, 2　　　　**2.** $\frac{1}{3}$, 4　　　　**3.** $\frac{11}{12}$, 2　　　　**4.** $\frac{13}{16}$, 2

**5.** $\frac{3}{4}$, 3　　　　**6.** $\frac{2}{5}$, 8　　　　**7.** $\frac{5}{6}$, 3　　　　**8.** $\frac{7}{10}$, 3

Find a fraction equivalent to the given fraction by dividing the numerator and the denominator by the number in red.

**9.** $\frac{4}{10}$, 2　　　**10.** $\frac{8}{12}$, 4　　　**11.** $\frac{12}{16}$, 4　　　**12.** $\frac{6}{8}$, 2

**13.** $\frac{10}{15}$, 5　　**14.** $\frac{20}{24}$, 4　　**15.** $\frac{24}{32}$, 8　　**16.** $\frac{10}{16}$, 2

Set 29　(Use after page 103.)

Reduce to lowest terms.

**1.** $\frac{6}{9}$　　　**2.** $\frac{14}{16}$　　　**3.** $\frac{8}{10}$　　　**4.** $\frac{9}{12}$　　　**5.** $\frac{8}{12}$

**6.** $\frac{18}{24}$　　**7.** $\frac{4}{6}$　　　**8.** $\frac{7}{28}$　　　**9.** $\frac{30}{36}$　　**10.** $\frac{6}{12}$

Set 30　(Use after page 105.)

Change to a decimal.

**1.** $\frac{85}{100}$　　**2.** $\frac{7}{100}$　　**3.** $\frac{15}{1000}$　　**4.** $\frac{125}{1000}$　　**5.** $\frac{5}{10}$

**6.** $\frac{17}{20}$　　**7.** $\frac{9}{20}$　　**8.** $\frac{3}{8}$　　　**9.** $\frac{21}{25}$　　**10.** $\frac{4}{5}$

Change to a fraction in lowest terms.

**11.** 0.75　　　**12.** 0.6　　　**13.** 0.35　　　**14.** 0.50　　　**15.** 0.15

**16.** 0.9　　　**17.** 0.875　　**18.** 0.625　　**19.** 0.24　　**20.** 0.065

*Set 31*   (Use after page 109.)

Add. Reduce to lowest terms.

1. $\dfrac{3}{8}$
   $+\dfrac{4}{8}$

2. $\dfrac{8}{12}$
   $+\dfrac{3}{12}$

3. $\dfrac{1}{5}$
   $+\dfrac{2}{5}$

4. $\dfrac{2}{6}$
   $+\dfrac{3}{6}$

5. $\dfrac{3}{10}$
   $+\dfrac{5}{10}$

6. $\dfrac{3}{16}$
   $+\dfrac{9}{16}$

7. $\dfrac{5}{12}$
   $+\dfrac{4}{12}$

8. $\dfrac{2}{10}$
   $+\dfrac{6}{10}$

9. $\dfrac{12}{20}$
   $+\dfrac{3}{20}$

10. $\dfrac{18}{24}$
    $+\dfrac{3}{24}$

*Set 32*   (Use after page 111.)

Change each pair of fractions to equivalent fractions with a common denominator.

1. $\dfrac{2}{3}, \dfrac{3}{4}$

2. $\dfrac{1}{2}, \dfrac{5}{6}$

3. $\dfrac{3}{4}, \dfrac{13}{16}$

4. $\dfrac{3}{8}, \dfrac{1}{3}$

5. $\dfrac{4}{9}, \dfrac{2}{3}$

6. $\dfrac{9}{10}, \dfrac{4}{5}$

7. $\dfrac{15}{16}, \dfrac{7}{8}$

8. $\dfrac{5}{36}, \dfrac{1}{9}$

9. $\dfrac{5}{8}, \dfrac{5}{6}$

*Set 33*   (Use after page 113.)

Add. Reduce to lowest terms.

1. $\dfrac{7}{10}$
   $+\dfrac{1}{5}$

2. $\dfrac{1}{8}$
   $+\dfrac{3}{4}$

3. $\dfrac{7}{12}$
   $+\dfrac{1}{3}$

4. $\dfrac{3}{4}$
   $+\dfrac{1}{6}$

5. $\dfrac{5}{6}$
   $+\dfrac{1}{12}$

6. $\dfrac{3}{16}$
   $+\dfrac{1}{4}$

7. $\dfrac{3}{20}$
   $+\dfrac{7}{10}$

8. $\dfrac{2}{3}$
   $+\dfrac{2}{9}$

9. $\dfrac{7}{24}$
   $+\dfrac{1}{3}$

10. $\dfrac{1}{2}$
    $+\dfrac{3}{7}$

Set 34    (Use after page 115.)

Solve.

1. A sheet of glass $\frac{1}{8}$ inch thick covers a sheet of wood $\frac{1}{4}$ inch thick. What is the total thickness of the wood and the glass?

2. A wall decoration needs $\frac{1}{4}$ yard of white ribbon and $\frac{2}{3}$ yard of blue ribbon. How much ribbon is needed in all?

3. Gloria drove 338.1 miles on 9.8 gallons of gas. How many miles per gallon did her car get?

4. An insulated window has a $\frac{3}{8}$-inch air space between two $\frac{1}{4}$-inch panes of glass. What is the total thickness of the window?

Set 35    (Use after page 117.)

Express as a mixed number. Simplify.

1. $\frac{35}{4}$    2. $\frac{50}{8}$    3. $\frac{22}{7}$    4. $\frac{65}{16}$    5. $\frac{15}{6}$

6. $\frac{64}{12}$    7. $\frac{48}{7}$    8. $\frac{54}{10}$    9. $\frac{25}{8}$    10. $\frac{35}{6}$

Express as a fraction.

11. $2\frac{7}{8}$    12. $8\frac{3}{4}$    13. $5\frac{1}{6}$    14. $7\frac{1}{4}$    15. $6\frac{2}{3}$

16. $10\frac{11}{16}$    17. $9\frac{3}{8}$    18. $12\frac{2}{5}$    19. $15\frac{7}{10}$    20. $25\frac{3}{4}$

Set 36    (Use after page 119.)

Add. Simplify.

1. $\frac{3}{4}$
$+\frac{7}{8}$

2. $\frac{3}{5}$
$+\frac{2}{3}$

3. $\frac{7}{10}$
$+\frac{5}{8}$

4. $\frac{3}{4}$
$+\frac{3}{16}$

5. $\frac{3}{10}$
$+\frac{2}{5}$

6. $\frac{2}{3}$
$+\frac{3}{4}$

7. $\frac{13}{15}$
$+\frac{4}{5}$

8. $\frac{11}{12}$
$+\frac{1}{6}$

9. $\frac{5}{6}$
$+\frac{2}{3}$

10. $\frac{1}{5}$
$+\frac{9}{10}$

**484**

(Use after page 121.)

Add. Simplify.

1. $4\frac{3}{5}$
   $+2\frac{3}{8}$

2. $7\frac{9}{10}$
   $+5\frac{2}{3}$

3. $3\frac{5}{8}$
   $+6\frac{3}{4}$

4. $8\frac{11}{12}$
   $+4\frac{3}{5}$

5. $16\frac{2}{3}$
   $+\ 9\frac{5}{6}$

6. $2\frac{3}{4}$
   $+18\frac{7}{12}$

7. $17\frac{1}{2}$
   $+\ 6\frac{4}{9}$

8. $12\frac{1}{2}$
   $+\ 5\frac{3}{4}$

9. $20\frac{7}{8}$
   $+\ 7\frac{2}{3}$

10. $19\frac{5}{8}$
    $+14\frac{5}{6}$

11. $26\frac{3}{4}$
    $+15\frac{7}{12}$

12. $13\frac{2}{15}$
    $+16\frac{7}{10}$

Set 38   (Use after page 123.)

Solve.

1. During one week a ski resort had the following snowfalls: $6\frac{1}{2}$ inches, 2 inches, $3\frac{1}{4}$ inches, and $5\frac{3}{4}$ inches. How many inches of snow was there during that week?

2. Maurice made a fruit salad, using $1\frac{1}{4}$ lb grapes, $1\frac{1}{2}$ lb apples, $2\frac{1}{8}$ lb bananas, $1\frac{3}{4}$ lb peaches, and $\frac{3}{4}$ lb strawberries. How many pounds of fruit did he use?

3. 1 gallon contains 128 fluid ounces. How many servings of 8 fluid ounces each are in 1 gallon?

4. A recipe calls for a mixture of $1\frac{1}{2}$ cups raisins and $1\frac{3}{4}$ cups nuts. How many cups of the mixture are there?

Set 39   (Use after page 133.)

Which symbol, $>$, $<$, or $=$, should replace each ●?

1. $\frac{5}{8}$ ● $\frac{3}{4}$

2. $\frac{2}{3}$ ● $\frac{7}{10}$

3. $\frac{3}{4}$ ● $\frac{2}{3}$

4. $\frac{1}{2}$ ● $\frac{3}{5}$

5. $2\frac{1}{3}$ ● $2\frac{1}{4}$

6. $5\frac{8}{10}$ ● $5\frac{4}{5}$

7. $6\frac{2}{8}$ ● $8\frac{1}{4}$

8. $4\frac{12}{24}$ ● $4\frac{8}{16}$

9. $7\frac{1}{8}$ ● $5\frac{15}{16}$

10. $6\frac{2}{3}$ ● $6\frac{8}{12}$

11. $9\frac{5}{8}$ ● $9\frac{7}{12}$

12. $3\frac{3}{4}$ ● $3\frac{4}{5}$

*Set 40*   (Use after page 137.)

Subtract. Reduce to lowest terms.

**1.**  $\dfrac{7}{8}$
$-\dfrac{3}{8}$

**2.**  $\dfrac{8}{9}$
$-\dfrac{2}{9}$

**3.**  $\dfrac{7}{12}$
$-\dfrac{1}{12}$

**4.**  $\dfrac{9}{10}$
$-\dfrac{3}{10}$

**5.**  $\dfrac{13}{16}$
$-\dfrac{7}{16}$

**6.**  $\dfrac{17}{20}$
$-\dfrac{7}{20}$

**7.**  $\dfrac{13}{18}$
$-\dfrac{7}{18}$

**8.**  $\dfrac{11}{16}$
$-\dfrac{5}{16}$

**9.**  $\dfrac{17}{25}$
$-\dfrac{7}{25}$

**10.**  $\dfrac{15}{16}$
$-\dfrac{7}{16}$

*Set 41*   (Use after page 139.)

Subtract. Reduce to lowest terms.

**1.**  $\dfrac{7}{8}$
$-\dfrac{1}{3}$

**2.**  $\dfrac{3}{4}$
$-\dfrac{3}{8}$

**3.**  $\dfrac{5}{6}$
$-\dfrac{1}{4}$

**4.**  $\dfrac{13}{16}$
$-\dfrac{5}{8}$

**5.**  $\dfrac{4}{5}$
$-\dfrac{1}{4}$

**6.**  $\dfrac{9}{10}$
$-\dfrac{2}{5}$

**7.**  $\dfrac{2}{3}$
$-\dfrac{1}{4}$

**8.**  $\dfrac{15}{16}$
$-\dfrac{3}{8}$

**9.**  $\dfrac{3}{5}$
$-\dfrac{1}{3}$

**10.**  $\dfrac{7}{12}$
$-\dfrac{1}{4}$

*Set 42*   (Use after page 141.)

Solve.

**1.** A recipe calls for $\frac{1}{2}$ cup of chopped celery and $\frac{1}{4}$ cup of diced green pepper. How much more celery than green pepper does the recipe call for?

**2.** If $\frac{1}{4}$ gallon of apple juice is mixed with $\frac{3}{8}$ gallon of cranberry juice, how much juice is in the mixture?

**3.** The fuel gauge on a car showed that there was $\frac{3}{4}$ tank of gasoline in the morning. At the end of the day, the gauge showed that there was $\frac{1}{4}$ tank. If no gasoline was added during the day, how much gasoline did the car use during the day?

**4.** It takes $\frac{3}{4}$ hour to dry a load of towels in the clothes dryer. It takes $\frac{1}{2}$ hour to dry a load of shirts. How much longer does the load of towels take to dry?

**486**

Set 43   (Use after page 143.)

Subtract. Simplify each answer.

**1.**  $15\frac{2}{3}$
$-\ 8\frac{3}{8}$

**2.**  $12\frac{7}{10}$
$-\ 7\frac{1}{2}$

**3.**  $11\frac{1}{3}$
$-\ 4\frac{3}{4}$

**4.**  $14\frac{1}{2}$
$-\ 6\frac{5}{8}$

**5.**  $18$
$-\ 9\frac{3}{5}$

**6.**  $21$
$-\ 7\frac{5}{12}$

**7.**  $9\frac{3}{10}$
$-2\frac{4}{5}$

**8.**  $13\frac{5}{12}$
$-\ 4\frac{7}{8}$

**9.**  $20$
$-11\frac{7}{10}$

**10.**  $16$
$-\ 5\frac{13}{16}$

Set 44   (Use after page 147.)

Solve.

**1.** A recipe calls for $1\frac{1}{4}$ cups of bread crumbs and $1\frac{3}{4}$ cups of flour. How many cups of the mixture are there?

**2.** If the top of a door is $1\frac{1}{2}$ feet from the ceiling and the ceiling is 8 feet high, how high is the top of the door from the floor?

**3.** Last week Bill worked $14\frac{3}{4}$ hours. This week he worked 18 hours. How many more hours did he work this week than last week?

**4.** The price of a stock went from $\$18\frac{1}{8}$ to $\$15\frac{3}{4}$. By how much did it go down?

Set 45   (Use after page 149.)

Complete.

**1.** 50 ft = ___ yd

**2.** 125 in. = ___ ft

**3.** 20 ft = ___ yd

**4.** 2 mi = ___ ft

**5.** 90 in. = ___ yd

**6.** 7 yd = ___ ft

**7.** 136 oz = ___ lb

**8.** 5500 lb = ___ tons

**9.** 6 lb = ___ oz

**10.** 9 c = ___ pt

**11.** 33 qt = ___ gal

**12.** 7 pt = ___ qt

**13.** 10 qt = ___ pt

**14.** 15 pt = ___ c

**15.** 5 gal = ___ qt

Set 46    (Use after page 161.)

Multiply.

1. $\frac{1}{5} \times \frac{3}{4}$      2. $\frac{2}{3} \times \frac{5}{7}$      3. $\frac{1}{6} \times \frac{5}{8}$      4. $\frac{2}{3} \times \frac{4}{9}$      5. $\frac{4}{5} \times \frac{1}{3}$

6. $\frac{3}{8} \times \frac{3}{4}$      7. $\frac{1}{2} \times \frac{3}{7}$      8. $\frac{2}{3} \times \frac{4}{15}$      9. $\frac{5}{6} \times \frac{1}{9}$      10. $\frac{3}{7} \times \frac{2}{5}$

11. $\frac{1}{4} \times \frac{3}{5}$      12. $\frac{3}{4} \times \frac{7}{8}$      13. $\frac{4}{5} \times \frac{2}{5}$      14. $\frac{6}{7} \times \frac{1}{5}$      15. $\frac{4}{7} \times \frac{3}{5}$

16. $\frac{2}{5} \times \frac{3}{11}$      17. $\frac{5}{7} \times \frac{4}{9}$      18. $\frac{3}{8} \times \frac{5}{11}$      19. $\frac{4}{15} \times \frac{2}{3}$      20. $\frac{9}{20} \times \frac{1}{2}$

Set 47    (Use after page 163.)

Multiply. Reduce to lowest terms.

1. $\frac{3}{4} \times \frac{2}{9}$      2. $\frac{2}{5} \times \frac{15}{16}$      3. $\frac{3}{4} \times \frac{5}{6}$      4. $\frac{1}{6} \times \frac{3}{4}$      5. $\frac{2}{5} \times \frac{5}{12}$

6. $\frac{3}{5} \times \frac{5}{6}$      7. $\frac{2}{3} \times \frac{9}{10}$      8. $\frac{6}{7} \times \frac{14}{15}$      9. $\frac{7}{8} \times \frac{4}{5}$      10. $\frac{4}{5} \times \frac{5}{6}$

11. $\frac{3}{8} \times \frac{4}{9}$      12. $\frac{5}{8} \times \frac{4}{15}$      13. $\frac{1}{3} \times \frac{9}{10}$      14. $\frac{6}{7} \times \frac{3}{8}$      15. $\frac{4}{9} \times \frac{3}{16}$

16. $\frac{9}{10} \times \frac{5}{18}$      17. $\frac{1}{6} \times \frac{8}{9}$      18. $\frac{2}{5} \times \frac{15}{32}$      19. $\frac{3}{16} \times \frac{8}{9}$      20. $\frac{7}{32} \times \frac{2}{7}$

Set 48    (Use after page 165.)

Solve.

1. A piece of wood trim was $\frac{1}{2}$ yard long. Jeri used $\frac{1}{3}$ of it. How long was the piece of trim she used?

2. A drinking glass holds $\frac{3}{4}$ cup of water. It is $\frac{2}{3}$ full. How much water is in it?

3. A recipe calls for $\frac{3}{4}$ teaspoon of cinnamon. How much should you use to make $\frac{2}{3}$ of the recipe amount?

4. Chris jogged for $\frac{3}{4}$ hour. Alan jogged for $\frac{1}{3}$ as long. How long did Alan jog?

Divide. Simplify the answer.

1. $\frac{3}{4} \div \frac{5}{8}$     2. $\frac{3}{8} \div \frac{9}{10}$     3. $\frac{4}{5} \div \frac{3}{10}$     4. $\frac{3}{10} \div \frac{1}{2}$     5. $\frac{3}{5} \div \frac{3}{10}$

6. $\frac{1}{2} \div \frac{2}{3}$     7. $\frac{6}{7} \div \frac{3}{4}$     8. $\frac{5}{6} \div \frac{3}{5}$     9. $\frac{2}{3} \div \frac{5}{6}$     10. $\frac{3}{4} \div \frac{3}{8}$

11. $\frac{1}{2} \div \frac{3}{10}$     12. $\frac{7}{10} \div \frac{2}{5}$     13. $\frac{3}{5} \div \frac{3}{4}$     14. $\frac{9}{10} \div \frac{2}{3}$     15. $\frac{4}{5} \div \frac{3}{7}$

16. $\frac{4}{9} \div \frac{5}{6}$     17. $\frac{7}{10} \div \frac{7}{12}$     18. $\frac{5}{12} \div \frac{5}{8}$     19. $\frac{4}{5} \div \frac{8}{15}$     20. $\frac{8}{15} \div \frac{4}{5}$

Multiply. Simplify each answer.

1. $1\frac{2}{3} \times 1\frac{4}{5}$     2. $2\frac{2}{5} \times 1\frac{3}{4}$     3. $2\frac{3}{8} \times 1\frac{1}{3}$     4. $3\frac{3}{4} \times 2\frac{4}{5}$     5. $6\frac{1}{2} \times 2\frac{2}{3}$

6. $1\frac{1}{4} \times 1\frac{2}{3}$     7. $3\frac{1}{2} \times 4\frac{2}{5}$     8. $6\frac{2}{9} \times 1\frac{7}{8}$     9. $4\frac{1}{2} \times 3\frac{7}{12}$     10. $6\frac{1}{4} \times 2\frac{3}{5}$

11. $1\frac{1}{2} \times 2\frac{1}{6}$     12. $5\frac{3}{8} \times 2\frac{2}{3}$     13. $3\frac{1}{8} \times 4\frac{1}{5}$     14. $3\frac{3}{4} \times 2\frac{5}{6}$     15. $8\frac{1}{3} \times 2\frac{1}{4}$

16. $6\frac{7}{8} \times 2\frac{1}{5}$     17. $1\frac{1}{7} \times 2\frac{1}{4}$     18. $3\frac{5}{6} \times 2\frac{2}{6}$     19. $3\frac{3}{4} \times 6\frac{2}{5}$     20. $4\frac{2}{3} \times 8\frac{1}{10}$

Divide. Simplify each answer.

1. $2\frac{1}{2} \div 3\frac{3}{4}$     2. $1\frac{1}{2} \div 1\frac{1}{4}$     3. $2\frac{2}{3} \div 1\frac{1}{3}$     4. $5\frac{1}{3} \div 1\frac{1}{10}$     5. $3\frac{1}{2} \div 1\frac{1}{8}$

6. $1\frac{2}{5} \div \frac{7}{10}$     7. $3\frac{1}{3} \div 1\frac{5}{9}$     8. $3\frac{3}{4} \div 2\frac{1}{12}$     9. $5\frac{2}{5} \div \frac{4}{15}$     10. $3\frac{3}{5} \div 2\frac{7}{10}$

11. $6\frac{1}{2} \div 1\frac{1}{4}$     12. $2\frac{4}{5} \div 1\frac{2}{5}$     13. $1\frac{3}{5} \div 3\frac{1}{5}$     14. $3\frac{1}{5} \div 1\frac{1}{5}$     15. $1\frac{1}{3} \div 2\frac{2}{9}$

16. $3\frac{3}{5} \div 1\frac{3}{7}$     17. $3\frac{1}{6} \div 1\frac{5}{8}$     18. $5\frac{1}{4} \div 1\frac{7}{8}$     19. $5\frac{2}{3} \div 1\frac{7}{9}$     20. $3\frac{1}{7} \div 1\frac{5}{7}$

Solve.

**1.** A serving is $\frac{3}{4}$ cup. How many servings are there in 6 cups?

**2.** How many $2\frac{1}{2}$-inch lengths can you cut from a wooden rod 36 inches long?

**3.** One seat cover for a chair requires $1\frac{1}{4}$ yards of material. How much material would you need for 6 chairs?

**4.** Darlene worked $5\frac{1}{2}$ hours per day. How many hours did she work in 5 days?

Set 53    (Use after page 181.)

Complete.

**1.** 12 pt = ___ gal

**2.** 2 yd = ___ in.

**3.** 75 in. = ___ yd

**4.** 8 gal = ___ c

**5.** 3 qt = ___ c

**6.** $\frac{1}{4}$ ton = ___ oz

**7.** 80,000 oz = ___ tons

**8.** 15 c = ___ qt

**9.** 16 c = ___ gal

**10.** 15 in. = ___ ft

**11.** $4\frac{1}{6}$ yd = ___ ft

**12.** 8 in. = ___ yd

**13.** $\frac{1}{9}$ yd = ___ in.

**14.** 18 c = ___ gal

**15.** 84 in. = ___ yd

Set 54    (Use after page 191.)

Use a protractor to measure each angle named below.

**1.** $\angle MNP$

**2.** $\angle PNR$

**3.** $\angle QNR$

**4.** $\angle QNO$

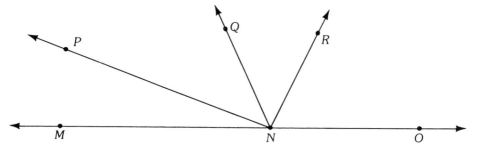

Using a protractor, draw each angle. Then label the angle with three letters and its measure.

**5.** $m\angle STU = 85°$        **6.** $m\angle MNP = 20°$        **7.** $m\angle STR = 105°$        **8.** $m\angle UVW = 145°$

Using a protractor, measure each angle. Then classify the angle as acute, right, obtuse, or straight.

**1.**      **2.**      **3.**

**4.** 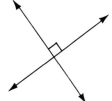     **5.**      **6.**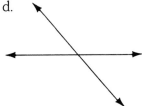

Set 56   (Use after page 195.)

**1.** Which of the following are perpendicular?

a. 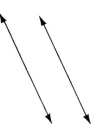     b. 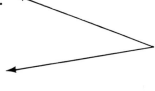     c.      d.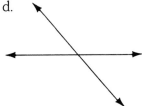

**2.** Which of the following are parallel?

a.      b. 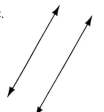     c. 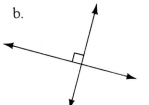     d.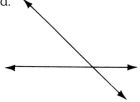

Classify each polygon and tell if it is regular or not. Use a ruler when necessary.

**1.** 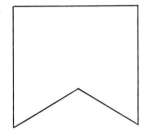   **2.** 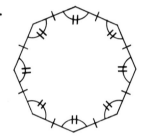   **3.**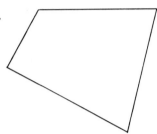

**4.** 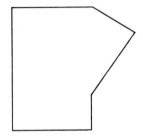   **5.** 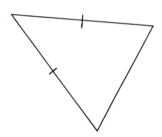   **6.**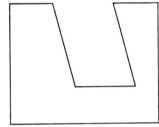

Set 58   (Use after page 199.)

The measures of 2 angles of a triangle are given. Find the measure of the third angle.

**1.** 53°, 28°          **2.** 80°, 75°          **3.** 105°, 25°

Measure the lengths of the sides of each triangle. Then classify the triangle according to the lengths of its sides. Measure the angles in each triangle. Then classify the triangle according to its angle measures.

**4.** 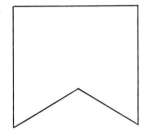   **5.**    **6.**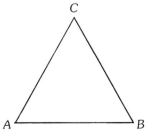

Set 59   (Use after page 205.)

Use the figure at the right to match the following. You may use an answer more than once.

**1.** $\overline{RT}$          a.   diameter

**2.** $\overline{ST}$          b.   center

**3.** $\overset{\frown}{VT}$          c.   radius

**4.** $\overline{WT}$          d.   arc

**5.** $\overset{\frown}{RW}$          e.   chord

**6.** $\overline{SV}$

**7.** S

**8.** $\overset{\frown}{RV}$

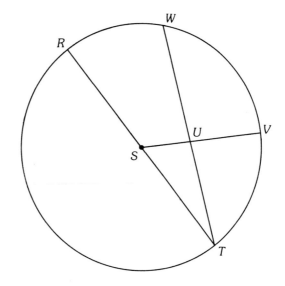

Set 60   (Use after page 207.)

Copy and complete. $\triangle QRS \cong \triangle TUV$

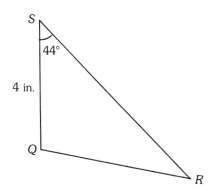

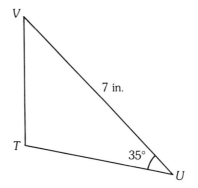

**1.** $m\angle V = $ ___.

**2.** $m\angle R = $ ___.

**3.** The length of $\overline{SR}$ is ___.

**4.** The length of $\overline{VT}$ is ___.

Is the dashed line a line of symmetry? Answer *yes* or *no*.

**1.**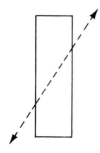

**2.**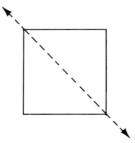

How many lines of symmetry, if any, do the following figures have?

**3.**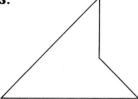

**4.**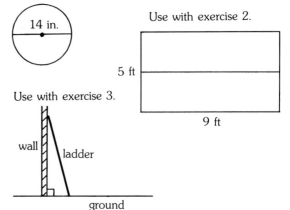

Set 62   (Use after page 211.)

Solve.

**1.** The diameter of a pizza pan is 14 inches. What is the radius?

**2.** How much tape do you need for a tennis table if you need to put a strip of tape on each outside edge and a strip down the center, as shown?

**3.** The ladder makes an angle of 15° with the wall. What angle does it make with the ground?

Use with exercise 1.

14 in.

Use with exercise 2.

5 ft

9 ft

Use with exercise 3.

wall

ladder

ground

Write each ratio as a fraction. Simplify each answer.

**1.** squares to all figures

**2.** all figures to triangles

**3.** hexagons to circles

**4.** circles to triangles

**5.** squares to triangles

Draw a picture to represent each ratio.

**6.** The ratio of squares to circles is 4 to 3.

**7.** The ratio of triangles to squares is 3 to 1.

Set 64 (Use after page 229.)

Determine if each proportion is true by simplifying the ratios.

**1.** $\frac{3}{5} = \frac{4}{8}$  **2.** $\frac{8}{4} = \frac{6}{3}$  **3.** $\frac{4}{6} = \frac{6}{9}$  **4.** $\frac{7}{5} = \frac{14}{8}$  **5.** $\frac{5}{9} = \frac{25}{45}$

**6.** $\frac{10}{4} = \frac{15}{5}$  **7.** $\frac{8}{10} = \frac{20}{24}$  **8.** $\frac{14}{18} = \frac{35}{45}$  **9.** $\frac{20}{14} = \frac{60}{42}$  **10.** $\frac{21}{9} = \frac{28}{14}$

Determine if each proportion is true by using cross products.

**11.** $\frac{2}{3} = \frac{4}{9}$  **12.** $\frac{3}{7} = \frac{6}{14}$  **13.** $\frac{6}{4} = \frac{15}{10}$  **14.** $\frac{12}{18} = \frac{6}{8}$  **15.** $\frac{28}{36} = \frac{14}{20}$

**16.** $\frac{3}{8} = \frac{6}{14}$  **17.** $\frac{5}{3} = \frac{10}{6}$  **18.** $\frac{7}{5} = \frac{21}{15}$  **19.** $\frac{3}{4} = \frac{12}{20}$  **20.** $\frac{3}{2} = \frac{12}{8}$

Set 65 (Use after page 231.)

Solve each proportion by copying and completing the table.

**1.** $\frac{4}{5}=\frac{?}{30}$

| 4 | | | | | |
|---|---|---|---|---|---|
| 5 | | | | | |

**2.** $\frac{12}{?}=\frac{3}{7}$

| 3 | | | |
|---|---|---|---|
| 7 | | | |

**3.** $\frac{6}{5}=\frac{36}{?}$

| 6 | | | | | |
|---|---|---|---|---|---|
| 5 | | | | | |

**4.** $\frac{?}{15}=\frac{8}{3}$

| 8 | | | |
|---|---|---|---|
| 3 | | | |

Set 66  (Use after page 235.)

Solve these proportions by using equivalent fractions.

**1.** $\frac{3}{2}=\frac{12}{?}$   **2.** $\frac{4}{3}=\frac{?}{12}$   **3.** $\frac{12}{10}=\frac{6}{?}$   **4.** $\frac{4}{?}=\frac{8}{4}$   **5.** $\frac{25}{15}=\frac{15}{?}$

**6.** $\frac{27}{6}=\frac{18}{?}$   **7.** $\frac{15}{6}=\frac{?}{8}$   **8.** $\frac{2}{3}=\frac{8}{?}$   **9.** $\frac{?}{15}=\frac{4}{3}$   **10.** $\frac{7}{?}=\frac{14}{16}$

**11.** $\frac{?}{3}=\frac{4}{12}$   **12.** $\frac{2}{3}=\frac{?}{36}$   **13.** $\frac{5}{3}=\frac{60}{?}$   **14.** $\frac{12}{10}=\frac{18}{?}$   **15.** $\frac{3}{?}=\frac{12}{8}$

**16.** $\frac{7}{6}=\frac{?}{30}$   **17.** $\frac{27}{?}=\frac{18}{16}$   **18.** $\frac{5}{6}=\frac{30}{?}$   **19.** $\frac{14}{8}=\frac{?}{4}$   **20.** $\frac{48}{18}=\frac{16}{?}$

Set 67  (Use after page 237.)

Solve each proportion by using cross products.

**1.** $\frac{12}{?}=\frac{3}{10}$   **2.** $\frac{5}{2}=\frac{?}{10}$   **3.** $\frac{?}{15}=\frac{2}{3}$   **4.** $\frac{15}{?}=\frac{5}{10}$   **5.** $\frac{4}{3}=\frac{24}{?}$

**6.** $\frac{10}{?}=\frac{8}{4}$   **7.** $\frac{30}{35}=\frac{6}{?}$   **8.** $\frac{10}{3}=\frac{?}{15}$   **9.** $\frac{?}{9}=\frac{14}{6}$   **10.** $\frac{42}{?}=\frac{7}{3}$

**11.** $\frac{11}{4}=\frac{33}{?}$   **12.** $\frac{16}{5}=\frac{?}{15}$   **13.** $\frac{17}{5}=\frac{?}{20}$   **14.** $\frac{15}{?}=\frac{30}{22}$   **15.** $\frac{?}{45}=\frac{28}{18}$

**16.** $\frac{?}{26}=\frac{20}{65}$   **17.** $\frac{18}{?}=\frac{63}{77}$   **18.** $\frac{28}{21}=\frac{?}{15}$   **19.** $\frac{45}{?}=\frac{30}{16}$   **20.** $\frac{9}{18}=\frac{?}{50}$

Solve by using a proportion.

**1.** A car can be driven 400 miles on 20 gallons of gas. How far can it be driven on 35 gallons of gas?

**2.** A customer bought 10 boxes of tissue that were on sale at 5 boxes for $3. How much did the 10 boxes cost?

**3.** Two pairs of slacks cost $45. At that rate, what would three pairs cost?

**4.** A family drove 100 miles in 2 hours. At that rate, how long would it take to drive 240 miles?

Set 69   (Use after page 241.)

Copy each figure and draw the indicated enlargement or reduction.

**1.**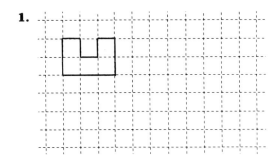

2:1 enlargement

**2.**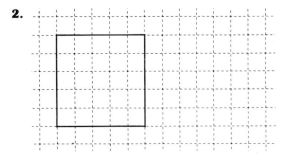

2:5 reduction

**3.**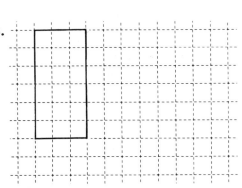

4:3 enlargement

**4.**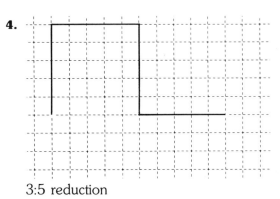

3:5 reduction

Set 70    (Use after page 243.)

Find the missing length for each pair of similar figures.

**1.**

3

15

1

x

**2.**

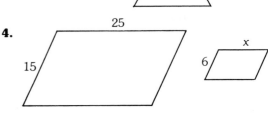

2   x

5   5

**3.**

40

24

60

x

**4.**

25

15

x

6

Set 71    (Use after page 245.)

Use the scale $\frac{1}{4}$ inch to 1 foot to answer the following:

**1.** The real length is 24 feet. What is the scale-drawing length?

**2.** The real length is 32 feet. What is the scale-drawing length?

**3.** The real length is 93 feet. What is the scale-drawing length?

**4.** The scale-drawing length is 2 inches. What is the real length?

**5.** The scale-drawing length is $3\frac{1}{2}$ inches. What is the real length?

**6.** The scale-drawing length is $6\frac{3}{4}$ inches. What is the real length?

Set 72    (Use after page 247.)

Solve.

**1.** A map was drawn to the scale of 1 inch to 10 miles. If two towns are shown $3\frac{1}{4}$ inches apart on the map, what is the distance between them?

**2.** A photograph 8 inches wide and 10 inches high is reduced so that the reduction is 3 inches wide. How high is the reduction?

**3.** A scale model of a car is $1\frac{1}{2}$ inches long. If the scale is $\frac{1}{8}$ inch to 1 foot, what is the actual length of the car?

**4.** A photograph is enlarged by a 5 to 1 ratio. If the photo is 3 inches high, how high is the enlargement?

**498**

Change each percent to a fraction in lowest terms.

**1.** 80%          **2.** 5%          **3.** 18%          **4.** 45%          **5.** 60%

**6.** 8%          **7.** 85%          **8.** 56%          **9.** 29%          **10.** 16%

Change each percent to a decimal.

**11.** 14%          **12.** 27%          **13.** 82%          **14.** 79%          **15.** 54%

**16.** 72.3%          **17.** 12.5%          **18.** $16\frac{1}{2}$%          **19.** $\frac{3}{5}$%          **20.** $4\frac{1}{5}$%

Change to a percent.

**1.** 0.43          **2.** 0.34          **3.** 0.26          **4.** 0.9          **5.** 0.4

**6.** 3.62          **7.** 5.9          **8.** 1.02          **9.** 3.1          **10.** 2.9

**11.** $\frac{7}{100}$          **12.** $\frac{3}{50}$          **13.** $\frac{4}{25}$          **14.** $\frac{9}{20}$          **15.** $\frac{4}{5}$

**16.** $\frac{3}{10}$          **17.** $1\frac{1}{5}$          **18.** $2\frac{3}{4}$          **19.** $1\frac{3}{10}$          **20.** $2\frac{9}{10}$

Find each number.

**1.** 80% of 25      **2.** 30% of 90      **3.** 5% of 200      **4.** 50% of 28      **5.** 75% of 200

**6.** 24% of 600      **7.** 40% of 20      **8.** 90% of 200      **9.** 8% of 400      **10.** 3% of 1000

Solve.

**11.** What number is 40% of 60?              **12.** What number is 2% of 300?

**13.** What number is 75% of 400?              **14.** What number is 60% of 700?

**1.** 3 is what percent of 12?

**2.** 63 is what percent of 70?

**3.** 8 is what percent of 25?

**4.** 7 is what percent of 20?

**5.** 13 is what percent of 50?

**6.** 84 is what percent of 200?

**7.** 0.06 is what percent of 10?

**8.** 129.15 is what percent of 630?

Solve.

**1.** Tom received $50 for his birthday. He plans to save 25% of this amount. How much money does he plan to save?

**2.** Judy bought a stereo for $400. She is making a 30% down payment. How much money is the down payment?

**3.** Connie received 453 votes of the 600 votes cast. What percent of the votes did she receive?

**4.** Carl spent $800 while on vacation. $120 of this amount was spent on gas. What percent of the money did Carl spend on gas?

Solve.

**1.** 3 is 20% of what number?

**2.** 16 is 32% of what number?

**3.** 24 is 30% of what number?

**4.** 18 is 25% of what number?

**5.** 4 is 0.8% of what number?

**6.** 80 is 16% of what number?

**7.** 43 is 8% of what number?

**8.** 42 is $10\frac{1}{2}$% of what number?

Set 79   (Use after page 269.)

Solve.

1. Insurance paid all but 20% of a hospital bill. If Mr. Andropolis had to pay $600, what was his hospital bill?

2. Kathy bought a coat at a cost that was 80% of the regular price. If she paid $90 for the coat, what was the regular price?

3. Mark must pay 2.5% of his income in state taxes. If he paid $412.50, what was his income for the year?

4. Juana has repaid $500 of her loan. If this is 40% of the loan, how much was the loan?

Set 80   (Use after page 270.)

Given the price and the percent of the sales tax, find the total cost.

1. $80, 5%          2. $15, 6%          3. $23, 4%          4. $34, 6%

5. $120, $5\frac{1}{2}$%          6. $296, 3%          7. $150, 6.5%          8. $347, 5%

9. $24.90, 6%     10. $126.30, 4%     11. $536.40, 5.5%     12. $274.50, $4\frac{1}{2}$%

Set 81   (Use after page 273.)

Find the total cost.

| | Original price | Percent of discount | Percent of sales tax |
|---|---|---|---|
| 1. | $420 | 15% | 5% |
| 2. | $130 | 20% | 6% |
| 3. | $53 | 10% | 4% |
| 4. | $80 | 25% | 5% |
| 5. | $50.40 | 20% | 6% |
| 6. | $140.75 | 20% | 5% |

Copy and complete.

| | Sales | Rate of commission | Amount of commission |
|---|---|---|---|
| **1.** | $630 | 20% | ____ |
| **2.** | $460 | 8% | ____ |
| **3.** | $1290 | 12% | ____ |
| **4.** | $3000 | ____ | $600 |
| **5.** | $1200 | ____ | $300 |
| **6.** | ____ | 20% | $850 |
| **7.** | ____ | 12% | $600 |

Solve.

**1.** A baseball player has a 0.427 batting average. What percent is that?

**2.** A quarterback completed 5 out of 8 passes in a game. What percent of the passes were completed?

**3.** A basketball player made 6 out of 12 free throws. What percent is that?

**4.** A bowling team won 45 games out of 60 played. What percent is that?

For each segment below, find the length in millimeters. Then rewrite the same length, using centimeters.

**1.** ————

**2.** ————————————————————

**3.** ————————————

**4.** ——————————

Draw line segments with the following lengths:

**5.** 81 mm          **6.** 23 mm          **7.** 2.6 cm          **8.** 5.4 cm

Set 85 (Use after page 285.)

Complete each statement with *mm*, *cm*, *m*, or *km* so that the statement is reasonable.

1. The length of a kitchen table is about 1.5 ___.

2. The width of a postage stamp is about 23 ___.

3. The thickness of a cheese slice is about 2 ___.

4. The width of a pencil is about 0.8 ___.

5. The distance of a car trip is about 200 ___.

6. The width of a sheet of notebook paper is about 21.5 ___.

Set 86 (Use after page 287.)

Copy and complete.

1. 1 m = ___ mm

2. 42 mm = ___ cm

3. 382 mm = ___ m

4. 84 km = ___ m

5. 8 m = ___ km

6. 15 km = ___ m

7. 9 mm = ___ cm

8. 24 m = ___ cm

9. 0.3 km = ___ m

10. 2.3 cm = ___ mm

11. 8200 mm = ___ m

12. 15 cm = ___ m

Set 87 (Use after page 291.)

Copy and complete.

1. 2 g = ___ mg

2. 8.3 kg = ___ g

3. 246 mg = ___ g

4. 4000 mg = ___ g

5. 25 g = ___ kg

6. 52 kg = ___ g

7. 4.2 g = ___ mg

8. 3.9 mg = ___ g

9. 43 280 mg = ___ g

10. 0.4 kg = ___ g

11. 1.5 kg = ___ g

12. 0.007 kg = ___ g

Set 88   (Use after page 293.)

Copy and complete.

**1.** 700 mL = ___ L

**2.** 23.6 L = ___ mL

**3.** 3 L = ___ mL

**4.** 15 L = ___ mL

**5.** 23 000 mL = ___ L

**6.** 8.6 mL = ___ L

**7.** 2.6 L = ___ mL

**8.** 14.5 L = ___ mL

**9.** 0.03 L = ___ mL

**10.** 0.3 mL = ___ L

**11.** 3400 mL = ___ L

**12.** 0.74 L = ___ mL

Set 89   (Use after page 295.)

Solve.

**1.** How many 250-mL servings can be poured from a full 4-L container?

**2.** One can weighs 238 grams. How many kilograms would 12 of the cans weigh?

**3.** Last year, Nancy was 141 cm tall. She has grown 2.5 cm. How tall is she now?

**4.** Sara and Karl want to hike a distance of 5 km. They stopped to rest after 3000 m. How much farther do they have to go?

Set 90   (Use after page 297.)

What is the most reasonable temperature for each of the following?

**1.** boiling water
   0°C   100°C   212°C

**2.** an ice cube
   50°F   32°F   ⁻20°F

**3.** a hot summer day
   35°C   195°C   93°C

**4.** a glass of lemonade
   8°C   45°C   ⁻3°C

**5.** inside a refrigerator
   95°F   38°F   75°F

**6.** a cold winter day
   89°F   105°F   22°F

**7.** a bowl of hot soup
   70°C   20°C   15°C

**8.** room temperature
   50°C   20°C   70°C

Given the length and the width, find the perimeter of each rectangle.

**1.** $l = 7$ m, $w = 3$ m    **2.** $l = 45$ cm, $w = 5.6$ cm    **3.** $l = 15\frac{1}{4}$ in., $w = 4\frac{1}{2}$ in.

Given the number of sides ($n$) and the length of each side ($l$), find the perimeter of each regular polygon.

**4.** $n = 3$, $l = 10$ cm    **5.** $n = 6$, $l = 7$ in.    **6.** $n = 4$, $l = 9$ ft

**7.** $n = 3$, $l = 2.4$ cm    **8.** $n = 8$, $l = 3\frac{1}{2}$ in.    **9.** $n = 5$, $l = 73$ mm

Find the circumference of each circle, given the radius or the diameter. Use 3.14 for $\pi$.

**1.** $r = 55$ mm    **2.** $r = 9$ cm    **3.** $r = 5$ m    **4.** $r = 35$ cm

**5.** $d = 26$ mm    **6.** $d = 15.5$ m    **7.** $r = 42$ cm    **8.** $d = 5$ cm

Find the circumference of each circle, given the radius or the diameter. Use $\frac{22}{7}$ for $\pi$.

**9.** $r = 7$ ft    **10.** $r = 21$ ft    **11.** $r = 14$ in.    **12.** $d = 56$ ft

**13.** $r = 6\frac{1}{8}$ yd    **14.** $d = 35$ yd    **15.** $r = 4.2$ in.    **16.** $d = 63$ ft

Find the area of each rectangle, given the length and the width.

**1.** $l = 8$ in., $w = 5$ in.    **2.** $l = 15$ cm, $w = 8$ cm    **3.** $l = 20$ m, $w = 10$ m

**4.** $l = 12\frac{1}{2}$ ft, $w = 5$ ft    **5.** $l = 135$ in., $w = 67$ in.    **6.** $l = 45.4$ m, $w = 0.5$ m

Find the area of each parallelogram, given the length of the base and the height.

**7.** $b = 9$ mm, $h = 3$ mm    **8.** $b = 25$ in., $h = 18$ in.    **9.** $b = 56$ m, $h = 34$ m

Set 94  (Use after page 319.)

Given the base and the height, find the area of each triangle.

**1.** $b=5$ ft, $h=3$ ft
**2.** $b=6$ m, $h=5$ m
**3.** $b=10$ ft, $h=8$ ft

**4.** $b=24$ cm, $h=24$ cm
**5.** $b=52$ mm, $h=30$ mm
**6.** $b=100$ in., $h=50$ in.

**7.** $b=8.5$ cm, $h=6$ cm
**8.** $b=2\frac{1}{2}$ ft, $h=1\frac{1}{2}$ ft
**9.** $b=0.4$ m, $h=1.2$ m

Set 95  (Use after page 321.)

Find the area of each circle, given the radius or the diameter. Use 3.14 for $\pi$.

**1.** $r=5$ m
**2.** $r=10$ mm
**3.** $r=6$ cm
**4.** $d=70$ cm

**5.** $r=24$ mm
**6.** $d=18$ m
**7.** $r=0.3$ km
**8.** $r=25$ mm

Find the area of each circle, given the radius or the diameter. Use $\frac{22}{7}$ for $\pi$.

**9.** $d=14$ ft
**10.** $r=7$ in.
**11.** $r=14$ yd
**12.** $r=70$ in.

**13.** $d=7$ ft
**14.** $d=3\frac{1}{2}$ in.
**15.** $r=56$ ft
**16.** $r=35$ in.

Set 96  (Use after page 329.)

Find the volume of each rectangular prism, given the length, the width, and the height.

**1.** $l=8$ ft
$w=5$ ft
$h=3$ ft

**2.** $l=10$ cm
$w=8$ cm
$h=5$ cm

**3.** $l=35$ in.
$w=20$ in.
$h=20$ in.

**4.** $l=7.6$ cm
$w=5$ cm
$h=3.5$ cm

**5.** $l=6\frac{1}{2}$ ft
$w=3$ ft
$h=2$ ft

Find the volume of each cylinder, given the radius and the height. Use 3.14 for $\pi$.

**6.** $r=3$ cm
$h=2$ cm

**7.** $r=7$ cm
$h=5$ cm

**8.** $r=5$ m
$h=5$ m

**9.** $r=5$ mm
$h=12$ mm

**10.** $r=7$ m
$h=6$ m

**11.** $r=8$ cm
$h=12$ cm

**12.** $r=1$ m
$h=8$ m

**13.** $r=14$ cm
$h=50$ cm

Set 97   (Use after page 331.)

Find the surface area of each right prism.

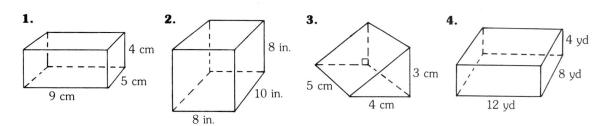

**1.**  4 cm  5 cm  9 cm

**2.**  8 in.  10 in.  8 in.

**3.**  5 cm  3 cm  4 cm

**4.**  4 yd  8 yd  12 yd

Set 98   (Use after page 333.)

Solve.

**1.** A tire has a diameter of 64 cm. How far does the tire roll in one complete turn?

**2.** The air-traffic radar at an airport covers a circular region with a 25-mile radius. What is the area of this region?

**3.** What is the area of a circular ice-skating rink with a diameter of 24 feet?

**4.** How much fencing is needed to fence in a square garden that is 3.5 meters on a side?

Set 99   (Use after page 343.)

Use the bar graph at the right to answer the following:

**1.** What is the title of the graph?

**2.** Which region has the largest population?

**3.** Which region has the smallest population?

**4.** How many people live in the northeast?

**5.** How many people live in the south?

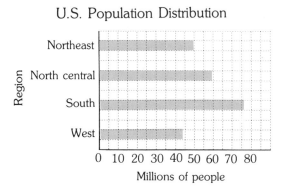

U.S. Population Distribution

Region

Northeast
North central
South
West

0  10  20  30  40  50  60  70  80
Millions of people

Use the line graph at the right to answer the following:

1. How many years are listed on the graph?

2. For which year does the graph show the greatest number of systems?

3. Was there a decrease in the number of systems for any five-year period listed?

4. What five-year period has the smallest increase?

5. Estimate the number of systems in each year listed.

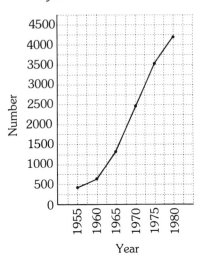

Number of Cable Television Systems in the U.S.

Use the picture graph at the right to answer the following:

1. What does each 🌽 stand for?

2. How many states are listed on the graph?

3. Which state listed on the graph produced the least amount of corn?

4. Estimate the amount of corn produced in each state.

One Year's Production of Corn

Nebraska

Illinois

Ohio

South Dakota

Minnesota

Key:  Each 🌽 stands for 100 million bushels of corn.

Set 102   (Use after page 351.)

Use the 100% bar graph at the right to answer the following:

If there are 2,000,000 people in the armed forces, how many are in the

**1.** Army

**2.** Navy

**3.** Marines

**4.** Air Force

**5.** Coast Guard

Distribution of Armed-Forces Personnel

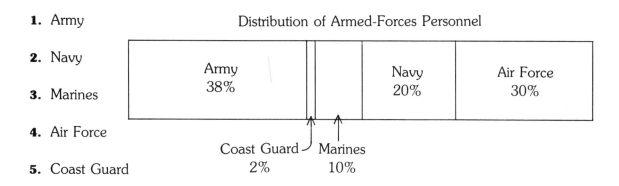

Set 103   (Use after page 353.)

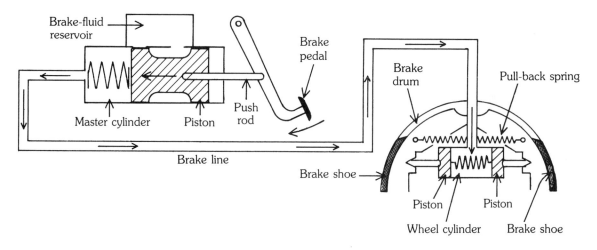

Use the schematic above to answer the following:

**1.** What does the brake fluid flow into after it flows through the brake line?

**2.** How many brake shoes are in the brake drum?

**3.** What is the brake pedal connected to?

**4.** How many pistons are in this schematic?

Make a bar graph for the table.

**1.**    Building Stone Production
        in the United States

| Stone | Thousands of tons |
| --- | --- |
| Granite | 575 |
| Limestone | 410 |
| Sandstone | 270 |
| Slate | 58 |
| Marble | 56 |

Make a line graph for the table.

**1.** Number of Unemployed Persons
    Over 16 Years Old in the U.S.

| Year | Millions |
| --- | --- |
| 1973 | 4.4 |
| 1975 | 8.0 |
| 1977 | 7.0 |
| 1979 | 6.1 |
| 1981 | 8.3 |

Make a circle graph for the table.

**1.**    U.S. Population Distribution by Age

| Age | Percent of population |
| --- | --- |
| 65 and over | 11% |
| 18–64 | 61% |
| Under 18 | 28% |

Set 107   (Use after page 373.)

**1.** Copy the frequency table at the right. Use the numbers below to complete it.

24, 15, 21, 18, 17, 23, 18, 21, 23, 21, 22, 19, 21, 23, 18, 15, 20, 22, 19, 18, 21, 19, 23, 24

**2.** Find the range for the frequency table.

| Quiz scores | Tally | Frequency |
|---|---|---|
| 24 | ⌐ | ? |
| 23 | ? | ? |
| 22 | ? | ? |
| 21 | ▨ | 5 |
| 20 | ? | ? |
| 19 | ? | ? |
| 18 | ? | ? |
| 17 | ? | ? |
| 16 | ? | ? |
| 15 | ? | ? |
| | total | 24 |

Set 108   (Use after page 377.)

Find the mean and the median for each set of numbers. Round to the nearest tenth when necessary.

**1.** 6, 8, 5, 3, 9, 4, 6, 8

**2.** 11, 18, 15, 12, 15, 16, 12, 11, 15, 16, 15

**3.** 46, 51, 48, 53, 51, 47, 52, 48, 46

**4.** 11, 21.5, 18, 16.3, 20, 15.5, 17.3

**5.** 8, 17, 15, 9, 10, 13, 17, 15, 8, 14, 9, 15, 16, 18, 9, 10, 11

**6.** 210, 305, 280, 150, 215, 265, 315, 305, 215, 175, 305, 315

**7.** 8, 10, 9, 12, 7, 9, 8, 13, 9, 14, 10, 8, 10, 12, 8, 15, 11, 8, 10, 7, 9, 9, 8, 9, 7, 14, 11, 11, 10, 13, 8, 7, 5

**8.** 134, 127, 125, 127, 127, 146, 153, 146, 153, 160, 123, 140, 151, 128, 153

Find the mean, the median, and the mode or modes for each of the frequency tables.

**1.**

| Number | Frequency |
|--------|-----------|
| 3 | 4 |
| 4 | 5 |
| 5 | 3 |
| 6 | 4 |
| 8 | 3 |
| total | 19 |

**2.**

| Number | Frequency |
|--------|-----------|
| 36 | 1 |
| 34 | 2 |
| 33 | 3 |
| 30 | 2 |
| 28 | 2 |
| total | 10 |

**3.**

| Number | Frequency |
|--------|-----------|
| 24 | 1 |
| 26 | 1 |
| 29 | 3 |
| 33 | 4 |
| 45 | 3 |
| 50 | 4 |
| total | 16 |

**4.**

| Number | Frequency |
|--------|-----------|
| 146 | 11 |
| 149 | 16 |
| 150 | 9 |
| 151 | 24 |
| 152 | 23 |
| 156 | 10 |
| 158 | 25 |
| 160 | 8 |
| total | 126 |

Solve.

**1.** Cindy Saavich is a construction worker. Her income depends on the weather. The first six months of last year she earned $4200, $1050, $1200, $1800, $3400, and $3350. What was her mean monthly income?

**2.** The prices of 5 houses for sale are $64,000, $175,000, $82,000, $68,000, and $73,000. Find the mean selling price and the median selling price. Which seems a more typical selling price?

**3.** The selling prices of 4 different models of video recorders are $699, $850, $549, and $975. What is the mean price? What is the median price?

**4.** The daily high temperatures for 9 days were 73°, 72°, 69°, 68°, 72.8°, 74°, 67°, 68.2°, and 75°. What is the mean high temperature? How many days were above the mean?

Set 111   (Use after page 401.)

Find each probability. Without looking, you pick one disk.

1. p (6)                2. p (red)

3. p (black)            4. p (odd number)

5. p (gray)             6. p (white)

7. p (number less than 10)

8. p (yellow)           9. p (not a 5)

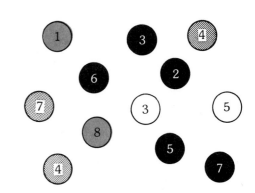

Set 112   (Use after page 403.)

Find each probability. The spinner is spun.

1. p (red or 3)         2. p (1 or 3)

3. p (white or 2)       4. p (2 or 3)

5. p (black or white)   6. p (black or 2)

7. p (black or 1)       8. p (red or black)

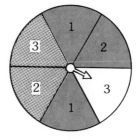

Set 113   (Use after page 407.)

Find each probability. A die is rolled and the spinner is spun.

1. p (1 and red)        2. p (3 and gray)

3. p (4 and white)      4. p (even number and red)

5. p (prime number and white)

6. p (odd number and gray)

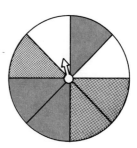

Set 114 (Use after page 409.)

Find each probability. A card is picked from a standard deck of 52 playing cards, and then another card is picked without replacing the first card.

**1.** p (both cards red)

**2.** p (both cards are jacks)

**3.** p (both cards are clubs)

**4.** p (both cards are 8's)

**5.** p (both cards are diamonds)

**6.** p (both cards are aces)

**7.** p (first card is a king and second card is a jack)

Set 115 (Use after page 425.)

List all the factors of each number.

**1.** 3    **2.** 4    **3.** 6    **4.** 5    **5.** 9

**6.** 10    **7.** 12    **8.** 18    **9.** 25    **10.** 30

**11.** 36    **12.** 40    **13.** 45    **14.** 48    **15.** 50

**16.** 72    **17.** 117    **18.** 81    **19.** 100    **20.** 250

Set 116 (Use after page 427.)

Write each composite number as the product of prime factors.

**1.** 4    **2.** 6    **3.** 8    **4.** 10    **5.** 12

**6.** 14    **7.** 16    **8.** 18    **9.** 20    **10.** 21

**11.** 27    **12.** 36    **13.** 40    **14.** 55    **15.** 64

**16.** 44    **17.** 57    **18.** 84    **19.** 81    **20.** 110

**21.** 132    **22.** 72    **23.** 75    **24.** 100    **25.** 210

(Use after page 429.)

Find the greatest common factor (GCF) of each pair of numbers.

**1.** 6 and 12     **2.** 2 and 8     **3.** 4 and 10     **4.** 8 and 12

**5.** 9 and 27     **6.** 12 and 24     **7.** 10 and 15     **8.** 15 and 30

**9.** 9 and 12     **10.** 6 and 10     **11.** 6 and 9     **12.** 6 and 18

**13.** 9 and 15     **14.** 10 and 12     **15.** 8 and 24     **16.** 6 and 15

**17.** 6 and 20     **18.** 12 and 18     **19.** 15 and 18     **20.** 48 and 54

(Use after page 431.)

Find the least common multiple (LCM) of each pair of numbers.

**1.** 4 and 5     **2.** 2 and 3     **3.** 3 and 4     **4.** 6 and 9

**5.** 4 and 6     **6.** 3 and 6     **7.** 3 and 12     **8.** 4 and 8

**9.** 4 and 10     **10.** 2 and 6     **11.** 6 and 8     **12.** 8 and 12

**13.** 8 and 10     **14.** 6 and 18     **15.** 18 and 48     **16.** 8 and 32

**17.** 6 and 15     **18.** 4 and 18     **19.** 5 and 12     **20.** 12 and 15

(Use after page 433.)

Solve.

**1.** Linda works every fourth Saturday. Bill works every fifth Saturday. If they both work this Saturday, how many weeks will pass before both work on the same Saturday again?

**2.** Can 57 pictures be arranged in more than one row with the same number of pictures in each row?

**3.** How many different ways can 18 buttons be packaged if each package must contain the same number of buttons? (Hint: One way is 2 packages of 9 buttons each.)

**4.** Both a 45-cm-wide piece of material and a 48-cm-wide piece of material are to be cut into strips of equal width, without wasting any material. What is the greatest width of the strips that can be cut?

Give the output.

**1.** 1Ø PRINT "COMPUTERS"
   2Ø PRINT "CAN BE FUN"

**2.** 1Ø PRINT "1Ø − 8"
   2Ø PRINT 1Ø − 8

**3.** 1Ø LET A = 9
   2Ø PRINT "A"
   3Ø PRINT A
   4Ø PRINT A/3

**4.** 1Ø LET X = 12
   2Ø LET Y = 2
   3Ø LET Z = X∗Y
   4Ø PRINT "X TIMES Y EQUALS"
   5Ø PRINT Z

Set 121   (Use after page 449.)

Find each value.

**1.** $10 - 2 \times 3$  **2.** $7 + 4 - 3$  **3.** $18 - 5 + 4$

**4.** $15 - 16 \div 4$  **5.** $5 \times 6 + 9$  **6.** $(8 - 3) \times 2$

**7.** $12 + (9 - 3)$  **8.** $4 + 7 \times 3 - 5$  **9.** $16 - (3 + 5) \div 2$

Find the value of each expression if $a = 5$ and $b = 7$.

**10.** $25 - a + b$  **11.** $b + 14$  **12.** $a \times 6$

**13.** $a + b$  **14.** $b - a$  **15.** $(a + 4) \div 3$

**16.** $35 - b - a$  **17.** $(a + b) - 2 \times 3$  **18.** $4 \times a - b + 3$

Set 122   (Use after page 451.)

Solve.

**1.** $d + 16 = 20$  **2.** $a - 8 = 3$  **3.** $b - 5 = 10$

**4.** $c + 3 = 15$  **5.** $d - 4 = 17$  **6.** $x + 14 = 35$

**7.** $k + 9 = 16$  **8.** $a - 5 = 22$  **9.** $s + 20 = 40$

**10.** $c - 8 = 31$  **11.** $b + 3 = 17$  **12.** $x + 18 = 43$

**13.** $45 = b - 12$  **14.** $50 = c + 16$  **15.** $a + 56 = 138$

Set 123  (Use after page 453.)

Solve.

1. $6a = 30$

2. $2b = 8$

3. $\frac{m}{2} = 6$

4. $5c = 20$

5. $4x = 28$

6. $\frac{b}{6} = 4$

7. $\frac{a}{8} = 5$

8. $9m = 54$

9. $\frac{d}{10} = 7$

10. $15a = 30$

11. $20c = 60$

12. $\frac{d}{15} = 10$

13. $12c = 9$

14. $27 = 3a$

15. $16 = \frac{a}{2}$


Set 124  (Use after page 455.)

Solve each problem by using an equation.

1. A pair of roller skates costs $35. Ted has $18. How much more does he need to buy the skates?

2. Christine earned $4 an hour and was paid $36. How many hours did she work?

3. After spending $15 on dinner, Glen had $12 left. How much did he have originally?

4. Sandy bought a blouse for $12 on sale. If the blouse originally cost $28, how much less is the sale price than the original price?


Set 125  (Use after page 462.)

Add.

1. $^+5 + {}^-6$

2. $^+4 + {}^-3$

3. $^+6 + {}^-8$

4. $^-4 + {}^+3$

5. $^-9 + {}^+10$

6. $^-5 + {}^-3$

7. $^-7 + {}^-8$

8. $^+8 + {}^-11$

9. $^-12 + {}^-4$

10. $^+15 + {}^-5$

11. $^-20 + {}^+8$

12. $^+32 + {}^-16$

13. $^-45 + {}^-12$

14. $^-30 + {}^+10$

15. $^+3.4 + {}^-0.8$

16. $^+\left(\frac{3}{4}\right) + {}^-\left(\frac{1}{2}\right)$

Set 126   (Use after page 465.)

Solve.

1. On the first play a football team went $^+19$ yards. On the next play they went $^-12$ yards. What was the change in yardage after both plays?

2. A checking account had a balance of $^-\$110$. (The account was overdrawn.) After a deposit of $250 ($^+\$250$), how much money was in the account?

3. The temperature was 2° below zero ($^-2°$). The temperature dropped 6° ($^-6°$). What was the temperature after the drop?

4. An airplane's altitude was $^+28,000$ feet. The pilot changed the altitude by $^-1500$ feet. What was the altitude after the change?

Set 127   (Use after page 469.)

Give the ordered pair for each point.

1. A          2. B          3. G          4. I

5. E          6. J          7. L          8. N

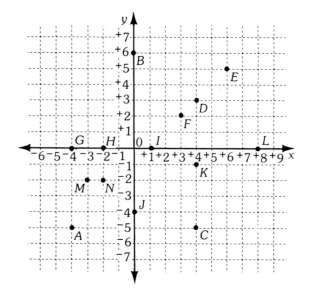

Give the letter for each ordered pair.

9. ($^+3,^+2$)     10. ($^-2,0$)     11. ($^+4,^-5$)

12. ($^-3,^-2$)     13. ($^+4,^+3$)     14. ($^+4,^-1$)

Complete each table and draw the graph.

15. $y = x - {}^+3$

| x | $^+1$ | $^+2$ | $^+3$ | $^+4$ | $^+5$ |
|---|---|---|---|---|---|
| y | | | | | |

16. $y = x + {}^+6$

| x | $^-1$ | 0 | $^+1$ | $^+2$ | $^+3$ | $^+4$ |
|---|---|---|---|---|---|---|
| y | | | | | | |

17. $y = {}^+3x$

| x | $^-2$ | $^-1$ | 0 | $^+1$ | $^+2$ | $^+3$ |
|---|---|---|---|---|---|---|
| y | | | | | | |

18. $y = x + {}^+3$

| x | $^-3$ | $^-2$ | $^-1$ | 0 | $^+1$ |
|---|---|---|---|---|---|
| y | | | | | |

# GLOSSARY

**acute angle**  An angle measuring between 0° and 90°.

**acute triangle**  A triangle with three acute angles.

**angle**  Two rays with the same endpoint. ∠XYZ has sides $\overrightarrow{YX}$ and $\overrightarrow{YZ}$ and vertex Y.

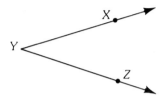

**arc**  Part of a circle.

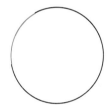

**area**  The amount of surface enclosed by a figure. Area is measured in square units.

**average**  In statistics, the average can be the mean, the median, or the mode. In most cases, the average of a set of numbers is considered to be the mean, found by adding the numbers and dividing by how many numbers there are.

**BASIC**  **B**eginner's **A**ll-purpose **S**ymbolic **I**nstruction **C**ode is a computer language.

**Celsius (°C)**  The metric temperature scale, on which water freezes at 0°C and boils at 100°C.

**central angle**  An angle whose vertex is the center of a circle.

**chord**  A segment with endpoints on a circle.

**circle**  A set of points in a plane that are the same distance from a given point, called the center.

**circumference**  The distance around a circle.

**commission**  An amount (paid to a salesperson or to an agency) that is a percent of the amount of sales.

**composite number**  Any whole number greater than one that is not a prime number. The first 6 composite numbers are 4, 6, 8, 9, 10, and 12.

**cone**  A solid figure with a circular base. The base is joined by a curved surface to a point, called the vertex.

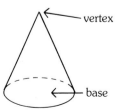
vertex
base

**congruent figures** Figures that have the same size and shape.

**coordinates** The numbers in an ordered pair that name a point on a plane.

**cross products** In the proportion $\frac{3}{4} = \frac{9}{12}$, the products of $3 \times 12$ and $4 \times 9$ are the cross products.

**cube** A solid figure with six faces, all square.

**cylinder** A solid figure with two circular bases of the same size in planes that would never meet.

**decimal** A number that includes place-value positions to the right of the ones place.

5.2 is five and *two tenths*.

0.04 is *four hundredths*.

1.987 is one and *nine hundred eighty-seven thousandths*.

**degree** A unit (on a protractor) for measuring angles or a unit (on a thermometer) for measuring temperature.

**denominator** *See fraction.*

**diameter** A segment through the center of a circle with endpoints on the circle.

**discount** An amount deducted from the original price.

**dividend** A number that is divided by another number.

In $18 \div 6$ and $6\overline{)18}$, 18 is the dividend.

**divisor** A number that is used to divide another number.

In $18 \div 6$ and $6\overline{)18}$, 6 is the divisor.

**equation** A mathematical sentence that uses the $=$ symbol.

**equilateral triangle** A triangle with all three sides of equal length.

**equivalent fractions** Fractions that stand for the same amount.

$\frac{3}{4}$ and $\frac{9}{12}$ are equivalent fractions.

**estimate** To find an approximate answer.

**experimental probability** Probability that is found by using the outcomes of an experiment.

**factor** A number to be multiplied.

In $5 \times 6 = 30$, 5 and 6 are factors of 30.

**formula** A rule or principle stated in shortened form.

$$P = 2w + 2l$$

perimeter of a rectangle        width        length

**fraction** In the fraction $\frac{3}{4}$, the numerator 3 tells the number of equal parts being considered. The denominator 4 tells the number of those equal parts in a whole. A fraction can also represent division: $\frac{3}{4}$ means $4\overline{)3}$.

**frequency table**  A list of numbers in increasing order, showing how many times each of the numbers occurs.

**gram**  A unit of mass (commonly called weight) in the metric system.

**greatest common factor (GCF)**  The largest number that is a factor of two or more numbers.

For 24 and 36, the greatest common factor is 12.

**improper fraction**  A fraction that has a numerator greater than or equal to the denominator.

$\frac{4}{4}$ and $\frac{8}{3}$ are improper fractions.

**integers**  The whole numbers and their opposites.

. . . , $^-3$, $^-2$, $^-1$, 0, $^+1$, $^+2$, . . .

**intersecting lines**  Lines that meet at a point.

**isosceles triangle**  A triangle with two sides of equal length.

**least common denominator (LCD)**  The least common multiple of the denominators of two or more fractions.

For $\frac{3}{8}$ and $\frac{5}{6}$, the least common denominator is 24.

**least common multiple (LCM)**  The smallest nonzero number that is a common multiple of two numbers.

Multiples of 6:   6, 12, 18, 24, 30, 36, . . .

Multiples of 9:   9, 18, 27, 36, 45, . . .

The least common multiple of 6 and 9 is 18.

**line**  A geometric figure extending in opposite directions without end along a straight path.

$\longleftrightarrow$

**liter**  A unit of capacity in the metric system.

**mean**  An average found by adding the numbers and dividing by how many numbers there are.

**median**  The middle number in a set of numbers when the numbers are listed in order (or if there are two middle numbers, their mean).

**meter**  A unit of length in the metric system.

**mixed number**  A number that stands for the sum of a whole number and a fraction.

$2\frac{3}{4}$ is a mixed number. $2\frac{3}{4} = 2 + \frac{3}{4}$.

**mode**  The number that occurs the most often in a set of numbers.

**multiple**  The nonzero multiples of a number are found by multiplying the number by 1, 2, 3, 4, and so on.

Multiples of 6:   6, 12, 18, 24, 30, 36, . . .

**negative number**  Any number less than 0.

**numerator**  *See fraction.*

**obtuse angle** An angle measuring between 90° and 180°.

**obtuse triangle** A triangle with one obtuse angle.

**odds** The ratio of a number of successful outcomes to the number of unsuccessful outcomes, or vice versa.

**opposite** On a number line, a number and its opposite are the same distance from 0 but in opposite directions.

+2 and ‾2 are opposites.

**ordered pair** A pair of numbers that names a point on a plane.

**outcome** A possible result in a probability experiment or event.

**parallel lines** Lines in the same plane that do not intersect.

**parallelogram** A quadrilateral with opposite sides parallel and of equal length.

**percent (%)** A ratio comparing a number to 100. Percent means "per 100," "hundredths," or "for every 100."

33 percent (33%) means 0.33, or $\frac{33}{100}$.

**perimeter** The distance around a polygon.

**period** A group of three place values in a number.

In 123,456,789, there are 123 *millions*, 456 *thousands*, and 789 *units*, or *ones*.

**perpendicular lines** Two lines that intersect to form right angles.

**pi (π)** The ratio of the circumference to diameter for any circle. π is approximately equal to $\frac{22}{7}$ or to 3.14.

**place value** The value of a digit depends on its place in a number. In the base-ten system, each place value is ten times the value of the place to its right.

In the number 2045, the digit 4 has a place value of 10, so its value is $4 \times 10$, or 40.

**plane** A flat surface with no thickness that extends without end.

**point** A geometric figure that has no size at all. It shows only position.

**polygon** A plane figure formed by three or more segments joined to one another at their endpoints.

**positive number** Any number that is greater than 0.

**prime number** A whole number greater than 1 that has only 1 and itself as factors. The first 6 prime numbers are 2, 3, 5, 7, 11, and 13.

**probability** The ratio of the number of ways a certain outcome can occur to the total number of ways all possible outcomes in an event can occur.

**product** The result of multiplying two or more numbers.

In $4 \times 5 = 20$, 20 is the product of 4 and 5.

**proportion** A statement that two ratios are equal.

$\frac{3}{5} = \frac{6}{10}$ is a proportion.

**protractor** An instrument used to measure angles.

**pyramid** A solid figure with a base in the shape of a polygon and 3 or more triangular faces that meet at a common point, called the vertex.

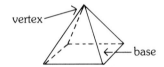

**quadrilateral** A polygon with four sides.

**quotient** The result in a division.

In $24 \div 4 = 6$, 6 is the quotient.

**radius** A segment from the center of a circle to a point on the circle.

**range** The difference between the largest and smallest numbers in a set of numbers.

**rate** A ratio that compares unlike measurements, usually written so that the denominator of the ratio is 1.

$\frac{300 \text{ mi}}{6 \text{ h}} = \frac{50 \text{ mi}}{1 \text{ h}}$, or 50 mi/h.

**ratio** A comparison of two numbers.

3 to 4      3:4      $\frac{3}{4}$

**ray** A geometric figure that extends without end in only one direction from an endpoint.

**reciprocals** Two numbers whose product is 1.

$\frac{3}{4}$ and $\frac{4}{3}$ are reciprocals because $\frac{3}{4} \times \frac{4}{3} = 1$.

**rectangle** A parallelogram with four right angles.

**rectangular solid** A solid figure with six rectangular faces.

**regular polygon** A polygon whose sides are all of equal length and whose angles all have the same measure.

**repeating decimal** A decimal in which one or more digits repeat without end.

$0.333 \cdots$ or $0.\overline{3}$ and

$4.123123 \cdots$ or $4.\overline{123}$ are repeating decimals.

**rhombus** A parallelogram with all four sides of equal length.

**right angle** An angle that has a measure of 90°.

**right prism** A solid with two bases that are congruent polygons and other faces that are rectangles.

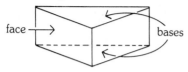

**right triangle** A triangle with one right angle.

**round (a number)** To change a number to a multiple of a particular place value.

2453 rounded to the nearest hundred is 2500.

364 rounded to the nearest ten is 360.

**scale drawing** A drawing that has the same shape as an object. Each length on the scale drawing is in a given ratio to the corresponding length on the actual object.

**scalene triangle** A triangle with no sides of equal length.

**segment** A part of a line with two endpoints.

A                    B

**ar figures** Geometric figures that
xactly the same shape but not nec-
he same size.

**res** Geometric figures that
'mensions—length, width, and

**sphere** A set of all points in space at a fixed distance from a given point, called the center.

**square** A rectangle with all four sides of equal length.

**statistics** The branch of mathematics that deals with organizing and interpreting data.

**straight angle** An angle that has a measure of 180°.

**surface area** The amount of surface (in square units) of a solid figure.

**trapezoid** A quadrilateral with only one pair of opposite sides parallel.

**triangle** A polygon with three sides.

**unit price** The price of 1 ounce, 1 gram, and so on. (Divide the total price by the amount.)

"$1.60 for 4 oz" gives a unit price of $0.40 per oz.

**variable** A letter that stands for a number.

**volume** The amount of space enclosed by a solid figure. Volume is measured in cubic units.

**whole numbers** 0, 1, 2, 3, 4, . . .

# INDEX